LINEAR INEQUALITIES AND RELATED SYSTEMS

G. B. DANTZIG
R. J. DUFFIN
K. FAN
L. R. FORD, JR.
D. R. FULKERSON
D. GALE
A. J. GOLDMAN
I. HELLER
A. J. HOFFMAN
J. B. KRUSKAL
H. W. KUHN
H. D. MILLS
G. L. THOMPSON
C. B. TOMPKINS
A. W. TUCKER
P. WOLFE

Edited by

H. W. Kuhn and A. W. Tucker

Princeton, New Jersey
Princeton University Press
1956

London: Geoffrey Cumberlege, Oxford University Press

L. C. Card 56-8385

This research was supported in part by the Office of Naval Research. Reproduction, translation, publication, use and disposal in whole or in part by or for the United States Government is permitted. Papers 7, 11, and 12 are published by permission of The RAND Corporation.

Printed in the United States of America

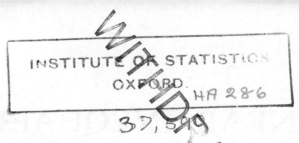

PREFACE

The eighteen papers collected here explore various aspects of one mathematical theme, the theory of linear inequalities. Although they are related by this fact, the papers are bound together more closely by the areas of intended application. Without exception, the direction or technique of each is determined by recent developments in the subjects of linear programming, matrix games, and related or derivative economic models. In their rapid growth during the last decade, these disciplines have not only posed questions of direct economic importance, but have also suggested peripheral mathematical problems of interest in themselves and have stimulated a thorough reconsideration of several mathematical topics. Following these lines of development, the papers of this volume fall roughly into three categories. Papers of the first type present a detailed exposition of the fundamental mathematical results which form a basis for the models. Such an inventory is peculiarly necessary in fields such as these, where the pressure for practical results is so great that there is little time for reflective appraisal of past accomplishment. The second type of paper answers purely mathematical questions that have appeared in the elaboration of the economic theory, or else exploits results such as the duality theorem of linear programming for independent, mathematical purposes. The third type considers problems that bear on the economic applications of the models.

The first five papers of this study are in the first category, and offer expository treatments of those facets of the theory of linear inequalities that have been highlighted by the needs of linear programming and the theory of matrix games. PAPER 1 studies pairs of finite systems of homogeneous linear inequalities (written uniformly $\geqq 0$) and/or equations involving variables that are nonnegative and/or unrestricted. To each inequality or equation in one system there corresponds a nonnegative or unrestricted variable in the other, and conversely; the array of coefficients in one system is the <u>negative transpose</u> of the array in the other. This formal tabular duality furnishes the foundation for the duality of matrix games and linear programming. Various pairs of dual systems give rise to sharpened "transposition theorems" of classical type and to a new property of "complementary slackness." In particular, it is shown that a self-dual system $KW \geqq 0$, $W \geqq 0$, where K is skew-symmetric, possesses a solution W^* such that $KW^* + W^* > 0$ (in each component). Since

$$\sum_{i,j} w_i k_{ij} w_j = 0$$

for all W, it follows that either $w_i^* > 0$ or $\Sigma_j k_{ij} w_j^* > 0$, but <u>not</u> both, for each i.

PAPER 2 deals with the set A^* of solutions of a finite system $AX \leqq 0$ of homogeneous linear inequalities in n variables, represented in n-dimensional (real) vector space as the intersection of finitely many halfspaces, and also with the set A^{**} of vectors Y such that $YX \leqq 0$ for each X in A^*. It is shown that A^* and A^{**} are convex hulls of finitely many halflines, A^* being spanned by the column-vectors of some matrix B and A^{**} by the row-vectors of A itself. These two basic results (Theorems of Minkowski and Farkas) are established for use in Paper 3, and as keys to the rich geometry of polyhedral convex cones which finds elegant expression in the lattice properties formulated by David Gale. At the outset the <u>polyhedral</u> structure of the convex cone A^* is made evident by partitioning A^* into a finite system of (open) "faces." At the end it appears that A^* is the convex hull of its "extreme" faces, and thus can be generated in a minimal manner.

PAPER 3 extends the vector-space geometry of homogeneous systems to the solution set of a finite nonhomogeneous system $AX \leqq B$. Among other results, it is shown that such a solution set (if not empty) is the vector sum of (1) the convex hull of a finite set of particular solutions and (2) the polyhedral convex cone A^* of solutions of the homogeneous system $AX \leqq 0$.

PAPER 4 presents a thorough <u>theoretical</u> treatment of linear programming -- as distinguished from the important practical techniques of formulating and solving actual programs. The fundamental duality and existence theorems for dual programs in nonnegative variables constrained by linear inequalities are obtained in the strongest possible form by means of the theorem for a skew-symmetric (self-dual) system of linear inequalities proved in Paper 1, and cited above. The scope of these results is then extended to mixed constraints (both inequalities and equations) in variables partly nonnegative and partly unrestricted. Basic connections are established with the theory of matrix games and the classical method of Lagrange multipliers, and theoretical characterizations are given for "extreme" and "infinite" solutions. Finally, the analysis of linear programs is inverted to provide a means of "synthesizing" dual programs which have solutions as arbitrary as possible.

PAPER 5 bears a close relation to those preceding it. The main problems considered are essentially the same, and include the solvability of systems of linear relations, consequences of such systems (i.e., relations which hold for all solutions of the system), extreme solutions, and saddlepoint problems. However, the point of view here is one of extreme generality and the paper is organized around sets of assumptions of varying strength. While the first half of the paper is of algebraic nature, most results of the second half belong to the domain of functional analysis. Thus, the first part of the paper is devoted to finite systems of linear inequalities defined in a real linear space without a norm or topology. The second part narrows the discussion to such spaces of finite dimension, allowing the treatment of theorems on rank and determinantal criteria for consistency. The systems of the third part are unrestricted as to the number of inequalities, but are defined in real linear spaces with a norm or topology. For these cases, it is natural to replace the concept of a linear system by the notion of a linear transformation. Inequalities are then expressed by means of the idea of a "nonnegative vector," namely, a vector lying in a certain distinguished closed convex cone of vectors. This part of the paper contains a study of infinite systems of linear inequalities in a normed real linear space, a discussion of the special cases of Euclidean and Hilbert spaces, and a "moment problem" in topological real linear spaces; it concludes with a proof of the Minimax Theorem for compact Hausdorff spaces, due to Fan and Glicksberg. The fourth, and final, part of the paper considers inequalities (of absolute value) defined in complex linear spaces, and includes a generalization of the Fredholm-Riesz-Schauder alternative theorem to inequalities involving completely continuous linear operators.

With systems of linear inequalities possessing satisfactory analogues in infinite dimensional spaces, it is natural to define "infinite programs" and to question the existence of duality relationships for such programs. This is done in PAPER 6, which considers programs which are defined by means of locally convex, linear topological spaces U and V, in which a notion of "nonnegative vector" has been introduced by means of closed cones. An infinite program is a triple (A, b, a), where A is a continuous linear transformation defined on the conjugate space U^* into V, $b \in V$, and $a \in U$. Consistency for such an infinite program means the existence of a feasible vector $x \in U^*$, such that $x \geqq 0$ and $Ax \geqq b$. The value of the program is $M = \inf (a, x)$ for such x. The dual to a program (A, b, a) consists of the triple $(-A^*, -a, -b)$, where A^* is the transformation adjoint to A. The value of the dual is denoted by M'.

PREFACE

For a finite program there are essentially three situations to be distinguished; a program can only be inconsistent, consistent with infinite value, or consistent with a finite value which is necessarily achieved. Of these three exhaustive and mutually exclusive possibilities, the first is dual to itself or to the second, while the third is self-dual. To discuss the analogous situation for infinite programs, a program is defined to be sub-consistent if there exist sequences $x_n \geqq 0$ and $q_n \geqq 0$ such that $\lim(Ax_n - q_n) = b$; the totality of such sequences (x_n) defines a sub-value for the program, $m' = \inf \underline{\lim} (a, x_n)$. Then a program is consistent and has a finite value M if and only if the dual program is sub-consistent and has the finite sub-value m'; under these conditions, $M + m' = 0$. A program (A, b, a) is said to be super-consistent if there is an x such that $x \geqq 0$ and $Ax > b$. Then a program is consistent with a feasible vector x achieving the finite value $(a, x) = M$ if the dual program is super-consistent with finite value; under these conditions, $m = M = - M' = - m'$.

Methods designed for special classes of linear programs have dominated recent work on computational routines. One phase of this development has been the construction of a special algorithm for the transportation problem by Ford and Fulkerson; partial evidence indicates that their method is quite efficient. PAPER 7 generalizes their process to solve the general linear programming problem. The distinctive feature of the routine is the use of a feasible solution to the dual program to define an alteration of the original program (called the "restricted primal") in which several of the variables are dropped, and the objective is changed to that of finding a solution as nearly feasible as possible. Optimal solutions of the "restricted primal" are then used to improve the feasible solution to the dual program. After a finite number of repetitions, the optimal solutions of the "restricted primal" coincide with those of the unaltered primal program. The particular efficacy of this algorithm for the transportation problem is due to the fact that the optimization of the "restricted primal" program can be performed without recourse to the Simplex Method. Otherwise, the procedure can be considered as a promising variant of the Simplex Method.

PAPER 8 investigates the rate of change of the value (i.e., the "marginal" value) of a matrix game, or the rate of change of the optimum value (i.e., the "marginal" optimum value) of the objective function of a linear program, as the payoffs of the game or the coefficients of the program are varied. This study promises practical application whenever these parameters can be controlled or altered since it indicates which changes will have a beneficial effect on the value. The determination of the marginal value of a matrix game is straightforward and uncomplicated by existence questions. Let $v(G)$ denote the value of the matrix game G, and let H be a matrix of the same size as G. The marginal value of G with respect to H is defined as the one-sided derivative

$$\frac{\partial v(G)}{\partial H} = \lim_{\alpha \longrightarrow 0+} \frac{v(G+\alpha H) - v(G)}{\alpha} .$$

It is shown that this marginal value is equal to the value of the matrix game H when the players are constrained to play in H from among the optimal strategies for G. The search for the marginal value of a linear program is handled simultaneously for a pair of dual programs by combining them into a single saddlepoint problem. Consider the function

$$\emptyset(x, y, A) = a_{oo} + \sum_{i=1}^{m} x_i a_{io} + \sum_{j=1}^{n} a_{oj} y_j + \sum_{i,j} x_i a_{ij} y_j$$

defined by the $(m+1)$ by $(n+1)$ matrix

$$A = \begin{pmatrix} a_{oo} & a_{oj} \\ a_{io} & a_{ij} \end{pmatrix} ,$$

where $i = 1, \ldots, m$ and $j = 1, \ldots, n$, $x = (x_i) \geqq 0$ and $y = (y_j) \geqq 0$. Any pair (x^o, y^o) such that $\emptyset(x, y^o, A) \leqq \emptyset(x^o, y^o, A) \leqq \emptyset(x^o, y, A)$ for all $x \geqq 0$ and $y \geqq 0$ is called a saddlepoint for $\emptyset$; such pairs are exactly the solutions to the dual linear programs: (1) maximize $a_{oo} + \Sigma_i x_i a_{io}$ subject to $a_{oj} + \Sigma_i x_i a_{ij} \geqq 0$, $x_i \geqq 0$, for all i and j, and (2) minimize $a_{oo} + \Sigma_j a_{oj} y_j$ subject to $a_{io} + \Sigma_j a_{ij} y_j$, $y_j \geqq 0$, for all i and j. The number $\emptyset(A) = \emptyset(x^o, y^o, A)$ is the common value of the programs if either program has a solution. Let H be a matrix of the same size as A; then the marginal value of the dual programs is defined as the one-sided derivative

$$\frac{\partial \emptyset(A)}{\partial H} = \lim_{\alpha \longrightarrow 0+} \frac{\emptyset(A+\alpha H) - \emptyset(A)}{\alpha} ,$$

<u>if this limit exists</u>. It is shown that, if $\emptyset(A + \alpha H)$ exists for some interval $0 \leqq \alpha < \alpha_o$, then this marginal value equals the saddle-value of the function $\emptyset(x, y, H)$ when x and y are restricted to be saddlepoints of $\emptyset(x, y, A)$. With the same assumption, a final result characterizes the marginal value of a pair of dual programs directly as the value of a certain composite program, if this latter value exists. Several

questions regarding the weakening of these assumptions remain unsettled.

The subject of PAPER 9 is a problem that arose naturally in connection with the sensitivity analysis of matrix games and linear programs treated in Paper 8. Let X and Y be polyhedral convex sets in two Euclidean spaces of dimension m and n, respectively, and let A be an n by m matrix. Under what conditions are $v_1 = \sup \inf xAy$ and $v_2 = \inf \sup xAy$ equal (where each supremum is taken over $x \in X$ and each infimum over $y \in Y$)? It is shown that they are always equal unless $v_1 = -\infty$ and $v_2 = +\infty$. If v_1 and v_2 are finite (and hence equal) the common value is attained for suitable $x \in X$ and $y \in Y$.

The origins of linear programming, in the work of G. B. Dantzig and Marshall Wood on program planning for the U. S. Air Forces and in the research of Hitchcock and Koopmans on static models of transportation, are innately practical in character. Supported by the simultaneous development of efficient computational techniques, linear programming has since found many areas of application as a concrete approach to problems of allocating limited resources, and has never lost its orientation toward practice. The practical nature of the subject is underlined by the fact that, almost by definition, the theoretical aspects are somewhat restricted. It is not entirely inaccurate to assert that the mathematical foundations of the subject are no more extensive than the theory of finite systems of linear inequalities. Thus, in view of its strictly utilitarian origins on the one hand, and its modest mathematical extent on the other, the next group of papers presents a development of the subject that is both unexpected and gratifying. The authors investigate various instances of a new method, that employs the results and techniques of linear programming to treat certain combinatorial problems.[1]

The problems dealt with in these papers have one feature in common: they ask either for an extreme value of an integral valued function defined on a finite set or for a member of a finite set that can be characterized by such an extremal property. In discussing the problems, it is suggestive to call the elements of the set "trials" and the function an "objective function." The first step of the method is the expression of the trials as points of an Euclidean space in such a manner that the objective function can be presented as a linear form. Clearly, this can always be done in many ways; the mode of expression in each case is suggested by the original setting of the problem and by conditions that

[1] The use of linear inequalities (precisely, the theorem of Farkas cited in the discussion of Paper 2 above) in graph theory seems to have been introduced by R. Rado (Ann. Math. (2) 44 (1943), 268-270).

must be met in the later stages of the method. Once the problem has been given its geometric formulation, it is not changed essentially if the objective function is examined on the convex hull of the set of trial points, since the extreme values are achieved at extreme points of this polyhedron and these are a subset of the trial points. In some cases, the later stages of the method are simplified by using an even larger convex polyhedron, constructed so that every face on which the form assumes its extreme value contains a trial point.

The problem is now a linear program since it asks for an extreme value of a linear form on a convex polyhedron. This may be true only in a non-effective sense if the polyhedron is presented in terms of its extreme points rather than by linear inequalities. To express the program explicitly, the equations of the faces of the convex polyhedron must be found. This is a difficult step for most polyhedra; it has been possible for the cases considered here because they have been recognized as programs of the transportation type.

Once the program has been stated explicitly, it is a routine matter to write out the dual program. The dual program presents itself explicitly as the problem of finding an extreme value of a linear form subject to linear equations and inequalities. The aim of the original formulation of the trials and objective function as points and as a linear form, respectively, can now be explained. It is to make the candidates for a solution (whether they are the extreme points of the constraint set or merely points in the faces on which the form assumes its extreme value) have all integral coordinates, and thus admit a combinatorial interpretation. If this is possible, then the dual program yields a combinatorial problem that is equivalent, according to the duality theorem of linear programming, to the original combinatorial problem.

The steps in the method just outlined can be illustrated by the solution of the classical problem of choosing a system of distinct representatives from a family of sets. To pose the problem, let $\{S_1, \ldots, S_n\}$ be a family of subsets of the set $S = \{a_1, \ldots, a_m\}$, where $m \geqq n$. A set of n distinct elements $a_{i_1}, \ldots, a_{i_n}$ is said to be a system of distinct representatives (abbreviated S.D.R.) if $a_{i_j} \in S_j$ for $j = 1, \ldots, n$. Thus, a trial for this problem is quite naturally an assignment of n distinct elements to the sets $\{S_j\}$. If the objective function is defined to count the number of elements in a trial that are in the sets to which they are assigned, the existence of an S.D.R. is reduced to the question of whether the maximum of this function is n.

Each trial can be expressed as a point of an mn-dimensional space by forming the m by n matrix $X = (x_{ij})$ with a 1 in row i and column

j if a_i is assigned to S_j and a zero, otherwise. The trials are thus identified with the m by n matrices formed of zeros with the exception of a single 1 in each column, and no more than a single 1 in each row. If the membership of the elements in the sets is also expressed by the m by n matrix

$$A = (a_{ij}) \text{ with } \begin{cases} a_{ij} = 1 & \text{if } a_i \in S_j \\ a_{ij} = 0 & \text{otherwise,} \end{cases}$$

then the objective function is given by the linear form

$$A \cdot X = \sum_{i,j} a_{ij} x_{ij}$$

The convex hull of the trial points is easily calculated to be the set of all $X = (x_{ij})$ such that:

(1) $$x_{ij} \geqq 0 \qquad (i = 1,\ldots,m;\ j = 1,\ldots,n)$$

(2) $$\sum_i x_{ij} = 1 \qquad (j = 1,\ldots,n)$$

(3) $$\sum_j x_{ij} \leqq 1 \qquad (i = 1,\ldots,m).$$

(This assertion is easily reduced to the theorem of D. Kőnig that the convex hull of the n by n permutation matrices is exactly the doubly stochastic matrices; this is a somewhat uncomfortable fact since the same theorem will also solve the problem of choosing an S.D.R. However, this does not vitiate the problem as an illustration of the method.) To simplify the treatment of the dual program, it is convenient to enlarge this polyhedron, replacing (2) by

(2') $$\sum_i x_{ij} \leqq 1 \qquad (j = 1,\ldots,n).$$

The dual program then asks for the minimum of $\Sigma_i u_i + \Sigma_j v_j$ where $u_i \geqq 0$ and $v_j \geqq 0$ are chosen so that $u_i + v_j \geqq a_{ij}$ for all i and j. Trivially, all of the u_i and v_j can be chosen to be 0 or 1, and the dual combinatorial problem is:

> Choose the smallest total number of elements a_i and sets S_j such that, if $a_i \in S_j$, then a_i or S_j is chosen.

By the duality theorem of linear programming, this minimum is equal to the maximum number of distinct representatives in a trial. If there is no S.D.R and hence both maximum and minimum are less than n, then the k sets not chosen in the solution to the dual program must contain fewer than k distinct elements among them. Since the converse is trivial, this proves the theorem of P. Hall:

> There exists an S.D.R if and only if every k of the sets of the family contain at least k distinct elements.

In PAPER 10, this method is applied to prove the following generalization of Hall's Theorem:

> Let $\{S_1, \ldots, S_n\}$ be a family of subsets of a given set S. Let there be given a finite partition of S into disjoint subsets T_k with associated integers $0 \leqq c_k \leqq d_k$, for $k = 1, \ldots, p$. The cardinality of a set A is denoted by $\bar{A}$. In order that there exist a subset R of S that is an S.D.R. with $c_k \leqq \overline{R \cap T_k} \leqq d_k$ for $k = 1, \ldots, p$, it is necessary and sufficient that
>
> $$\overline{(\cup_{j\in A} S_j) \cap (\cup_{k\in B} T_k)} \geqq \bar{A} - n + \sum_{k\in B} c_k$$
>
> and
>
> $$\overline{(\cup_{j\in A} S_j) \cap (\cup_{k\notin B} T_k)} \geqq \bar{A} - \sum_{k\in B} d_k$$
>
> for all subsets $A \subset \{1, \ldots, n\}$ and $B \subset \{1, \ldots, p\}$.

The methods used in this paper parallel the treatment of Hall's Theorem given above.

The problem of PAPER 11 asks for the smallest number of disjoint chains contained in a finite partially ordered set P such that every element of the set belongs to one of the chains. Thus, a trial is a decomposition of P into disjoint chains and the objective function (to be minimized) counts the number of chains in a trial. Suppose P contains n elements, denoted by $1, 2, \ldots, n$. A trial can be realized as an $(n+1)$ by $(n+1)$ matrix $X = (x_{ij})$ of zeros and ones as follows:

$x_{0j} = 1$ if j is the initial element of a chain;
$x_{i0} = 1$ if i is the terminal element of a chain;
$x_{00} = n - k$ if k is the number of chains;
$x_{ij} = 1$ if i immediately precedes j in a chain;

where $i, j = 0, 1, 2, \ldots, n$ and all other $x_{ij} = 0$. The objective function (to be maximized) can then be taken to be the linear form

$$C \cdot X = \sum_{i,j} c_{ij} x_{ij}$$

where $C = (c_{ij})$ is defined by $c_{00} = 1$ and $c_{ij} = 0$ otherwise. If i does not immediately precede j in P, the definition of c_{ij} is immaterial since $x_{ij} = 0$ for such pairs in all trials.

To convert this problem into one of transportation type, the authors use the convex polyhedron composed of all $X = (x_{ij})$ which are nonnegative and satisfy

$$\sum_{j=0}^{n} x_{0j} = \sum_{i=0}^{n} x_{i0} = n$$

$$\sum_{j=0}^{n} x_{ij} = 1 \qquad (i = 1, \ldots, n)$$

$$\sum_{i=0}^{n} x_{ij} = 1 \qquad (j = 1, \ldots, n)$$

and redefine $c_{ij} = -\infty$ for those i not preceding j. The extreme points of the polyhedron which have $x_{ij} = 0$ for $c_{ij} = -\infty$ have an obvious interpretation as trials. The dual to this linear program asks in a natural way for the largest number of mutually incomparable elements of P. Therefore, the duality theorem asserts the equality of this number with the smallest number of chains in a trial decomposition and proves the finite case of a theorem of Dilworth.

The problem discussed in PAPER 12 arose in the study of transportation networks and, although it is not as clearly combinatorial as the situations of Papers 10 and 11, it yields to a similar attack. Consider a network connecting two nodes by way of a number of intermediate arcs and nodes, and suppose that these can handle certain limited amounts of traffic per unit time. Assuming a steady state condition, find a maximal flow of traffic from one given node (the source) to the other (the sink). When this problem is formulated as a linear program, the dual program asks for a "cut" in the network (i.e., a collection of nodes and arcs that meets every chain from source to sink) with minimum total capacity. A simple device permits the derivation of the following theorem of Menger as a corollary: The maximum number of pairwise node-disjoint chains joining two given disjoint sets of nodes of a linear graph is equal to the minimum number of nodes necessary to separate the sets.

In applying the method of Papers 10, 11, and 12 to combinatorial problems, the most difficult step is the formulation of a linear program equivalent to the original situation. Although almost any choice of variables suggests natural linear constraints, the difficulty consists in showing that these insure solutions among the original integral trials. For example, in the problem of systems of distinct representatives discussed above, the natural constraints are given by (1), (2), and (3). It is clear that the trials are among the extreme points of the polyhedron defined by these relations, but this does not exclude the existence of extreme points other than the trials. However, if it were known that every extreme solution of this system had all integral coordinates, then every extreme solution must be a trial. This follows directly from the fact that the only integral values for the x_{ij} are 0 or 1, and thus (1), (2), and (3), when applied to integral values, parallel the definition of a trial exactly. In varying degrees, the same statement is true of each of the problems in Papers 10, 11, and 12; namely, if it were known that the only extreme solutions of the relations used in the linear program formulations had all integral coordinates, then the appropriateness of those formulations could be established directly.

PAPER 13 was written to fill this need; it seeks to characterize a wide class of linear programs which have integral solutions irrespective of their objective functions. In geometric terms, let P be a convex polyhedron defined as the set of all n-vectors x, such that $b \leq Ax \leq b'$ for a given integral m by n matrix A and m-vectors b and b', whose components are integers or $\pm\infty$. Let the rank of A be r. It is shown that every face of P contains an integral point (for all vectors b and b') if and only if, in every set of r linearly independent rows of A, the greatest common divisor of all r by r minor determinants is 1. If P is further restricted by the inequalities $c \leq x \leq c'$ (for n-vectors c and c', whose components are integers or $\pm\infty$), then every face contains an integral point (for all b, b', c, and c') if and only if every minor determinant of A is 0 or ± 1. Applied to a linear program with a matrix A enjoying this "unimodular property," this theorem asserts that both the program and its dual will have polyhedra of feasible vectors with all integral extreme points. Therefore, it is important to have convenient sufficient conditions for a matrix to have the unimodular property. The most general result of this type proved in the paper is the following:

> Suppose G is an oriented graph (with no singular edges and at most one edge joining two vertices), P is a set of directed paths in G, and A is the incidence matrix

> of the vertices of G versus the paths in P. If every cycle in G contains an even number of edges and has adjacent pairs of edges oppositely oriented, then the matrix A has the unimodular property.

Two special cases of this theorem are stated, applying directly to the matrix A, and deriving from the integrality of the transportation problem and certain caterer-type problems, respectively.

The historical source of interest in integral solutions to linear programs can be found in the transportation problem, where Dantzig first noted that his Simplex Method only involved additions and subtractions, and thus yielded integral answers from integral data. Without entering into the details of the Simplex Method one can describe Dantzig's observation as follows: Let A be the $(m+n)$ by mn constraint matrix of a transportation problem with m sources and n destinations. In each column there are exactly two entries equal to 1, one in the first m rows, the other in the last n rows. All other entries are 0. Every possible pair of non-zero entries satisfying these conditions appears in some column. Then, the Dantzig Property is:

> If a column of A is represented as a linear combination of linearly independent columns, then the coefficients in the combination are 0, + 1, or - 1.

PAPER 14 considers a natural extension of this theorem; in a somewhat simplified form, it may be paraphrased in the following terms. Let A be a matrix with $m+n$ rows and such that, in each column, the non-zero entries are either: (a) a single entry of 1, or (b) two entries of 1, one in the first m rows, the other in the last n rows, or (c) two entries, + 1 and - 1, both appearing in the first m rows or in the last n rows. It is then shown that this wider class of matrices still enjoys the Dantzig Property. A straightforward application of Cramer's Rule establishes that this is equivalent to the unimodular property discussed in Paper 13. An editorial appendix to Paper 14 establishes this connection explicitly and demonstrates that, for matrices with but two non-zero elements in each column, the enlarged class of matrices is the best possible.

Although it is cast in purely geometric terms, the problem solved in PAPER 15 arose in an attempt to apply linear programming techniques to a combinatorial problem. This paper deals with the convex hulls of finite sets of points in a Euclidean space, i.e., with bounded convex polyhedra. The intersection of such a polyhedron with any one of its supporting hyperplanes is called a face. Two distinct vertices are said to be neighbors if the segment joining them is a face or, less explicitly, if they are joined by an edge of the polyhedron. It is shown that, for every positive integer n, there exists a polyhedron in $2m$-space with n vertices such that the convex hull of every set of m of the vertices is a face. Thus, in four-dimensional Euclidean space, there exist polyhedra with an arbitrary number of vertices such that every two vertices are neighbors. The construction is carried out by means of an even distribution of points on the surface of a k-sphere in $(k+1)$-space. Precisely, for any positive integers k and j there always exist sets of $2j + k$ points on the surface of the k-sphere such that every open hemisphere contains at least j points, and the existence of such sets leads directly to the required polyhedra.

Viewed with the hindsight provided by recent research, linear programming and matrix games share historical and mathematical sources with certain models of general economic equilibrium. This connection is seen most clearly in the work of Wald on the existence and uniqueness of a solution to the Walrasian equation systems of mathematical economics, and in the original expanding linear model of production studied by von Neumann. Papers 16, 17, and 18 continue the investigations initiated by these pioneers.

Wald dealt with a static model of production in which a prescribed endowment of the factors of production is used to produce certain goods; the output of each good is assumed to be a linear form in the inputs of the factors of production. A static demand structure, relating the prices of the goods to the quantities produced, is also assumed. The object of the model is to determine the bill-of-goods to be produced and the prices of the goods and of the factors of production. At equilibrium, the cost of each good in factors of production is to equal its market price. The endowment of each factor of production is to be sufficient for the goods produced; any factor present in excess is priced zero. Wald's achievement was the construction of a simple set of hypotheses, sufficient to establish a unique solution with nonnegative quantities and prices. Although the economic validity of these assumptions is questionable, this was the first time that a system of equations for a static general equilibrium had been shown to have a solution by rigorous methods. The proof given by Wald is highly ingenious, but also extremely difficult, so that the paper has been often cited but little read. In PAPER 16, Wald's theorem is re-examined in the light of linear programming techniques and the interplay of the various assumptions is analyzed in some detail. It is shown that there is a pair of dual linear programs implicit in the Walrasian equations of equilibrium, one asking for a maximum revenue from the goods produced, the other demanding a minimum accounting cost for the available factors of production. By this observation, the existence of an equilibrium for a set of fixed prices for the goods becomes a consequence of the duality theorem for linear programming, and the problem is reduced to that of satisfying the demand relations. This question, intrinsically non-algebraic, is settled by an application of the Kakutani fixed-point theorem. A final section treats a modification of Wald's hypotheses that is suggested by the linear programming proof.

Von Neumann's closed linear model of production, which was constructed independently, contains limited dynamic aspects. It describes an economy that operates within a unit time period to convert certain nonnegative amounts $a = (a_1, \ldots, a_n)$ of n goods into nonnegative amounts $b = (b_1, \ldots, b_n)$ of the same goods. The model of production is defined by giving the set Z of all achievable processes $c = (a, b)$ as a subset of 2n-space. Von Neumann imposed the following conditions:

(1) The set Z is a polyhedral convex cone spanned by m basic processes $c_i = (a_{i1}, \ldots, a_{in}, b_{i1}, \ldots, b_{in})$ for $i = 1, \ldots, m$. In economic terms, this means that the goods are produced by a finite set of basic processes with constant returns to scale and that the processes can be operated simultaneously at any nonnegative intensities $x = (x_1, \ldots, x_m)$ with additive outputs. Thus, every achievable process can be represented as (xA, xB) for suitable intensities x, where A and B are the two m by n matrices (a_{ij}) and (b_{ij}), respectively.

(2) Every good appears either as an input or as an output of each basic process. That is, $a_{ij} + b_{ij} > 0$ for all i and j.

The economy, when operating the process $c = (a, b)$, assures an expansion of the amount of good j available for input in the next time period by the factor $\alpha_j(a, b) = b_j/a_j$ (where $\alpha_j = \infty$ if $a_j = 0$ and $b_j \neq 0$ but is undefined if $a_j = b_j = 0$). The rate of productive expansion of the economy for the process (a, b) is defined to be $\alpha(a, b) = \min \alpha_j(a, b)$. The basic processes can then be operated at intensities x such that $xB \geqq \alpha xA$. To define an equilibrium for this model, introduce prices $y = (y_1, \ldots, y_n)$ that are not all zero. At these prices, the process (a, b) will be said to operate at the economic expansion rate $\beta(a, b; y) = \Sigma_j b_j y_j / \Sigma_j a_j y_j$. The rate of economic expansion of the economy at the prices y is then defined to be

$$\beta(y) = \max_{(a,b)} \beta(a, b; y)$$

and satisfies $By \leqq \beta Ay$. This vector can be given the following economic interpretation: $\beta(y)$ determines an interest rate; no process yields a greater money return than could be achieved by investing money at this rate. An equilibrium for this model is achieved when the goods that are overproduced (as measured by α) are priced zero, and the processes that are inefficient (as measured by β) are operated at zero intensity. With these definitions and assuming (1) and (2), von Neumann's theorem asserts the existence of equilibrium intensities and prices with a unique common value $\alpha = \beta$ for the productive and economic expansion rates.

Most of the criticism of the von Neumann model has been directed at the economic naturalness of (2). PAPER 17 considers the effect of replacing (2) by:

(2') Every basic process needs some good as an input; every good is the output of some basic process. That is, each row of A and each column of B contains a positive entry.

The main theorem of this paper (obtained by G. Thompson with J. G. Kemeny and O. Morgenstern and given a new proof here) asserts the existence of equilibrium intensities and prices with a common value for the expansion rates. This common rate is no longer unique; however, there are but a finite number of expansion rates for which $xBy > 0$, i.e., for which the total value of all goods produced is positive. The proof uses the natural equivalence between the equilibria and the optimal mixed strategies for the matrix game with payoff matrix $B - \alpha A$, where the rate α is chosen so as to give this game the value zero. A numerical example demonstrates that the problem is not always solvable over the rational field even if the basic processes have integral components.

The von Neumann model is also the starting point of PAPER 18, which presents a detailed treatment of the consequences of various sets of hypotheses. A distinctive feature of this paper is the elementary nature of the proofs which provide an essentially self-contained account of the theory. For the most general model considered, the following assumptions are made:

(1') The set Z of processes is a closed convex cone (and is not necessarily polyhedral).

(2') Every non-zero process needs some good as input; every good is the output of some process.

In this paper the productive expansion rate of the model is defined to be $\alpha_M = \max \alpha(a, b)$, where the maximum is taken over all non-zero processes in Z, and the economic expansion rate is defined to be $\beta_m = \min \beta(y)$, where the minimum is taken over all prices y. Processes that achieve the expansion rate α_M are said to be optimal. The first main result then asserts that there is always an optimal process $(\bar{a}, \bar{b})$ and prices y such that

$$\max_{(a,b)} \beta(a, b; y) = \beta(\bar{a}, \bar{b}; y) = \alpha_M .$$

Such prices are said to be optimal; goods that are overproduced in an optimal process are necessarily optimally priced zero. If every good is produced in every optimal process, the model is said to be regular and $\alpha_M = \beta_m$.

When Z is specialized to be a polyhedral cone, the existence of von Neumann equilibria (with possibly non-unique expansion rates) is assured. If, in addition, the model is regular, the equality of α_M and β_m leads to statements that are analogous to the duality theorem of linear programming and the main theorem of matrix games. As a natural condition to insure regularity for von Neumann models, the following is proposed:

> Every submodel (i.e., subset of the basic processes that produces every good consumed within the subset) has all of the goods as outputs.

Three examples illustrate the numerical irrationality of the equilibria, the possible multiplicity of equilibria when $\alpha_M > \beta_m$, and the possibility of $\alpha_M = \beta_m$ for non-regular models. A final section treats the special case of a Leontief model, i.e., a von Neumann model in which each basic process produces exactly one of the goods; the principal results here concern the possible reduction of the model into submodels.

This Study concludes with a Bibliography that presents a selection of papers and books bearing on linear inequalities. In the main, the entries have been chosen from the areas treated in the papers of this volume. Recent research in linear programming, both practical and theoretical, has been given particular attention.

The editing and preparing of this Study has been done at Princeton University in the Department of Mathematics, as part of the work of a Logistics Project sponsored by the Office of Naval Research. Members of the Project who have participated in this work have been M. Frank, A. J. Goldman, J. H. Griesmer, J. J. Kohn, R. Z. Norman, M. Richardson, M. Sion, Philip Wolfe, and the undersigned. The papers have been refereed by members of the Project with the generous assistance of A. Charnes, G. B. Dantzig, Ky Fan, D. R. Fulkerson, David Gale, J. W. Green, O. Gross, I. Heller, A. J. Hoffman, J. B. Kruskal, J. T. Robacker, and R. Solow. The inclusion of a Bibliography has been made possible by painstaking effort on the part of Mrs. Lily Atiyah and J. H. Griesmer. The typing of the master copy has been done with care and dispatch by Mrs. Euthie Anthony; special characters and the figures were prepared by Mrs. Ruth Hoff and Richard Snedeker. The entire endeavor has benefited from the sympathetic interest of H. S.

Bailey, Jr., Director of the Princeton University Press. To all these individuals, for their friendly cooperation, and to the contributing authors, for their patience, we express our sincere thanks.

July 1956

H. W. Kuhn
A. W. Tucker

CONTENTS

LINEAR INEQUALITIES AND RELATED SYSTEMS

DUAL SYSTEMS OF HOMOGENEOUS LINEAR RELATIONS*

A. W. Tucker

The aim of this paper is to furnish some fundamental information about the homogeneous linear systems which underlie the nonhomogeneous linear systems arising in Matrix Games and dual Linear Programs. In part, this information can be regarded as sharpening and consolidating certain "transposition theorems": the classical theorems of Farkas [3], Gordan [5] and Stiemke [9], the Transposition Theorem of Motzkin [7], and the Theorem of the Alternative for Matrices of von Neumann and Morgenstern [8] (numbers in square brackets refer to the bibliography at the end of the paper). But, in part, it is quite new information about a formal tabular property of "complementary slackness" which pertains to dual systems of wide generality (see Theorem 6) and to self-dual systems (see Theorem 7).

The systems of homogeneous linear relations to be studied consist of homogeneous linear inequalities, written uniformly $\geqq 0$, and possibly also linear equations. Specifically, we deal with the following systems, four pairs of "dual" systems and one "self-dual" system:

1. $A^T U \geqq 0,$ and $AX > 0, \quad X \geqq 0.$

2. $A^T U \geqq 0, \quad B^T U = 0,$ and $AX + BY = 0, \quad X \geqq 0.$

3. $V \geqq 0, \quad C^T V \geqq 0,$ and $-CX \geqq 0, \quad X \geqq 0.$

4. $V \geqq 0, \quad A^T U + C^T V \geqq 0, \quad B^T U + D^T V = 0$ and $-AX - BY = 0, \quad -CX - DY \geqq 0, \quad X \geqq 0.$

5. $KW \geqq 0, \quad W \geqq 0, \quad (K^T = -K).$

The letters A, B, C, D, K denote matrices (rectangular in general, except K which is square) and U, V, W, X, Y denote vectors (treated as one-column matrices). The superscript T indicates transposition; each

---

* This paper was written for the Office of Naval Research Logistics Project in the Department of Mathematics at Princeton University.

vector inequality ($\geqq 0$) holds for every component individually. It will be noticed that the first three pairs of dual systems can be regarded as special cases of the fourth: take B, C, D vacuous and change $-AX = 0$ into $AX = 0$ to get the first pair; take C, D vacuous and change $-AX - BY = 0$ into $AX + BY = 0$ to get the second pair; and take A, B, D vacuous to get the third pair. The self-dual system (No. 5), which has special importance in the Theory of Linear Programming (see Paper 4 in this Study), arises from the third pair of dual systems by taking C skew-symmetric and setting $K = C^T$.

To explain the sense in which the term <u>dual</u> is here being used, we exhibit the left and right systems of the general case (No. 4, above) in the following greater detail:

$$
\begin{array}{rlr}
(u_h \text{ unrestricted}) & -\Sigma_j a_{hj} x_j - \Sigma_k b_{hk} y_k = 0 & (h = 1,\dots,p) \\
v_i \geqq 0 & -\Sigma_j c_{ij} x_j - \Sigma_k d_{ik} y_k \geqq 0 & (i = 1,\dots,m) \\
\Sigma_h a_{hj} u_h + \Sigma_i c_{ij} v_i \geqq 0 & x_j \geqq 0 & (j = 1,\dots,n) \\
\Sigma_h b_{hk} u_h + \Sigma_i d_{ik} v_i = 0 & (y_k \text{ unrestricted}) & (k = 1,\dots,q)
\end{array}
$$

It will be noticed (1) that there is a one-to-one correspondence between unrestricted variables in one system and equations in the other, indexed by h and k, and between nonnegative variables in one system and "fully coefficiented" inequalities in the other, indexed by i and j, and (2) that the arrays of coefficients at lower left and upper right are such that the array in one system is the <u>negative transpose</u> of the array in the other. This prescription enables one to pass by a well-defined procedure from a given system of homogeneous linear inequalities and/or equations involving nonnegative and/or unrestricted variables to a second such system. The procedure is reversible, as duality should be: if system α has system β as dual, then β has α as dual. The following small-scale example serves to illustrate a general pair of dual systems (No. 4, above).

					$-x_1$	$+x_2$		$-x_4$	$-y_1$	$+y_2$	$= 0$
	v_1			$\geqq 0$*	$-x_1$	$+x_2$	$-x_3$		$-y_1$		$\geqq 0$
		v_2		$\geqq 0$	x_1		$+x_3$	$-x_4$	$-y_1$	$-y_2$	$\geqq 0$*
			v_3	$\geqq 0$*		$-x_2$	$-x_3$	$-x_4$		$+y_2$	$\geqq 0$
u_1	$+v_1$	$-v_2$		$\geqq 0$	x_1						$\geqq 0$*
$-u_1$	$-v_1$		$+v_3$	$\geqq 0$*		x_2					$\geqq 0$
	v_1	$-v_2$	$+v_3$	$\geqq 0$*			x_3				$\geqq 0$
u_1		$+v_2$	$+v_3$	$\geqq 0$				x_4			$\geqq 0$*
u_1	$+v_1$	$+v_2$		$= 0$							
$-u_1$		$+v_2$	$-v_3$	$= 0$							

REMARK. The starred inequalities in this example exhibit the property of "complementary slackness" that will be established in Theorem 6 for a general pair of dual systems. For reference at that time, we observe that

$$(u_1;\ v_1,v_2,v_3) = (-1;\ 1,0,1) \quad \text{and} \quad (x_1,x_2,x_3,x_4;\ y_1,y_2) = (2,0,0,1;\ -2,1)$$

are solutions of the left and right systems which satisfy the starred inequalities as strict inequalities (> 0) and the remaining relations as equations $(= 0)$.

* * * * * * *

We begin with a lemma concerning the pair of dual systems $A^TU \geqq 0$ and $AX = 0,\ X \geqq 0$, where

$$A = [A_1,\ \ldots,\ A_n]$$

is an n-columned matrix with arbitrary real entries (but we could work equally well in the rational field or in any ordered field). We use an argument adapted from an unpublished proof by David Gale of the Fundamental Theorem of Hermann Weyl [13] that the convex hull of finitely many half-lines is the intersection of finitely many halfspaces.

LEMMA. The dual systems

$$A^TU \geqq 0 \quad \text{and} \quad AX = 0,\ X \geqq 0$$

possess solutions U and X such that

$$A_1^TU + x_1 > 0.$$

PROOF. We proceed by induction on n, the number of columns in A. The initial case $n = 1$ is trivial: if $A_1 = 0$, take $U = 0$ and $x_1 = 1$; if $A_1 \neq 0$ take $U = A_1$ and $x_1 = 0$.

We now assume that the Lemma holds for a matrix A of n columns and proceed to prove it for a matrix

$$\bar{A} = [A,\ A_{n+1}] = [A_1,\ \ldots,\ A_n,\ A_{n+1}]$$

of $n + 1$ columns. Applying the Lemma to A, we get U and X such that

$$A^TU \geqq 0,\ AX = 0,\ X \geqq 0,\ A_1^TU + x_1 > 0.$$

If $A_{n+1}^T U \geqq 0$, we take $\bar{X} = (X, 0)$. Then

$$\bar{A}^T U \geqq 0, \ \bar{A}\bar{X} = 0, \ \bar{X} \geqq 0, \ A_1^T U + x_1 > 0,$$

which extends the Lemma to the matrix $\bar{A} = [A, A_{n+1}]$.

However, if $A_{n+1}^T U < 0$, we apply the Lemma again to a matrix

$$B = [B_1, \ldots, B_n] = [A_1 + \lambda_1 A_{n+1}, \ldots, A_n + \lambda_n A_{n+1}],$$

where

$$\lambda_j = - A_j^T U / A_{n+1}^T U \geqq 0 \qquad (j = 1, \ldots, n)$$

so that

$$B^T U = 0.$$

This second use of the Lemma yields V and Y such that

$$B^T V \geqq 0, \ BY = 0, \ Y \geqq 0, \ B_1^T V + y_1 > 0.$$

We take $\bar{Y} = (Y, \Sigma \lambda_j y_j)$. Then

$$\bar{A}\bar{Y} = 0 \quad \text{and} \quad \bar{Y} \geqq 0$$

because $Y \geqq 0$, $\Sigma \lambda_j y_j \geqq 0$ and because

$$\bar{A}\bar{Y} = [A, A_{n+1}]\bar{Y} = BY = 0.$$

We now take $W = V + \mu U$, where

$$\mu = - A_{n+1}^T V / A_{n+1}^T U,$$

so that

$$A_{n+1}^T W = 0.$$

Then

$$\bar{A}^T W \geqq 0 \quad \text{and} \quad A_1^T W + y_1 > 0$$

because

$$\begin{aligned} A^T W &= B^T W && \text{(since } A_{n+1}^T W = 0\text{)} \\ &= B^T V && \text{(since } B^T U = 0\text{)} \\ &\geqq 0 && \text{(by choice of } V \text{ above)} \end{aligned}$$

and because

$$A_1^T W + y_1 = B_1^T V + y_1 > 0 \qquad \text{(by above).}$$

Thus, by means of W and Y, we have extended the Lemma to the matrix $\bar{A} = [A, A_{n+1}]$.

In the last two paragraphs, by considering the two mutually exclusive possibilities $A_{n+1}^T U \geqq 0$ and $A_{n+1}^T U < 0$, we have succeeded in extending the Lemma from the n-columned matrix A to the (n+1)-columned matrix $\bar{A} = [A, A_{n+1}]$. Therefore the induction on n is fully established and the Lemma must hold for all n. This completes the proof of the Lemma.

COROLLARY. If the inequality $A_0^T U \geqq 0$ holds for all solutions U of the system $A^T U \geqq 0$, then $A_0 = AX$ for some $X \geqq 0$.

PROOF. We apply the Lemma to the dual systems

$$[-A_0, A]^T U \geqq 0 \quad \text{and} \quad [-A_0, A] \begin{bmatrix} x_0 \\ X \end{bmatrix} = 0, \begin{bmatrix} x_0 \\ X \end{bmatrix} \geqq 0,$$

in which $-A_0$ and x_0 assume the leading positions held by A_1 and x_1 in the Lemma itself. We are thus assured of some U and x_0, X such that

$$-A_0^T U \geqq 0, \; A^T U \geqq 0, \; -A_0 x_0 + AX = 0, \; x_o \geqq 0, \; X \geqq 0,$$

$$\text{and} \quad -A_0^T U + x_0 > 0.$$

But, by the hypothesis of the Corollary, $A_0^T U \geqq 0$ since $A^T U \geqq 0$. Hence $x_0 > A_0^T U \geqq 0$. Therefore $A_0 = AX^0$ for $X^0 = X/x_0 \geqq 0$. This completes the proof.

This Corollary is a classical theorem of J. Farkas (see [3], page 5). It will recur in geometric form in Paper 2, "Polyhedral Convex Cones," as the theorem (Theorem 3) that a polyhedral convex cone is the polar of its polar, and in Paper 3, "Resolution and Separation Theorems for Polyhedral Convex Sets," as the separation theorem (Lemma 3) for a polyhedral convex cone and an individual vector.

THEOREM 1. The dual systems

$$A^T U \geqq 0 \quad \text{and} \quad AX = 0,\ X \geqq 0$$

possess solutions U^* and X^* such that

$$A^T U^* + X^* > 0.$$

[Note: $A^T U^* + X^* > 0$ means that all components of $A^T U^* + X^*$ are positive.]

PROOF. In the Lemma the column A_1 played a special rôle. But, by renumbering, any column A_j could equally well play that special rôle. Consequently, for $j = 1, \ldots, n$, there exist pairs U^j, X^j such that

$$A^T U^j \geqq 0,\ AX^j = 0,\ X^j \geqq 0,\ A_j^T U^j + x_j^j > 0.$$

Take $U^* = \Sigma_j U^j$, $X^* = \Sigma_j X^j$. Then

$$A^T U^* = \Sigma_j A^T U^j \geqq 0,\ AX^* = \Sigma_j AX^j = 0,\ X^* = \Sigma_j X^j \geqq 0.$$

Moreover, for $j = 1, \ldots, n$,

$$A_j^T U^* + x_j^* = \Sigma_k \left(A_j^T U^k + x_j^k \right) \geqq A_j^T U^j + x_j^j > 0$$

because

$$A_j^T U^k + x_j^k \geqq 0 \qquad (\text{since } A^T U^k \geqq 0,\ X^k \geqq 0)$$

and

$$A_j^T U^j + x_j^j > 0 \qquad (\text{as constructed above}).$$

Therefore

$$A^T U^* + X^* > 0,$$

which completes the proof.

COROLLARY 1A. The system of equations $AX = 0$ has (i) a fully positive solution X (> 0) if there is no U such that $A^T U \geqq 0$ and $\neq 0$, and (ii) a nonnegative non-trivial solution X $(\geqq 0$ and

$\neq 0$) if there is no U such that $A^T U > 0$.

PROOF. By Theorem 1 there exist U^* and X^* such that

$$A^T U^* \geqq 0, \ AX^* = 0, \ X^* \geqq 0, \quad \text{and} \quad A^T U^* + X^* > 0.$$

Either $A^T U^* = 0$ or $A^T U^* \neq 0$; in the former case $X^* > 0$. This establishes (i). Also, either $X^* \neq 0$ or $X^* = 0$; in the latter case $A^T U^* > 0$. This establishes (ii) and completes the proof.

Parts (i) and (ii) of Corollary 1A are Theorems I and II of E. Stiemke [9]. Part (ii) was published still earlier by P. Gordan [5]; it seems to be the earliest known instance of a "transposition theorem."

THEOREM 2. The dual systems

$$A^T U \geqq 0, \ B^T U = 0 \quad \text{and} \quad AX + BY = 0, \ X \geqq 0$$

possess solutions U^* and X^*, Y^* such that

$$A^T U^* + X^* > 0.$$

PROOF. We apply Theorem 1 to the dual systems

$$[A, B, -B]^T U \geqq 0 \quad \text{and} \quad [A, B, -B] \begin{bmatrix} X \\ Y_1 \\ Y_2 \end{bmatrix} = 0, \ \begin{bmatrix} X \\ Y_1 \\ Y_2 \end{bmatrix} \geqq 0$$

to get U^* and X^*, Y_1^*, Y_2^* such that

$$A^T U^* \geqq 0, \ B^T U^* \geqq 0, \ -B^T U^* \geqq 0, \ AX^* + BY_1^* - BY_2^* = 0, \ X^* \geqq 0, \ Y_1^* \geqq 0, \ Y_2^* \geqq 0$$

and

$$A^T U^* + X^* > 0, \ B^T U^* + Y_1^* > 0, \ -B^T U^* + Y_2^* > 0.$$

Take $Y^* = Y_1^* - Y_2^*$. Then

$$A^T U^* \geqq 0, \ B^T U^* = 0, \ AX^* + BY^* = 0, \ X^* \geqq 0$$

and

$$A^T U^* + X^* > 0.$$

This completes the proof.

COROLLARY 2A. Let the dual systems

$$A^T U \geqq 0,\ B^T U = 0 \quad \text{and} \quad AX + BY = 0,\ X \geqq 0$$

have the partitioned presentation

$$A^{1T} U \geqq 0,\ A^{2T} U \geqq 0,\ B^T U = 0$$

and

$$A^1 X_1 + A^2 X_2 + BY = 0,\ X_1 \geqq 0,\ X_2 \geqq 0,$$

where A^1 is any nonvacuous set of columns of A and A^2 is the set (possibly vacuous) of remaining columns of A. Then (i) either the left system has a solution U such that $A^{1T}U \neq 0$ or the right system has a solution X such that $X_1 > 0$. Also (ii) either the left system has a solution U such that $A^{1T}U > 0$ or the right system has a solution X such that $X_1 \neq 0$.

PROOF. By Theorem 1 there exist $U*$ and X_1^*, X_2^* such that

$$A^{1T}U* \geqq 0,\ A^{2T}U* \geqq 0,\ B^T U* = 0,\ A^1 X_1^* + A^2 X_2^* + BY* = 0,\ X_1^* \geqq 0,\ X_2^* \geqq 0,$$

and

$$A^{1T}U* + X_1^* > 0,\ A^{2T}U* + X_2^* > 0.$$

Either $A^{1T}U* \neq 0$ or $A^{1T}U* = 0$; in the latter case $X_1^* > 0$, since $A^{1T}U* + X_1^* > 0$. This establishes (i). Also, either $X_1^* = 0$ or $X_1^* \neq 0$; in the former case $A^{1T}U* > 0$, since $A^{1T}U* + X_1^* > 0$. This establishes (ii) and completes the proof.

The alternatives in parts (i) and (ii) of Corollary 2A are mutually exclusive because $U^T(AX + BY) = 0$ for any solutions of the dual systems (this is an aspect of the general "complementary slackness" to be established later in Theorem 6). Part (ii) is the Transposition Theorem of T. S. Motzkin (see [7], page 51). When the matrix B is vacuous, (i) and (ii) become "theorems of alternatives" for the pair of matrices A^1, A^2 (see [10], [1]); these two-matrix transposition theorems have various geometric interpretations (see [10], [11]), one of which appears as the Separation Theorem (Theorem 2) of Paper 3 in this Study. From a standpoint of logic, transposition theorems may be viewed as asserting the disjoint alternatives of solvability <u>or</u> contradiction via linear combination (see [6]).

THEOREM 3. The dual systems

$$V \geqq 0,\ C^T V \geqq 0 \quad \text{and} \quad -CX \geqq 0,\ X \geqq 0$$

possess solutions V^* and X^* such that

$$V^* - CX^* > 0 \quad \text{and} \quad C^T V^* + X^* > 0.$$

PROOF. We apply Theorem 1 to the dual systems

$$[I, C]^T V \geqq 0 \quad \text{and} \quad [I, C] \begin{bmatrix} W \\ X \end{bmatrix} = 0,\ \begin{bmatrix} W \\ X \end{bmatrix} \geqq 0,$$

where I is an identity matrix. Thus there exist V^* and W^*, X^* such that

$$[I, C]^T V^* \geqq 0,\ [I, C] \begin{bmatrix} W^* \\ X^* \end{bmatrix} = 0,\ \begin{bmatrix} W^* \\ X^* \end{bmatrix} \geqq 0,\ [I, C]^T V^* + \begin{bmatrix} W^* \\ X^* \end{bmatrix} > 0.$$

That is,

$$V^* \geqq 0,\ C^T V^* \geqq 0,\ -CX^* = W^* \geqq 0,\ X^* \geqq 0,\ V^* - CX^* > 0,\ C^T V^* + X^* > 0.$$

This completes the proof.

By applying Theorem 3 to the payoff matrix C of a "fair" zero-sum two-person game, it is possible to obtain not only the Main Theorem of von Neumann and Morgenstern (see [8], page 154) but also the characterization of the "essential" or "active" pure strategies (first indicated by Bohnenblust, Karlin and Shapley in [2], page 54). [To make any given matrix game "fair" we subtract from all the given payoffs the least constant k which will produce a matrix C with the property that $-CX \geqq 0$ for some $X \geqq 0$ with $\Sigma x_j = 1$. This constant k, uniquely determined by a Dedekind cut, is the "value" of the given game; it can be imagined as the least side-payment from the first player to the second that would induce the second player to play the given game.]

COROLLARY 3A. The dual systems

$$V \geqq 0,\ C^T V \geqq 0 \quad \text{and} \quad -CX \geqq 0,\ X \geqq 0$$

possess solutions V^* and X^* for which the following alternatives hold:

$$
\begin{array}{llll}
(\;\text{i}) & \text{either} \quad C^TV^* \neq 0 & \text{or} & X^* > 0, \\
(\;\text{ii}) & \text{either} \quad C^TV^* > 0 & \text{or} & X^* \neq 0, \\
(\text{iii}) & \text{either} \quad V^* > 0 & \text{or} & -CX^* \neq 0, \\
(\;\text{iv}) & \text{either} \quad V^* \neq 0 & \text{or} & -CX^* > 0.
\end{array}
$$

This Corollary is an immediate consequence of Theorem 3. The alternatives in (i) - (iv) are mutually exclusive because $V^TCX = 0$ for all solutions of the dual systems (this is an aspect of the general "complementary slackness" to be established in Theorem 6). Parts (ii) and (iv) yield dual forms of the Theorem of the Alternative for Matrices of J. von Neumann and O. Morgenstern (see [8], pp. 140-141), as well as a similar earlier theorem of J. Ville (see [12], page 105).

THEOREM 4. The general dual systems

$$
\begin{array}{rcr}
(U \text{ unrestricted}) & \qquad & -AX - BY = 0 \\
V \geqq 0 & & -CX - DY \geqq 0 \\
A^TU + C^TV \geqq 0 & & X \geqq 0 \\
B^TU + D^TV = 0 & & (Y \text{ unrestricted})
\end{array}
$$

possess solutions U^*, V^* and X^*, Y^* such that

$$V^* - CX^* - DY^* > 0,$$

$$A^TU^* + C^TV^* + X^* > 0.$$

PROOF. We apply Theorem 3 to the dual systems

$$
\begin{bmatrix} U_1 \\ U_2 \\ V \end{bmatrix} \geqq 0, \quad
\begin{bmatrix} -A & -B & B \\ A & B & -B \\ C & D & -D \end{bmatrix}^T
\begin{bmatrix} U_1 \\ U_2 \\ V \end{bmatrix} \geqq 0
\quad \text{and} \quad
-\begin{bmatrix} -A & -B & B \\ A & B & -B \\ C & D & -D \end{bmatrix}
\begin{bmatrix} X \\ Y_1 \\ Y_2 \end{bmatrix} \geqq 0, \quad
\begin{bmatrix} X \\ Y_1 \\ Y_2 \end{bmatrix} \geqq 0.
$$

Thus there exist

$$U_1^* \geqq 0,\ U_2^* \geqq 0,\ V^* \geqq 0 \quad \text{and} \quad X^* \geqq 0,\ Y_1^* \geqq 0,\ Y_2^* \geqq 0$$

such that

$$
\begin{aligned}
- A^TU_1^* + A^TU_2^* + C^TV^* &\geqq 0 & AX^* + BY_1^* - BY_1^* &\geqq 0 \\
- B^TU_1^* + B^TU_2^* + D^TV^* &\geqq 0 & - AX^* - BY_1^* + BY_2^* &\geqq 0 \\
B^TU_1^* - B^TU_2^* - D^TV^* &\geqq 0 & - CX^* - DY_1^* + DY_2^* &\geqq 0 \\
- A^TU_1^* + A^TU_2^* + C^TV^* + X^* &> 0 & V^* - CX^* - DY_1^* + DY_2^* &> 0 \;.
\end{aligned}
$$

Take $U^* = U_2^* - U_1^*$ and $Y^* = Y_1^* - Y_2^*$. Then

$$
\begin{aligned}
A^TU^* + C^TV^* &\geqq 0 & - AX^* - BY^* &= 0 \\
B^TU^* + D^TV^* &= 0 & - CX^* - DY^* &\geqq 0 \\
A^TU^* + C^TV^* + X^* &> 0 & V^* - CX^* - DY^* &> 0 \;.
\end{aligned}
$$

This completes the proof.

THEOREM 5. The self-dual system

$$KW \geqq 0, \quad W \geqq 0 \qquad (K^T = - K)$$

has a solution W^* such that

$$KW^* + W^* > 0.$$

PROOF. We apply Theorem 3 (which depends on Theorem 1 and its preceding Lemma) to the skew-symmetric matrix $C = K^T = - K$. Then there exist V^* and X^* such that

$$V^* \geqq 0,\ KV^* \geqq 0,\ KX^* \geqq 0,\ X^* \geqq 0,\ V^* + KX^* > 0,\ KV^* + X^* > 0.$$

Hence

$$K(V^* + X^*) \geqq 0,\ V^* + X^* \geqq 0,\ K(V^* + X^*) + (V^* + X^*) > 0.$$

Take $W^* = V^* + X^*$. This completes the proof.

This theorem will be used in Paper 4, "Theory of Linear Programming," as an omnibus means of proving the basic duality and existence theorems of Linear Programming. It can also be used to establish the Main ("Minimax") Theorem for symmetric zero-sum two-person games and to characterize at the same time the "essential" or "active" pure strategies of such a game. [The solution of any zero-sum two-person game in normalized form can be obtained through the solution of an associated symmetric game (see [4]).]

* * * * * * *

The final section of this paper deals with the property of "complementary slackness" in pairs of dual systems and in a self-dual system.

DEFINITION. A <u>slack</u> inequality in a system is an inequality ($\geqq 0$) which is satisfied as a strict inequality (> 0) by some solution of the system.

Given a (mixed) system $A^TU \geqq 0$, $B^TU = 0$, let J denote the set of indices j such that $A_j^TU_j > 0$ for some solution U_j of the system; then ΣU_j, summed for all j in J, is a solution of the system which makes $A_j^T(\Sigma U_j) > 0$ for all j in J. This shows that the slack inequalities in a system can be characterized collectively as the maximum set of inequalities of the system which are satisfied as strict inequalities by some solution of the system. The remaining inequalities in a system are those which are satisfied as equations by all solutions of the system.

THEOREM 6. In the general dual systems

(U unrestricted)	$-AX - BY = 0$
$V \geqq 0$	$-CX - DY \geqq 0$
$A^TU + C^TV \geqq 0$	$X \geqq 0$
$B^TU + D^TV = 0$	(Y unrestricted)

each of the $m + n$ pairs of corresponding inequalities

$$v_i \geqq 0 \qquad -\Sigma_j c_{ij}x_j - \Sigma_k d_{ik}y_k \geqq 0 \qquad (i = 1, \ldots, m)$$

$$\Sigma_h a_{hj}u_h + \Sigma_i c_{ij}v_i \geqq 0 \qquad x_j \geqq 0 \qquad (j = 1, \ldots, n)$$

contains exactly one inequality that is slack (relative to its system).

PROOF. Let U, V and X, Y be <u>any</u> solutions of the dual systems. Then, by multiplying together corresponding items in the dual systems and summing, we have

$$(1) \quad -U^TAX - U^TBY = U^T(-AX - BY) = 0$$

$$(2) \quad -V^TCX - V^TDY = V^T(-CX - DY) \geqq 0$$

$$(3) \quad U^TAX + V^TCX = (A^TU + C^TV)^TX \geqq 0$$

$$(4) \quad U^TBY + V^TDY = (B^TU + D^TV)^TY = 0.$$

Adding (1) and (3) and also (2) and (4), we have

$$- U^T BY + V^T CX \geqq 0 \quad \text{and} \quad U^T BY - V^T CX \geqq 0.$$

So $U^T BY - V^T CX = 0$. Combining this with (1) and (4), we get

$$- U^T AX = U^T BY = V^T CX = - V^T DY.$$

When use is made of these equalities in (2) and (3), we see that

$$0 = V^T(- CX - DY) = \Sigma_i v_i (- \Sigma_j c_{ij} x_j - \Sigma_k d_{ik} y_k)$$

$$0 = (A^T U + C^T V)^T X = \Sigma_j (\Sigma_h a_{hj} u_h + \Sigma_i c_{ij} v_i) x_j .$$

These two equations show that in each pair of dual inequalities

$$v_i \geqq 0 \quad \text{and} \quad - \Sigma_j c_{ij} x_j - \Sigma_k d_{ik} y_k \geqq 0 \qquad (i=1,\ldots,m)$$

$$\Sigma_h a_{hj} u_j + \Sigma_i c_{ij} v_i \geqq 0 \quad \text{and} \quad x_j \geqq 0 \qquad (j=1,\ldots,n)$$

at least one sign of equality (=) must hold for all solutions; otherwise we would have $V^T(- CX - DY) > 0$ or $(A^T U + C^T V)^T X > 0$ for some solutions. Therefore each pair of dual inequalities contains at most one inequality that is slack.

But, by Theorem 4, there exist solutions U^*, V^* and X^*, Y^* of the dual systems such that

$$v_i^* + \left(- \Sigma_j c_{ij} x_j^* - \Sigma_k d_{ik} y_k^*\right) > 0 \qquad (i=1,\ldots,m)$$

$$\left(\Sigma_h a_{hj} u_h^* + \Sigma_i c_{ij} v_i^*\right) + x_j^* > 0 \qquad (j=1,\ldots,n).$$

Therefore each pair of corresponding inequalities contains at least one inequality that is slack.

Taken together, the last two paragraphs assert that each pair of corresponding inequalities in the dual systems contains exactly one inequality that is slack (relative to its system). This completes the proof.

The property that Theorem 6 attributes to the individual inequalities in a pair of dual systems can be described collectively as complementary slackness: the set of slack inequalities in the one system is exactly complementary to the set of slack inequalities in the other system. This is illustrated by the small-scale example of a general pair of dual systems given in the introductory part of this paper. The slack inequalities in each system of the example are starred to make it quite evident that opposite each slack inequality (at left or right) there is a non-slack inequality (at right or left), and conversely. The fact that the starred inequalities are slack (relative to their systems) is verified in a remark following the example; the fact that the remaining inequalities are not slack is a consequence of the first paragraph of the proof of Theorem 6.

The property of complementary slackness applies, of course, to the pairs of dual systems considered in Theorems 1-3, since Theorem 6 can be specialized to these pairs of dual systems by letting certain of the matrices A, B, C, D become vacuous. In particular, this shows that the alternatives in the various parts of Corollaries 1A, 2A and 3A are mutually exclusive.

THEOREM 7. In the self-dual system

$$KW \geqq 0, \; W \geqq 0 \qquad\qquad (K^T = -K)$$

each of the n pairs of corresponding inequalities

$$\Sigma_j k_{ij} w_j \geqq 0 \quad \text{and} \quad w_i \geqq 0 \qquad\qquad (i = 1, \ldots, n)$$

contains exactly one inequality that is slack (relative to the full self-dual system).

PROOF. For any W, $W^T KW = \Sigma\Sigma w_i k_{ij} w_j = 0$ because

$$W^T KW = \Sigma\Sigma w_i k_{ij} w_j = \Sigma\Sigma w_i(-k_{ji})w_j = -\Sigma\Sigma w_j k_{ji} w_i = -W^T KW.$$

Hence, in each pair of corresponding inequalities

$$\Sigma_j k_{ij} w_j \geqq 0 \quad \text{and} \quad w_i \geqq 0 \qquad\qquad (i = 1, \ldots, n)$$

at least one sign of equality (=) must hold for all solutions W; otherwise we would have $W^T KW > 0$ for some solution W. Therefore each pair of corresponding inequalities contains <u>at most</u> one inequality that is slack.

But, by Theorem 5, there exists a solution W^* such that

$$\Sigma_j k_{ij} w_j^* + w_i^* > 0. \qquad\qquad (i = 1, \ldots, n).$$

Therefore each pair of corresponding inequalities contains <u>at least</u> one inequality that is slack.

Taken together, the last two paragraphs assert that each pair of corresponding inequalities contains <u>exactly</u> one inequality that is slack (relative to the full self-dual system). This completes the proof.

The following small-scale example illustrates the complementary slackness within a self-dual system.

$$\begin{array}{rrrrl|rl}
 & -w_2 & +w_3 & -w_4 & \geqq 0 & w_1 & \geqq 0* \\
w_1 & & -w_3 & +w_4 & \geqq 0 & w_2 & \geqq 0* \\
-w_1 & +w_2 & & -w_4 & \geqq 0 & w_3 & \geqq 0* \\
w_1 & -w_2 & +w_3 & & \geqq 0* & w_4 & \geqq 0
\end{array}$$

The starred inequalities are slack (relative to the full system), as can easily be verified: $W = (1, 1, 1, 0)$ is a solution of the system which satisfies all four starred inequalities as strict inequalities. The fact that the remaining four ("complementary") inequalities are satisfied as equations by all solutions W of the self-dual system is a consequence of the proof above.

BIBLIOGRAPHY

[1] ANTOSIEWICZ, H. A., "A theorem on alternatives for pairs of matrices," Pacific J. Math. 5 (1955), 641-642.

[2] BOHNENBLUST, H. F., KARLIN, S., and SHAPLEY, L. S., "Solutions of discrete, two-person games," Contributions to the Theory of Games, Vol. I, pp. 51-72, Annals of Mathematics Study No. 24, Princeton, 1950.

[3] FARKAS, J., "Über die theorie der einfachen Ungleichungen," J. Reine Angew. Math. 124 (1902), pp. 1-24.

[4] GALE, D., KUHN, H. W., and TUCKER, A. W., "On symmetric games," Contributions to the Theory of Games, Vol. I, pp. 81-87, Annals of Mathematics Study No. 24, Princeton, 1950.

[5] GORDAN, P., "Über die Auflösungen linearer Gleichungen mit reelen Coefficienten," Math. Ann. 6 (1873), 23-28.

[6] KUHN, H. W., "Solvability and consistency for linear equations and inequalities," Amer. Math. Monthly 63 (1956), 217-232.

[7] MOTZKIN, T. S., Beiträge zur Theorie der Linearen Ungleichungen (Dissertation, Basel, 1933) Jerusalem, 1936.

[8] von NEUMANN, J., and MORGENSTERN, O., Theory of Games and Economic Behavior, Princeton, 1944 (3rd edition 1953).

[9] STIEMKE, E., "Über positive Lösungen homogener linearer Gleichungen," Math. Ann. 76 (1915), 340-342.

[10] TUCKER, A. W., "Theorems of alternatives for pairs of matrices,"

Symposium on Linear Inequalities and Programming, A. Orden and L. Goldstein, eds., pp. 180-181, Comptroller, Hq. USAF, Washington, D. C., 1952. Also Abstract No. 76, Bull. Amer. Math. Soc. 56 (1950), 57.

[11] TUCKER, A. W., Game Theory and Programming, pp. 32-44, College Bookstore, Oklahoma A. and M. C., Stillwater, Okla. 1955. Also Abstract No. 214, Bull. Amer. Math. Soc. 61 (1955), 135.

[12] VILLE, J., "Sur la théorie générale des jeux où intervient l'habileté des joueurs," Traité du Calcul des Probabilités et de ses Applications, by E. Borel and collaborators, Vol. 4, Part 2, pp. 105-113, Paris, 1938.

[13] WEYL, H., "Elementare theorie der konvexen polyeder," Comm. Math. Helv. 7 (1935), 290-306; also (in English translation by H. W. Kuhn) Contributions to the Theory of Games, Vol. I, pp. 3-18, Annals of Mathematics Study No. 24, Princeton, 1950.

A. W. Tucker

Princeton University

POLYHEDRAL CONVEX CONES*

A. J. Goldman and A. W. Tucker

Introduction

Let X and Y be n-dimensional real vectors and let

$$YX = y_1x_1 + \cdots + y_nx_n .$$

For matrix purposes the components $x_1, \ldots, x_n$ form a column of n real numbers and the components $y_1, \ldots, y_n$ form a row of n real numbers. But we prefer to take the abstract point of view that X and Y belong to dual (conjugate) vector spaces, an "X-space" and a "Y-space", between which YX is a bilinear product that can be expressed as above when X and Y are referred to suitable (complementary) bases in the dual spaces. In Part 3 we will have occasion to combine the dual spaces into a single Euclidean vector space in which YX becomes an inner product $X \cdot Y$. A reader who prefers this more concrete point of view may take our X-space and Y-space as the same vector space from the outset, simply regarding X as a column-vector and Y as a row-vector. [We remark that our results actually hold in vector spaces over an arbitrary ordered field, although we use the real field for definiteness.]

Take any set A of vectors in Y-space and form the set in X-space

$$A^* = \{X \mid AX \leqq 0\} = \{X \mid YX \leqq 0;\ Y \in A\}$$

called the polar of A, consisting of all vectors X such that $YX \leqq 0$ for each vector Y in the set A. The set A* is a convex cone C in the sense that: (1) kX belongs to C if $k \geqq 0$ and X belongs to C, (2) $X_1 + X_2$ belongs to C if X_1 and X_2 belong to C. If A is a finite set $\{A_1, \ldots, A_p\}$, A* is called a polyhedral convex cone: A*

---

* This paper was written for the Office of Naval Research Logistics Project in the Department of Mathematics at Princeton University. It benefits from work done by J. J. Kohn [7].

is then the intersection of finitely many halfspaces

$$A_1X \leqq 0, \ \ldots, \ A_pX \leqq 0$$

whose boundary hyperplanes $A_1X = 0, \ldots, A_pX = 0$ pass through the origin 0. [Concretely, such an intersection of halfspaces is just the set of solutions of a finite system of homogeneous linear inequalities in n unknowns.] A set B is said to <u>span</u> a convex cone C if B is a subset of C and each vector of C can be expressed as a finite linear combination of vectors of B with nonnegative coefficients; since C is the "least" convex cone containing B, we say that C is the convex-cone <u>hull</u> of B and write $C = B^{\angle}$. If B is a finite set $\{B_1, \ldots, B_q\}$,

$$B^{\angle} = \{X \mid X = BV;\ V \geqq 0\} = \{X \mid X = B_1v_1 + \cdots + B_qv_q;\ v_j \geqq 0\}.$$

These definitions carry over to Y-space; thus, the polar of a set B in X-space is

$$B^* = \{Y \mid YX \leqq 0\} = \{Y \mid YX \leqq 0;\ X \in B\}$$

and the convex cone spanned by a finite set $A = \{A_1, \ldots, A_p\}$ is

$$A^{\angle} = \{Y \mid Y = UA;\ U \geqq 0\} = \{Y \mid Y = u_1A_1 + \cdots + u_pA_p;\ u_i \geqq 0\}.$$

In Part 2 we show (Theorem 3) that, for A finite,

$$A^{**} = A^{\angle}, \quad \text{i.e.,} \quad \{Y \mid YX \leqq 0 \text{ whenever } AX \leqq 0\} = \{Y \mid Y = UA;\ U \geqq 0\},$$

which expresses a classical result of J. Farkas (see [2], page 5). We also show (Theorems 2 and 4) that, given any finite A there is some finite B such that

$$A^* = B^{\angle}, \quad \text{i.e.} \quad \{X \mid AX \leqq 0\} = \{X \mid X = BV;\ V \geqq 0\},$$

and, at the same time,

$$A^{\angle} = B^*, \quad \text{i.e.} \quad \{Y \mid Y = UA;\ U \geqq 0\} = \{Y \mid YB \leqq 0\}.$$

The relation $A^* = B^{\angle}$ says that any intersection of finitely many halfspaces is the convex hull of finitely many halflines; as a "finite basis theorem" for the solutions of a finite system of homogeneous linear inequalities, this was stated by H. Minkowski (see [8], page 45) and proved by Farkas (see [2], page 9). The relation $A^{\angle} = B^*$ says that any convex hull of finitely many halflines is an intersection of finitely many halfspaces, a result established by H. Weyl for A of rank n (see [12], Theorem 1).

In Part 3 we show that, corresponding to any two polyhedral convex cones in X-space

$$C^1 = (A^1)^* = (B^1)^\angle \quad \text{and} \quad C^2 = (A^2)^* = (B^2)^\angle,$$

there is a "greatest" polyhedral convex cone

$$C^1 \cap C^2 = \{X \mid A^1X \leqq 0,\ A^2X \leqq 0\} \qquad (\cap \text{ is "cap"})$$

contained in both C^1 and C^2, and a "least" polyhedral convex cone

$$C^1 \cup C^2 = \{X \mid X = V^1B^1 + V^2B^2;\ V^1 \geqq 0,\ V^2 \geqq 0\} \qquad (\cup \text{ is "cup"})$$

containing both C^1 and C^2. Hence the system of polyhedral convex cones in X-space is a lattice with respect to set-inclusion $\subseteq$ (see [1] for lattice concepts). The correspondence

$$A^* = B^\angle = C \longleftrightarrow C^* = B^* = A^\angle$$

is a dual isomorphism (or involutory anti-isomorphism) between the lattice of polyhedral convex cones in X-space and that in Y-space. If we identify Y-space with X-space to form an n-dimensional Euclidean vector space with inner product $X \cdot Y = YX$, we find that for any polyhedral convex cone C

$$C \cap C^* = 0 \quad \text{and} \quad C \cup C^* = \text{the entire n-space.}$$

Hence, under this identification, the lattice of polyhedral convex cones is orthocomplemented by the dual automorphism

$$C \longleftrightarrow C^*.$$

These lattice properties of polyhedral convex cones under set-inclusion were formulated by David Gale (see [4] and [5]).

In Part 1, to lay a groundwork for proving that any intersection of finitely many halfspaces is a convex hull of finitely many halflines ($A^* = B^\angle$), we examine the face structure of a polyhedral convex cone

$$A^* = \{X \mid AX \leqq 0\} = \{X \mid A_1X \leqq 0, \ldots, A_pX \leqq 0\}$$

determined by a set $A = \{A_1, \ldots, A_p\}$ of rank $n - d$. We show (in Lemma

1) that a vector X_0 interior to a face of dimension greater than $d + 1$ can be expressed as a sum $X_0 = X_1 + X_2$ of vectors X_1, X_2 interior to boundary faces of dimensions greater than d. Through this reduction we establish that the polyhedral convex cone A^* is either just its d-face, which is the d-dimensional subspace $AX = 0$, or the convex hull of this d-face and its finitely many (d+1)-faces. The d-face and (d+1)-faces are shown in Part 4 to be precisely the extreme faces of the polyhedral convex cone A^*, and this fact is used in characterizing the minimal sets B such that $A^* = B^{\angle}$.

PART 1. Face Structure of the Convex Cone A^*

We turn first to the face-structure of the polyhedral convex cone

$$A^* = \{X \mid A_1X \leqq 0, \ldots, A_pX \leqq 0\}.$$

To each subset H (which may be the null set $\emptyset$) of the indices $1, \ldots, p$ there corresponds a subset F_H of A^* defined by the conditions

$$\begin{aligned} A_hX &< 0 \quad \text{for each } h \text{ in } H, \\ A_hX &= 0 \quad \text{for each } h \text{ not in } H. \end{aligned}$$

F_H is the (open) face of A^* corresponding to H. Since H can be chosen in 2^p possible ways, and since nonvacuous faces corresponding to distinct subsets of indices are clearly disjoint, we see that A^* is partitioned into 2^p faces, some of which may be vacuous. If F_H is not vacuous, then it is the intersection

$$F_H = O_H \cap L_H$$

of the (open) set O_H of all vectors X satisfying

$$A_hX < 0 \quad \text{for each } h \text{ in } H$$

and the linear subspace L_H consisting of all vectors X satisfying

$$A_hX = 0 \quad \text{for each } h \text{ not in } H.$$

The dimension d_H of L_H is given by

$$d_H = n - r_H,$$

where r_H is the maximal number of linearly independent equations in the system of equations determining L_H (i.e., the maximal number of linearly independent vectors in the set $\{A_h \mid h$ not in $H\}$). We say that F_H is a face of dimension d_H.

Let $r = r_\emptyset$ = rank of A and $d = d_\emptyset = n - r$. It is not hard to see that A^* has no faces of dimension $< d$ and has exactly one face of dimension d (namely, the linear subspace $F_\emptyset$ consisting of the solutions of the system of linear homogeneous equations $AX = 0$). We shall show later that A^* can be "built up" from its d-dimensional face and its (d+1)-dimensional faces (if any) in a sense made precise in Theorem 1.

A (d+1)-dimensional face F_H of A^* is an open halfspace of L_H bounded by $F_\emptyset$. To see this, write $F_H = C_H \cap L_H$ and observe that F_H is the intersection of the sets

$$\{X \mid A_h X < 0\} \cap L_H, \qquad h \in H.$$

Each such set is the intersection of L_H with an open halfspace, and so is either L_H itself or a halfspace of L_H bounded by a d-dimensional subspace $\{X \mid A_h X \leqq 0\} \cap L_H$ which contains $F_\emptyset$ and therefore coincides with $F_\emptyset$. As a nonvacuous intersection of such sets, F_H must itself be either L_H or an open halfspace in L_H bounded by $F_\emptyset$. The first alternative cannot occur because F_H is not a linear subspace (if X is in F_H then $(-X)$ is not).

If A is of rank n, then $d = 0$ and $F_\emptyset$ becomes the unique zero-dimensional face (or "vertex") of A^*, consisting of the vector 0 alone. If A is of rank $r < n$ then there are no vertices. Using a more geometrical language, we might say that the cone A^* is "pointed" in the first case and is "blunted" in the second case.

When $d = 0$, the (d+1)-dimensional faces are open halflines called <u>edges</u>. Since these are of particular importance (see Corollary 1B) when they exist, it is worthwhile to point out that they can be found systematically by a straightforward (though laborious) method. One chooses (in all possible ways) a subset of $n - 1$ linearly independent row vectors of A; the solution set of the corresponding system of homogeneous equations consists of all multiples tX of a particular nontrivial solution X. If X satisfies $AX \leqq 0$, then the open halfline tX for $t > 0$ is an edge of A^*; if X satisfies $AX \geqq 0$ then the open halfline $t(-X)$ for $t > 0$ is an edge of A^*.

The notion of "boundary face" must now be introduced. Suppose that H and G are subsets of the index set, that G is a proper subset of H, and that F_H and F_G are both nonvacuous. Then we say that F_G is a <u>boundary face</u> of F_H; note that (because we work with <u>open</u>

faces) F_G is not a subset of F_H, and is in fact disjoint from F_H. The set of all boundary faces of F_H constitutes the "boundary" of F_H.

If F_G is a boundary face of F_H, then $d_G < d_H$. To prove this, we note that the system of equations defining L_H is a subset of the system of equations defining L_G, so that $d_G \leqq d_H$. Choose an index g in $H - G$ (the part of H not in G); if $d_G = d_H$, then the equation $A_g X = 0$ would be linearly dependent on the equations $A_h X = 0$ for all h not in H, so that any vector X satisfying these last equations would also satisfy $A_g X = 0$. It would follow that F_H must be vacuous (contrary to hypothesis). Thus the assumption $d_G = d_H$ is untenable, and $d_G < d_H$ must hold.

Before proceeding further, we give two simple examples to illustrate the concepts just considered and the results soon to be proved.

EXAMPLE 1.

$$A = \begin{bmatrix} -1 & 0 \\ 0 & -1 \end{bmatrix} .$$

Here the cone A^* is the "first quadrant" $x_1 \geqq 0$, $x_2 \geqq 0$. (See Figure 1). We list the nonvacuous faces:

F_{12}	$x_1 > 0,\ x_2 > 0$	$d_{12} = 2$
F_1	$x_1 > 0,\ x_2 = 0$	$d_1 = 1$
F_2	$x_1 = 0,\ x_2 > 0$	$d_2 = 1$
$F_\emptyset$	$x_1 = 0,\ x_2 = 0$	$d = d_\emptyset = 0.$

F_1, F_2, and $F_\emptyset$ are boundary faces of F_{12}. F_1 and F_2 have $F_\emptyset$ as boundary face. The edges of A^* are found by the process described above to be

$$F_1 : tE_1 \quad \text{all } t > 0$$

and

$$F_2 : sE_2 \quad \text{all } s > 0$$

where E_1 and E_2 are the unit vectors along the x_1- and x_2-axes respectively. We point out that any nonzero vector in A^* can be expressed as a convex combination

$$\frac{x_1}{x_1+x_2}(x_1 + x_2)E_1 + \frac{x_2}{x_1+x_2}(x_1 + x_2)E_2$$

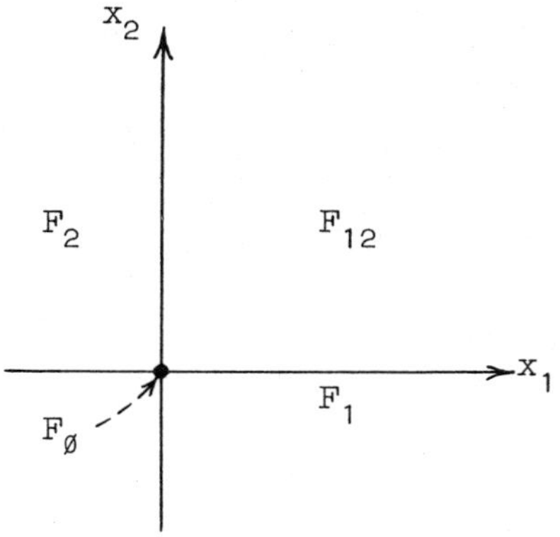

Figure 1

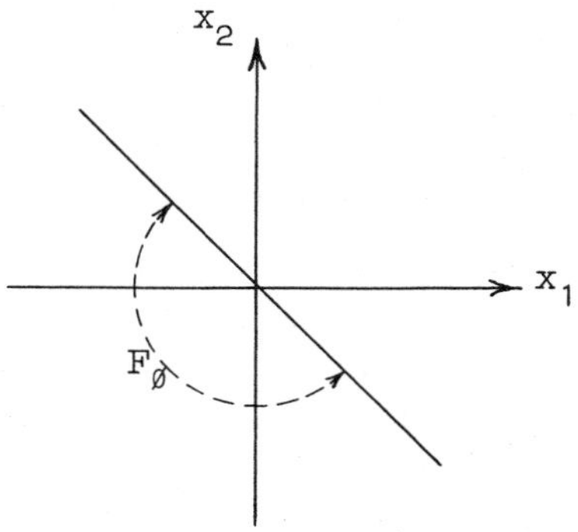

Figure 2

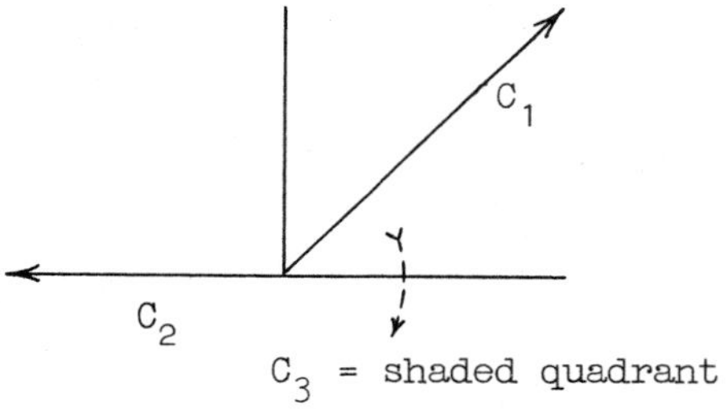

Figure 3

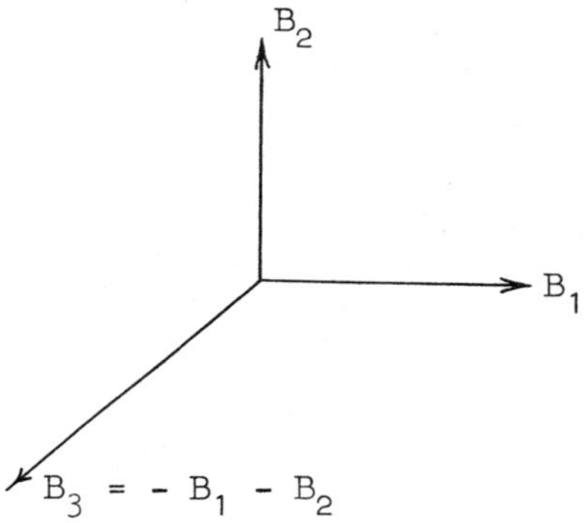

Figure 4

of vectors $(x_1 + x_2)E_1$ and $(x_1 + x_2)E_2$ in the edges, so that A^* is the convex hull of its edges and the vector 0.

EXAMPLE 2.

$$A = \begin{bmatrix} 1 & 1 \\ -1 & -1 \end{bmatrix} .$$

A^* here consists of the line $x_1 + x_2 = 0$ (see Figure 2). The only non-vacuous face is $F_\emptyset = A^*$, and $d = 1$. The edges of A^* are found to be

$$tE_1' \quad \text{all} \quad t > 0$$

and

$$sE_2' \quad \text{all} \quad s > 0,$$

where E_1' has components $(1, -1)$ and E_2' has components $(-1, 1)$.

In Example 1, we found that A^* was the convex hull of its d-dimensional face and its faces of dimension $d + 1$, while in Example 2, A^* coincided with its (unique) face $F_\emptyset$ of dimension d. We will show (Theorem 1) that these are the only possible cases. First we prove a "reduction lemma."

LEMMA 1. A vector X_0 lying in a face F_H of dimension $d_H > d + 1$ can be expressed as a sum

$$X_0 = X_1 + X_2$$

of vectors X_1, X_2 belonging to boundary faces of F_H of dimension $> d$ (and necessarily $< d_H$).

PROOF. The linear subspace L_H which "carries" F_H is of dimension $d_H > d + 1$. Therefore we can find in L_H a vector X' which is not in the linear subspace generated by X_0 and the vectors of the d-dimensional space $F_\emptyset$. X_0 and X' together span a 2-dimensional linear subspace L^o of L_H consisting of all vectors

$$X = tX_0 + sX'. \tag{1}$$

L^o intersects the cone A in a subset M^o consisting of the vectors X whose parameters t and s satisfy

$$A_hX = t(A_hX_0) + s(A_hX') \leqq 0 \tag{2}$$

for each index h.

A vector X of the form (1) is in L_H and therefore automatically satisfies (2) for each h not in H; thus X is in M^o if and only if it satisfies (2) for each h in H. H is not vacuous since $d_H > d = d_\emptyset$.

We now draw (see Figure 5) the graphs of the equations

$$t(A_hX_0) + s(A_hX') = 0 \qquad \text{each } h \text{ in } H$$

in the (s,t)-plane, obtaining a set of straight lines through the origin with slopes

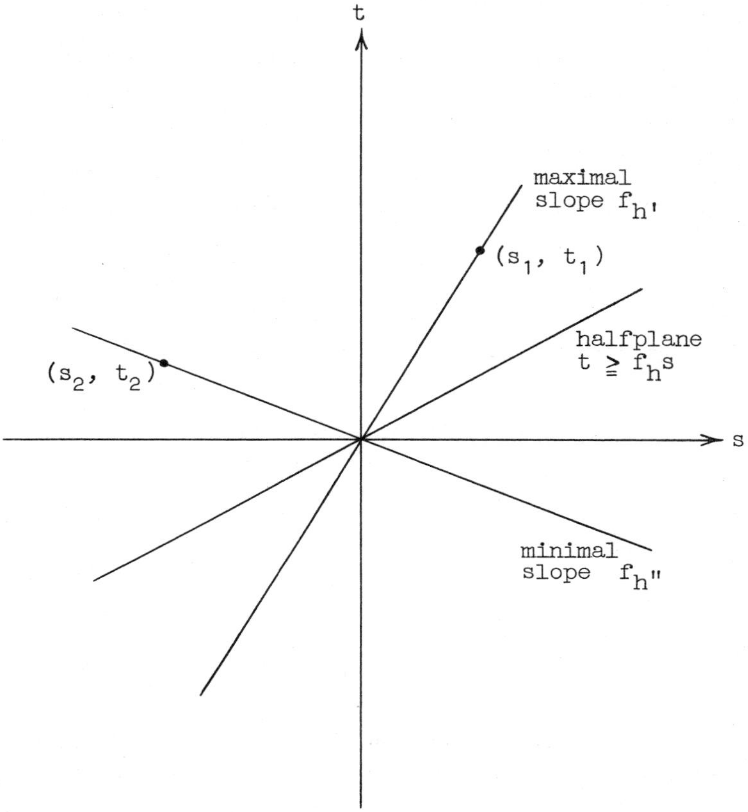

Figure 5

$$f_h = - A_h X'/A_h X_o \qquad \text{each } h \text{ in } H.$$

For h in H we have $A_h X_o < 0$ and so can rewrite (2) as

(3) $$t \geqq f_h s.$$

The set of straight lines in the (s,t)-plane does not consist of just a single straight line with some slope f. Otherwise we would have

$$A_h(fX_o + X') = 0 \qquad \text{each } h \text{ in } H$$

and the same equation would hold for h not in H because X_o and X'

lie in L_H. This would mean $A(fX_o + X') = 0$, so that $fX_o + X'$ would be in $F_\emptyset$, contradicting the way in which X' was chosen.

Therefore the set of lines contains distinct lines of maximal slope $f_{h'}$ and minimal slope $f_{h''}$, corresponding to certain h', h'' in H. We set

$$s_1 = \frac{1}{f_{h'}-f_{h''}}, \quad t_1 = \frac{f_{h'}}{f_{h'}-f_{h''}} \quad \text{to get} \quad X_1 = t_1X_o + s_1X'$$

and

$$s_2 = \frac{-1}{f_{h'}-f_{h''}}, \quad t_2 = \frac{-f_{h''}}{f_{h'}-f_{h''}} \quad \text{to get} \quad X_2 = t_2X_o + s_2X'.$$

These vectors X_1 and X_2 are such that

$$X_1 + X_2 = X_o.$$

For X_1 and X_2, (3) reduces to

$$f_{h'} \geqq f_h \quad \text{and} \quad f_h \geqq f_{h''}$$

respectively.

We see that X_1 satisfies (3) (and thus (2)) as an equation for $h = h'$ and as a strict inequality for $h = h''$, while X_2 satisfies (3) (and thus (2)) as an equation for $h = h''$ and as a strict inequality for $h = h'$. Thus each of X_1, X_2 satisfies (2) as a strict inequality for some but not all h in H; X_1 and X_2 lie in L_H and therefore satisfy (2) as an equation for each h not in H. It follows that each of X_1 and X_2 lies in a boundary face of F_H of dimension $> d$; this completes the proof of the lemma.

THEOREM 1. A^* is <u>either</u> just its unique d-face <u>or</u> the convex hull of this d-face and its (d+1)-dimensional faces.

PROOF. We have already pointed out that A^* has no faces of dimension $< d$. Suppose A^* does <u>not</u> consist only of its d-dimensional face. Consider first any vector X lying in a face of dimension $> d + 1$. We may apply Lemma 1 repeatedly to show that X is a finite sum of vectors each lying in a (d+1)-dimensional face of A^*, say

$$X = X_1 + \dots + X_m.$$

The vectors mX_1, ..., mX_m each lie in a (d+1)-dimensional face of A^*, and by writing

$$X = \frac{1}{m}(mX_1) + \cdots + \frac{1}{m}(mX_m)$$

we see that X is a convex combination of the vectors $mX_1, \ldots, mX_m$. As for the other vectors of A^*, which lie in faces of dimension d or $d + 1$, they certainly lie in the convex hull of these faces. The inclusion in the other direction follows immediately from the convexity of A^*, and so A^* is the convex hull of its d-face and its faces of dimension $d + 1$.

The following corollaries are direct consequences of Theorem 1 and our earlier comments on the nature of (d+1)-faces and edges.

COROLLARY 1A. The intersection of finitely many half-spaces is <u>either</u> a linear subspace (of dimension d) <u>or</u> the convex hull of finitely many half-subspaces (of dimension $d + 1$) bounded by a common subspace (of dimension d).

COROLLARY 1B. If the rank of A is n, then A^* is <u>either</u> just 0 <u>or</u> the convex hull of 0 and the edges of A^*.

PART 2. The Theorems of Minkowski, Farkas, and Weyl.

In Part 2 we consider, in addition to the convex cone

$$A^* = \{X \mid A_1X \leqq 0, \ldots, A_pX \leqq 0\}$$

a convex cone

$$B^{\angle} = \{X \mid X = BV;\ V \geqq 0\} = \{X \mid X = v_1B_1 + \cdots + v_qB_q;\ v_j \geqq 0\}$$

where $B = \{B_1, \ldots, B_q\}$ is a finite set of vectors in X-space and is said to <u>span</u> $B^{\angle}$. In other words, the set $B^{\angle}$ consists of all finite linear combinations with nonnegative coefficients of vectors in B. It is easy to see that $B^{\angle}$ is the convex hull of the halflines v_jB_j, $v_j \geqq 0$, generated by the vectors B_j of B. Conversely, the convex hull of <u>any</u> finite family of halflines can be written in the form $B^{\angle}$; to form B, one chooses a nonzero vector from each of the nondegenerate halflines (and chooses $B = \{0\}$ if the only halfline in the family is the degenerate one consisting of the single vector 0).

THEOREM 2. (Minkowski [8]). Given a finite set A of vectors in Y-space, there exists a finite set B of vectors in X-space such that $A^* = B^{\angle}$.

PROOF. We wish to prove that A^* has a spanning set B. By Theorem 1, it suffices to show that the d-face $F_\emptyset$ and the (d+1)-faces F_H each have (finite) spanning sets; B can then be taken as the union of these spanning sets.

If $d = 0$, then $F_\emptyset$ consists of 0 alone, and so $\{0\}$ is a spanning set for $F_\emptyset$. If $d > 0$, let $B_1, \ldots, B_d$ be a basis for $F_\emptyset$, so that any vector X in $F_\emptyset$ can be written in the form

$$X = c_1B_1 + \ldots + c_dB_d .$$

Set $u_i = \max(c_i, 0) \geqq 0$ and $v_i = \max(-c_i, 0) \geqq 0$; since

$$X = u_1B_1 + \ldots + u_dB_d + v_1(-B_1) + \ldots + v_d(-B_d),$$

it follows that $\{B_1, \ldots, B_d, -B_1, \ldots, -B_d\}$ spans $F_\emptyset$.

Now let F_H be any (d+1)-face. The (d+1)-dimensional linear subspace L_H which "carries" F_H contains the d-dimensional subspace $F_\emptyset$; thus L_H is linearly generated by the vectors of $F_\emptyset$ and any vector B_H which lies in F_H (and so lies in L_H but not in $F_\emptyset$). Therefore any vector X' in F_H can be written in the form

$$X' = X + cB_H; \qquad X \in F_\emptyset .$$

H is not vacuous; if we multiply the last equation on the left by A_h for some h in H and recall that $A_hX' < 0$, $A_hX = 0$, and $A_hB_H < 0$, we find that $c > 0$. It follows that a spanning set for F_H is obtained by adjoining B_H to any spanning set $\bar{B}$ of $F_\emptyset$. This completes the proof.

COROLLARY 2A. An intersection of finitely many half-spaces is a convex hull of finitely many halflines.

We recall that the <u>polar</u> E^* of a set E of vectors from X-space is by definition the (closed) convex cone

$$E^* = \{Y \mid YX \leqq 0;\ X \in E\}$$

in Y-space; in particular $A^{**} = (A^*)^*$ is defined whenever A is a set of vectors in X-space.

THEOREM 3 (Farkas [2]). If A is a finite set of vectors in Y-space, then $A^{**} = A^{\angle}$.

PROOF. The fact that A^{**} is a subset of $A^{\angle}$ follows immediately from the Corollary to the Lemma of the preceding paper, "Dual Systems of Homogeneous Linear Relations", which we rewrite as follows:

If the inequality $YX \leqq 0$ holds for all vectors X such that $AX \leqq 0$, then

$$Y = u_1 A_1 + \cdots + u_p A_p$$

for some $u_1 \geqq 0, \ldots, u_p \geqq 0$.

In this rewriting we have replaced the A^T of the Corollary by A, the column vector A_0 by a vector Y in Y-space (the space of "row-vectors"), the variable column vector U by a vector $(-X)$ in X-space (the space of "column vectors"), and the column vector X by a row vector $(u_1, \ldots, u_p)$.

To prove the inclusion in the other direction, we observe that if Y is in $A^{\angle}$, so that

$$Y = u_1 A_1 + \cdots + u_p A_p;\ u_1 \geqq 0, \ldots, u_p \geqq 0,$$

then $YX \leqq 0$ certainly holds for all X such that $AX \leqq 0$ (i.e., $A_1 X \leqq 0, \ldots, A_p X \leqq 0$), and so Y lies in A^{**}. This completes the proof.

THEOREM 4 (Weyl [12]). Let A be a finite set of vectors in Y-space. There exists a finite set B of vectors in X-space such that

$$A^* = B^{\angle} \quad \text{and} \quad A^{\angle} = B^*.$$

PROOF. By Theorem 2, there exists a finite set B such that $A^* = B^{\angle}$. It is easy to check that $(B^{\angle})^* = B^*$; thus we have $A^{**} = B^*$ and (by Theorem 3) $A^{\angle} = B^*$.

COROLLARY 4A. Every convex hull of finitely many halflines is the intersection of finitely many half-spaces, and conversely.

PROOF. If we begin with a set $B^{\angle}$ which is the convex hull of finitely many halflines, then we can reverse the roles of A and B in Theorem 4 and assert that there exists a finite set A such that $B^{\angle} = A^*$;

thus $B^{\angle}$ is expressed as the intersection of finitely many halflines. The converse statement is precisely Corollary 2A.

PART 3. The Lattice of Polyhedral Convex Cones

In this brief section, we derive an elegant formulation (due to David Gale, [4] and [5]) of certain properties of the system of <u>all</u> polyhedral convex cones in an n-dimensional vector space.

Consider first any two such cones in the X-space, which we express as intersections of finitely many halfspaces

$$C^1 = \{X \mid A^1X \leqq 0\} = (A^1)^* = \{A_1^1, \ldots, A_p^1\}^*$$

and

$$C^2 = \{X \mid A^2X \leqq 0\} = (A^2)^* = \{A_1^2, \ldots, A_r^2\}^*.$$

Their set-theoretic intersection is again a polyhedral convex cone, since it can be written

$$C^1 \cap C^2 = \{X \mid A^1X \leqq 0,\ A^2X \leqq 0\} = \{A_1^1, \ldots, A_p^1;\ A_1^2, \ldots, A_r^2\}^*.$$

$C^1 \cap C^2$ is clearly the "greatest" convex cone contained in both C^1 and C^2. (Thus $\cap$, called "cap", means intersection.)

Next we rewrite C^1 and C^2 as convex hulls of finitely many halflines,

$$C^1 = \{X \mid X = B^1V^1;\ V^1 \geqq 0\} = (B^1)^{\angle} = \{B_1^1, \ldots, B_q^1\}^{\angle}$$

and

$$C^2 = \{X \mid X = B^2V^2;\ V^2 \geqq 0\} = (B^2)^{\angle} = \{B_1^2, \ldots, B_s^2\}^{\angle}$$

and define

$$C^1 \cup C^2 = \{X \mid X = B^1V^1 + B^2V^2;\ V^1 \geqq 0,\ B^2 \geqq 0\} =$$

$$= \{B_1^1, \ldots, B_q^1;\ B_1^2, \ldots, B_s^1\}^{\angle}.$$

(Here $\cup$, called "cup", is <u>not</u> set-theoretic union.) The set $C^1 \cup C^2$ is a polyhedral convex cone which lies in any convex cone containing both C^1 and C^2; i.e., $C^1 \cup C^2$ is the "least" convex cone containing both C^1 and C^2.

The last two paragraphs show that the system of all polyhedral convex cones in the X-space forms a lattice $\mathfrak{C}$ with respect to partial ordering by set-inclusion ($\subseteqq$). The cone consisting of the single vector 0 is the "least" element in $\mathfrak{C}$, while the whole X-space constitutes a cone which is the "greatest". Clearly the polyhedral convex cones in Y-space form a similar lattice.

The linear subspaces L of X-space form an interesting sublattice $\mathfrak{L}$ of $\mathfrak{C}$. It is well known that $\mathfrak{L}$ is a modular lattice; i.e., that $L^1 \subseteqq L^3$ implies $L^1 \cup (L^2 \cap L^3) = (L^1 \cup L^2) \cap L^3$ for all L^2 in $\mathfrak{L}$. $\mathfrak{C}$ is not modular, however, for $n \geqq 2$, as is shown by setting up a coordinate system in the n-space and considering the example (see Figure 3)

$$C^1 = \{X \mid x_1 \geqq 0,\ x_2 \geqq 0,\ x_1 = x_2\}$$

$$C^2 = \{X \mid x_1 \leqq 0,\ x_2 = 0\}$$

$$C^3 = \{X \mid x_1 \geqq 0,\ x_2 \geqq 0\}$$

for which

$$C^1 \cup (C^2 \cap C^3) = C^1$$

but

$$(C^1 \cup C^2) \cap C^3 = \{X \mid x_1 \geqq 0,\ x_2 \geqq 0,\ x_1 \leqq x_2\}.$$

LEMMA 2. The correspondence $C \longleftrightarrow C^*$ is a dual isomorphism (involutory anti-isomorphism) between the lattice $\mathfrak{C}$ of polyhedral convex cones in X-space and the lattice of polyhedral convex cones in Y-space, that is

(a) $C^{**} = C$

(b) $(C^1)^* = (C^2)^*$ if and only if $C^1 = C^2$

(c) any polyhedral convex cone in Y-space can be written as C^*, where C is in $\mathfrak{C}$

(d) $(C^1)^* \subseteqq (C^2)^*$ if and only if $C^2 \subseteqq C^1$

(e) $(C^1 \cap C^2)^* = (C^1)^* \cup (C^2)^*$

(f) $(C^1 \cup C^2)^* = (C^1)^* \cap (C^2)^*$.

PROOF. (a) Write $C = A^*$, where A is a finite set of vectors in Y-space. Then $C^* = A^{**} = A^{\angle}$, and so $C^{**} = (A^{\angle})^* = A^* = C$.

(b) The "if" assertion is clear; to prove the "only if",

note that $(C^1)^* = (C^2)^*$ implies $(C^1)^{**} = (C^2)^{**}$ and thus (by (a)) $C^1 = C^2$.

(c) Let B^* be a polyhedral convex cone in Y-space, where B is a finite set of vectors in X-space. Then $B^{**} = B^{\angle}$, and so $B^{***} = (B^*)^{\angle} = B^*$; i.e., $B^* = C^*$ where $C = B^{**} = B^{\angle}$ is in $\mathfrak{C}$.

(d) The "if" assertion follows directly from the definition of "polar"; to prove the "only if", we suppose that $(C^*)^* \subseteq (C^2)^*$. By the part of (d) already proved, we have $(C^2)^{**} \subseteq (C^1)^{**}$, and so by (a) we have $C^2 \subseteq C^1$.

(e) and (f) These are easy consequences of (d) and the definitions of the lattice operations "cap" and "cup".

Let us now identify Y-space with X-space by a one-to-one bilinear correspondence. In terms of row and column vectors, this can be done by identifying each row vector with its transpose. Abstractly, one can choose a basis in each space, consider "components" with respect to these bases, and then identify each vector in Y-space with the vector in X-space having the same components. The form YX then becomes an inner product $X \cdot Y$ in X-space. The polyhedral convex cones C and C^* both lie in X-space, and C^* is the set of all vectors making a non-acute angle with every vector in C; the correspondence $C \longleftrightarrow C^*$ becomes a <u>dual automorphism</u> (involutory anti-automorphism) on $\mathfrak{C}$.

LEMMA 3. The dual automorphism $C \longleftrightarrow C^*$ on $\mathfrak{C}$ is an <u>orthocomplementation</u>; that is,

$$C \cap C^* = \{0\} \quad \text{and} \quad C \cup C^* = \text{the entire X-space.}$$

PROOF. If X is in $C \cap C^*$, then $X \cdot X \leq 0$ and so $X = 0$; i.e., $C \cap C^* = \{0\}$. Now we apply (a) and (e) of Lemma 2:

$$C \cup C^* = C^{**} \cup C^* = (C^* \cap C)^* = \{0\}^* = \text{the entire X-space.}$$

We summarize the results of Part 3 as follows:

THEOREM 5 (D. Gale). The polyhedral convex cones of an n-dimensional Euclidean vector space form a lattice $\mathfrak{C}$ under set-inclusion. $\mathfrak{C}$ is <u>orthocomplemented</u> by the dual automorphism

$$C \longleftrightarrow C^*$$

but is nonmodular for $n \geqq 2$.

PART 4. Extreme Faces and Minimal Spanning Sets

The results of this section tie in with those of Parts 1 and 2 (especially Theorems 1 and 2) but were deferred to this Part 4 so as not to interrupt the continuity of the earlier discussion. We deal throughout with the convex cone

$$A^* = \{X \mid AX \leqq 0\} = \{X \mid YX \leqq 0;\ Y \in A\}.$$

It is well known (and intuitively clear) that a bounded convex polyhedron is the convex hull of its extreme points. (This is proved in the following paper.) We next derive the analogous result (Theorem 6) for the convex cone A^*. An <u>extreme face</u> F_H of A^* is one with the following property: If any vector X_H in F_H is written as a sum

$$X_H = X_1 + X_2 \qquad (X_1,\ X_2 \text{ in } A^*),$$

then at least one of X_1, X_2 also lies in F_H.

LEMMA 4. If a vector X lies in a face F_H of A^*, and if

$$X = X_1 + \dots + X_m; \quad X_i \text{ in } A^*\ (1 \leqq i \leqq m),$$

then each X_i lies either in F_H or in a boundary face of F_H.

PROOF. For each h not in H we have

$$A_hX = A_hX_1 + \dots + A_hX_m = 0; \quad A_hX_i \leqq 0 \quad \text{for} \quad 1 \leqq i \leqq m.$$

These relations imply $A_hX_i = 0$ for $1 \leqq i \leqq m$ and all h not in H, which in turn implies the conclusion of the lemma.

LEMMA 5. The extreme faces of A^* are precisely the (unique) d-dimensional face $F_\emptyset$ and the (d+1)-dimensional faces (if any).

PROOF. It follows immediately from Lemma 1 that no face of dimension $> d + 1$ is extreme. To show that $F_\emptyset$ is an extreme face, we choose a vector $X_\emptyset$ in $F_\emptyset$ and suppose that

$$X_\emptyset = X_1 + X_2 \qquad (X_1,\ X_2 \text{ in } A^*).$$

$F_\emptyset$ has no boundary faces, and so by Lemma 4 both X_1 and X_2 lie in $F_\emptyset$.

To show that a (d+1)-dimensional face F_H is extreme, we choose a vector X_H in F_H and write

$$X_H = X_1' + X_2' \qquad (X_1',\ X_2' \text{ in } A^*).$$

Suppose neither X_1' nor X_2' were in F_H. By Lemma 4, X_1' and X_2' would be in boundary faces of F_H. But the only boundary face of the (d+1)-dimensional face F_H is the d-dimensional linear space $F_\emptyset$; thus X_1' and X_2' (together with their sum X_H) would have to lie in $F_\emptyset$, contradicting the choice of X_H in F_H. So either X_1' or X_2' lies in F_H; this completes the proof of the lemma.

We note that the edges of a pointed cone are often called its extreme rays; Lemma 5 (with $d = 0$) shows that our terminology is in harmony with this practice.

THEOREM 6. A^* is the convex hull of its extreme faces. Furthermore, if A^* is the convex hull of some set S of its faces, then S must include all the extreme faces of A^*.

PROOF. The first assertion follows immediately from Theorem 1 and Lemma 5. In proving the second assertion, we will use the term "S-face" for a face of A^* which is included in S. Let F_H be any extreme face; we want to show that F_H is an S-face. Choose a vector X_H in F_H; then we can write

$$X_H = t_1X_1 + \dots + t_mX_m$$

where each X_i $(1 \leq i \leq m)$ is in an S-face; $0 \leqq t_i \leqq 1$ and $\Sigma t_i = 1$. By deleting all summands which appear with zero coefficient and then renumbering if necessary, we may assume all $t_i > 0$; then t_iX_i lies in the same face as does X_i, and therefore lies in an S-face. So to prove F_H an S-face, we need only show that some t_iX_i lies in F_H. (We recall that distinct faces of A^* are disjoint.)

By Lemma 4, each t_iX_i lies either in F_h or in a boundary of F_H. If $F_H = F_\emptyset$, then F_H has no boundary face. If F_H is of dimension $d + 1$, then its only boundary face is $F_\emptyset$; some t_iX_i does not lie in $F_\emptyset$, however, for otherwise X_H would lie in $F_\emptyset$. So in either case some t_iX_i lies in F_H, which is therefore an S-face.

Theorem 2 asserts that $A^* = B^{\angle}$; i.e., that A^* has a spanning set B. In Theorem 7 we describe a <u>minimal</u> choice for B. Lemmas 6 and 7 sharpen the arguments used in proving Theorem 2.

LEMMA 6. Suppose $d > 0$. Let $\bar{B} = \{B_1, \ldots, B_d, B_{d+1}\}$, where $B_1, \ldots, B_d$ is a basis for $F_\emptyset$ and

$$B_{d+1} = - \sum_{i=1}^{d} B_i .$$

Then, $F_\emptyset = \bar{B}^\angle$. Any spanning set for $F_\emptyset$ contains at least $d + 1$ vectors.

PROOF. Suppose first that we try to express $F_\emptyset$ as $(B')^\angle$, where B' is a set of at most d vectors of $F_\emptyset$. $(B')^\angle$ is a subset of the linear subspace generated by the vectors of B', and so in order that $(B')^\angle = F_\emptyset$ it is necessary that $B' = \{B_1, \ldots, B_d\}$, a basis for $F_\emptyset$. But this condition is still not sufficient, for the vector

$$B_{d+1} = - \sum_{i=1}^{d} B_i$$

of $F_\emptyset$ can be expressed as a linear combination of the vectors of B' only by taking all coefficients as (-1), and therefore does not lie in $(B')^\angle$. (See Figure 4.)

If, however, we form $\bar{B}$ by adjoining B_{d+1} to the basis B', then $F_\emptyset = \bar{B}^\angle$. To prove this, we note that any vector X in $F_\emptyset$ can be written in the form

$$X = c_1 B_1 + \cdots + c_d B_d .$$

If all c_i are $\geqq 0$, then X clearly lies in $\bar{B}^\angle$. If some c_i is < 0, then we let v be the greatest of $-c_1, \ldots, -c_d$ and set $v_i = c_i + v$. Note that $v > 0$ and $v_i \geqq 0$. It is easy to check that

$$X = v_1 B_1 + \cdots + v_d B_d + v B_{d+1} ,$$

and so X lies in $\bar{B}^\angle$ in this case also. Thus the proof is complete.

LEMMA 7. Let B be a set of vectors in X-space such that $A^* = B^\angle$. Then

(i) B contains at least one vector from every $(d+1)$-face F_H;

(ii) if $d > 0$, then B contains a subset B^o such that $F_\emptyset = (B^o)^\angle$.

PROOF. To prove (i), form the set S of faces of A^* which consists of $F_\emptyset$ together with those faces of A^* that contain a vector of B. Since $A^* = B^\angle$, A^* is contained in (and thus coincides with) the convex hull of the set S of its faces, so that assertion (i) follows from the second part of Theorem 6.

Suppose now that $d > 0$, and let B^o be the subset of B consisting of all vectors of B which lie in $F_\emptyset$. We shall soon show that B^o is nonvacuous. Since $d > 0$, there is a nonzero vector X in $F_\emptyset$, which can be written

$$X = u_1B_1 + \dots + u_mB_m;\ u_i \geqq 0,\ B_i \in B.$$

By Lemma 4 (since $F_\emptyset$ has no boundary faces) each u_iB_i lies in $F_\emptyset$, and so B_i lies in $F_\emptyset$ whenever $u_i > 0$. In other words, $u_i = 0$ whenever B_i is not in B^o. Not all $u_i = 0$ (since $X \neq 0$) and so B^o is nonvacuous; furthermore, we see that the arbitrary nonzero vector X in $F_\emptyset$ has been expressed (after summands with $u_i = 0$ are deleted) as a vector of $(B^o)^\angle$. Clearly 0 lies in $(B^o)^\angle$, and so assertion (ii) is proved.

Let ν be the number of (d+1)-faces of A^*. If $\nu = d = 0$, then A^* consists of 0 alone, so that $\{0\}$ is a minimal spanning set for A^*. Thus we can omit this case in the next theorem.

THEOREM 7. If $A^* \neq \{0\}$, then a minimal set B such that $A^* = B^\angle$ is obtained by choosing an arbitrary vector B_H in each (d+1)-face F_H of A^*, and (in case $d > 0$) adjoining a set $\bar{B}$ of the sort considered in Lemma 6, such that $F_\emptyset = \bar{B}^\angle$.

PROOF. a) Let B be formed as in the statement of the theorem. If $d > 0$, then B contains a spanning set for $F_\emptyset$ and spanning sets for each (d+1)-face F_H (see the next-to-last sentence in the proof of Theorem 2), and so Theorem 1 ensures that B spans A. If $d = 0$ then each (d+1)-face is an edge and so is spanned by B_H, while $F_\emptyset = \{0\}$ is clearly contained in $B^\angle$; thus again B spans $A^\angle$ by Theorem 1.

b) To prove minimality, we observe that any spanning set for A^* must (by Lemma 7) contain at least one vector from each (d+1)-face, and if $d > 0$ must also contain a spanning set B' for $F_\emptyset$; by Lemma 6, B' contains at least as many vectors as a set $\bar{B}$.

SUPPLEMENTARY REMARK: We conclude with some comments on the nature of the "non-polyhedral" convex cones A^* and $B^\angle$ when A and B are allowed to be <u>infinite</u> sets. In this case

$$A^* = \{X \mid YX \leqq 0;\ Y \in A\}$$

will have infinitely many faces F_H corresponding to the subsets H of the infinite set needed to index A. Also,

$$B^{\angle} = \{X \mid X = \Sigma v_j B_j;\ v_j \geqq 0,\ B_j \in B\}$$

will consist of all finite nonnegative linear combinations of vectors chosen from a possibly infinite set B. If all occurrences of the word "finite" are deleted, with the one exception named in the last sentence, then the proofs and results of this paper up to and including Corollary 2A, and all those of Part 4, remain valid. The spanning set B required in Theorem 2 may now be infinite, and so might be obtained trivially by setting $B = A^*$.

Theorems 3 and 4, Corollary 3A, and the results of Part 3 do not remain valid, however. To show, for instance, that Theorem 3 $(A^{**} = A^{\angle})$ may fail if A is infinite, we take $A = \{Y \mid Y > 0\}$, so that A is the "open first orthant" in some coordinate system in Y-space. Then $A^{**} = (A^*)^*$ is the solution-set of a system of linear inequalities $(\leq)$ and is therefore a closed set, while $A^{\angle}$ consists of A together with the vector 0 and so is not closed. Thus $A^{**} \neq A^{\angle}$ in this example.

References

[1] BIRKHOFF, G., Lattice Theory, American Mathematical Society Colloquium Publications Vol. XXV, New York (1948).

[2] FARKAS, J., "Uber die theorie der einfachen Ungleichungen", Journal fur die reine und angewandte Mathematik 124 (1901), pp. 1-27.

[3] FENCHEL, W., "Convex cones, sets, and functions", Notes of Lectures at Princeton University (1951).

[4] GALE, D., "Convex polyhedral cones and linear inequalities", Cowles Commission Monograph No. 13 (1951), [13], pp. 287-297.

[5] GALE, D., and SHERMAN, S., "Solutions of finite two-person games", Annals of Mathematics Studies 24, Princeton (1950), [14], pp. 37-49.

[6] GERSTENHABER, M., "Theory of convex polyhedral cones", Cowles Commission Monograph No. 13 (1951), [13], pp. 298-316.

[7] KOHN, J. J., "Linear inequalities and polyhedral convex cones", O.N.R. Logistics Project Report, Department of Mathematics, Princeton University (1956).

[8] MINKOWSKI, H., Geometry der Zahlen, Teubner, Leipzig, 2nd edition, (1910).

[9] MOTZKIN, T. S., "Beitrage zur theorie der linearen Ungleichungen", Inaug. diss., Jerusalem (1936).

[10] TUCKER, A. W., "Linear inequalities and convex polyhedral sets", Proceedings of the Second Symposium in Linear Programming (National

Bureau of Standards and U.S. Air Force) Vol. 2 (1956), pp. 569-602.

[11] TUCKER, A. W., "Dual systems of homogeneous linear relations", this Study.

[12] WEYL, H., "The elementary theory of convex polyhedra", Annals of Mathematics Studies 24 (1950), [14], pp. 3-18.

[13] Activity Analysis of Production and Allocation, ed. by T. C. Koopmans, Cowles Monograph No. 13, John Wiley and Sons, New York (1951).

[14] Contributions to the Theory of Games (Vol. I), ed. by H. W. Kuhn and A. W. Tucker, Annals of Mathematics Study 24, Princeton (1950).

A. J. Goldman

A. W. Tucker

Princeton University

RESOLUTION AND SEPARATION THEOREMS FOR POLYHEDRAL CONVEX SETS*

A. J. Goldman

This paper is intended to serve as a bridge between the preceding one on "Polyhedral Convex Cones" (Paper 2, for short) and the one which follows, "Theory of Linear Programming" (Paper 4). As the title suggests, we stress geometric ideas and language throughout the paper.

We deal with polyhedral convex sets in an n-dimensional space of vectors X; such a set S is the intersection of m (closed) half-spaces

$$A_1X \leqq b_1, \ \ldots, \ A_mX \leqq b_m$$

in arbitrary positions in X-space. More concretely, we deal with the solution-set S of the system

$$\begin{matrix} a_{11}x_1 + \cdots + a_{1n}x_n \leqq b_1 \\ \vdots \qquad\qquad\qquad \vdots \\ a_{m1}x_1 + \cdots + a_{mn}x_n \leqq b_m \end{matrix}$$

of m nonhomogeneous linear inequalities in n unknowns. If A represents the set of row vectors $A_1, \ldots, A_m$ or the matrix $\|a_{ij}\|$, and B denotes the column vector formed by $b_1, \ldots, b_m$, then we can write

$$S = \{X \mid AX \leqq B\} .$$

Of course S may be vacuous. But, if nonvacuous, S will be shown to be the vector sum

$$S = P^{\Delta} \quad Q^{\angle}$$

of a bounded convex polyhedron

---

* This paper was written for the Office of Naval Research Logistics Project in the Department of Mathematics at Princeton University.

$$P^{\Delta} = \{X \mid X = u_1P_1 + \dots + u_pP_p; \quad u_i \geqq 0, \quad \Sigma u_i = 1\}$$

and a polyhedral convex cone

$$Q^{\angle} = \{X \mid X = v_1Q_1 + \dots + v_qQ_q; \quad v_j \geqq 0\} .$$

This twofold resolution of a polyhedral convex set is essentially equivalent to the threefold representation (or basis) theorem of T. S. Motzkin [7]; taken with its converse, this result constitutes our Resolution Theorem (Theorem 1). The significance of the extreme vectors of S when A has rank n is discussed in two corollaries (1A and 1B).

We remark that the symbols Δ and $\angle$ in P^{Δ} and $Q^{\angle}$ are chosen to be pictorially suggestive: a triangle Δ (interior and boundary) is a typical two-dimensional "bounded convex polyhedron" and an angle $\angle$ (interior and boundary) is a typical two-dimensional "polyhedral convex cone".

Our other main result (Theorem 2) asserts that a bounded convex polyhedron and a polyhedral convex cone can be separated by a hyperplane if they do not intersect. This Separation Theorem is a geometric variant of the Motzkin Transposition Theorem [7] (see remark following Corollary 2A of Paper 1 in this Study).

Our first aim, then, is the characterization of all sets of the form

$$S = \{X \mid AX \leqq B\} ,$$

where A represents the m by n matrix $\|a_{ij}\|$ or the set of row vectors $A_1, \dots, A_m$, and B represents the column vector formed by $b_1, \dots, b_m$. Such a set may, of course, be vacuous. If nonvacuous, it is convex, that is, whenever X_1 and X_2 are in S, and $t_1 \geqq 0$ and $t_2 \geqq 0$ are numbers such that $t_1 + t_2 = 1$, the vector $t_1X_1 + t_2X_2$ (a typical vector "with endpoint on the line segment joining the endpoints of X_1 and X_2") is also in S.

To emphasize the fact that S is the intersection of finitely many halfspaces we call it a polyhedral convex set. If the system of inequalities is homogeneous, i.e., $B = 0$, then S is a polyhedral convex cone: if X is in S, then the vectors tX for all $t \geqq 0$ ("the ray or halfline generated by X") are also in S. Theorem 2 of Paper 2 shows that such a polyhedral convex cone $\{X \mid AX \leqq 0\}$ can also be expressed as the convex-cone hull $Q^{\angle}$ of a finite set $Q = \{Q_1, \dots, Q_q\}$:

$$Q = \{X \mid X = v_1Q_1 + \dots + v_qQ_q; \quad v_j \geqq 0\} = \{X \mid X = QV; \quad V \geqq 0\}.$$

Concretely, Q is the n by q matrix with $Q_1, \dots, Q_q$ as columns.

One more type of geometric object will play a role in our discussion. This is the <u>bounded convex polyhedron</u> P^{Δ}, which is the convex hull of a finite nonvacuous set $P = \{P_1, \ldots, P_p\}$ of vectors:

$$P^{\Delta} = \{X \mid X = u_1P_1 + \ldots + u_pP_p; \quad u_i \geqq 0, \quad \Sigma u_i = 1\}$$

$$= \{X \mid X = PU; \quad U \geqq 0, \quad \Sigma u_i = 1\}.$$

Concretely, P is the n by p matrix with $P_1, \ldots, P_p$ as columns. Our results will imply that any bounded polyhedral convex set is a bounded convex polyhedron.

The key step in the method used below is the transition from polyhedral convex sets S in the n-dimensional X-space to polyhedral convex <u>cones</u> C^{n+1} in the (closed) halfspace $t \geqq 0$ of the (n+1)-dimensional space of vectors $\bar{X} = (X, t)$. The results of Paper 2 are then applied to these cones in $\bar{X}$-space. [We write (X, t) as a row instead of a column for typographical convenience.]

LEMMA 1. The rule

$$\{X \mid AX \leqq B\} \longleftrightarrow \{\bar{X} \mid AX - Bt \leqq 0, \ -t \leqq 0\}$$

yields a one-to-one inclusion-preserving correspondence between the nonvacuous polyhedral convex sets S in X-space and those polyhedral convex cones C^{n+1} which lie in the halfspace $t \geqq 0$ of $\bar{X}$-space and meet the hyperplane $t = 1$.

PROOF. (a) If X_o lies in $\{X \mid AX \leqq B\}$ (i.e., if $\{X \mid AX \leqq B\}$ is nonvacuous), then $(X_o, 1)$ lies in

$$C^{n+1} = \{\bar{X} \mid AX - Bt \leqq 0, \ -t \leqq 0\},$$

so that C^{n+1} has the desired properties.

Conversely, any polyhedral convex cone D^{n+1} in $\bar{X}$-space can be written in the form

$$D^{n+1} = \{\bar{X} \mid AX - Bt \leqq 0\};$$

if D^{n+1} lies in the halfspace $t \geqq 0$ and contains a vector $(X_o, 1)$, then we have

$$D^{n+1} = \{\bar{X} \mid AX - Bt \leqq 0, \ -t \leqq 0\}$$

and X_0 lies in $S = \{X \mid AX \leqq B\}$, which is therefore nonvacuous.

(b) Suppose $\{X \mid AX \leqq B\}$ is a nonvacuous subset of $\{X \mid CX \leqq D\}$, and let $\bar{X}_0 = (X_0, t_0)$ be any vector in $\{\bar{X} \mid AX - Bt \leqq 0, - t \leqq 0\}$. If $t_0 > 0$, then X_0/t_0 lies in $\{X \mid AX \leqq B\}$ and thus in $\{X \mid CX \leqq D\}$, so that $\bar{X}_0 = (X_0, t_0)$ lies in $\{\bar{X} \mid CX - Dt \leqq 0, - t \leqq 0\}$. If $t_0 = 0$, then X_0 lies in $\{X \mid AX \leqq 0\}$; we pick a fixed vector X_1 in $\{X \mid AX \leqq B\}$ and note that $X_1 + \lambda X_0$ lies in $\{X \mid AX \leqq B\}$, and thus in $\{X \mid CX \leqq D\}$, for all $\lambda \geqq 0$. It follows readily that X_0 lies in $\{X \mid CX \leqq 0\}$, and so $\bar{X}_0 = (X_0, 0)$ lies in $\{\bar{X} \mid CX - Dt \leqq 0, - t \leqq 0\}$. Thus $\{\bar{X} \mid AX - Bt \leqq 0, - t \leqq 0\}$ is a subset of $\{\bar{X} \mid CX - Dt \leqq 0, - t \leqq 0\}$, and so the correspondence is inclusion-preserving in the direction $S \longrightarrow C^{n+1}$.

(c) It readily follows from (b) that if

$$\{X \mid AX \leqq B\} = \{X \mid CX \leqq D\},$$

then

$$\{\bar{X} \mid AX - Bt \leqq 0, - t \leqq 0\} = \{\bar{X} \mid CX - Dt \leqq 0, - t \leqq 0\}.$$

Thus the correspondence is well-defined in the direction $S \longrightarrow C^{n+1}$. That it is well-defined and inclusion-preserving in the direction $C^{n+1} \longrightarrow S$ follows from the fact that

$$S = \{X \mid (X, 1) \in C^{n+1}\}.$$

We can write the correspondence studied in Lemma 1 as

$$S \longrightarrow C^{n+1} = C^{n+1}(S)$$

and

$$C^{n+1} \longleftarrow S = S(C^{n+1})$$

and note that

$$S(C^{n+1}) = \{X \mid (X, 1) \in C^{n+1}\}.$$

A fundamental theorem established by T. S. Motzkin (see [7] page 40) guarantees the existence of a finite "basis" $\{P_1, \ldots, P_p; Q_1, \ldots, Q_q\}$ for any nonvacuous polyhedral convex set. We now state and prove this theorem and its converse.

THEOREM 1. A polyhedral convex set

$$S = \{X \mid AX \leqq B\},$$

if nonvacuous, can be expressed as the vector sum

$$P^{\Delta} + Q^{\angle} = \{X \mid X_1 + X_2,\ X_1 \in P^{\Delta},\ X_2 \in Q^{\angle}\} =$$

$$= \{X \mid X = PU + QV,\ U \geqq 0,\ \Sigma u_i = 1,\ V \geqq 0\}$$

of a bounded convex polyhedron

$$P^{\Delta} = \{X \mid X = PU,\ U \geqq 0,\ \Sigma u_i = 1\}$$

and a polyhedral convex cone

$$Q^{\angle} = \{X \mid X = QV,\ V \geqq 0\}.$$

In any such decomposition, $Q^{\angle} = \{X \mid AX \leqq 0\}$. Conversely, any nonvacuous set of the form $P^{\Delta} + Q^{\angle}$ is a convex polyhedral set.

PROOF. (a) Let $S = \{X \mid AX \leqq B\}$ be a nonvacuous polyhedral convex set in X-space, and form the polyhedral convex cone $C^{n+1}(S)$ in the halfspace $t \geqq 0$ of $\bar{X}$-space. By Corollary 2A of Paper 2, there is a finite set of vectors in $\bar{X}$-space which span $C^{n+1}(S)$. Some of these vectors (call them $(P_1, t_1), \ldots, (P_p, t_p)$) will have positive last components t_i and (since $C^{n+1}(S)$ is a cone) can be normalized so that $t_i = 1$; the others (call them $(Q_1, 0), \ldots, (Q_q, 0)$) have last component zero. Since $C^{n+1}(S)$ meets the hyperplane $t = 1$, we must have $p > 0$; in case $q = 0$, we set $(Q_1, 0) = (0, 0)$. Thus $C^{n+1}(S)$ consists of all vectors of the form

$$\bar{X} = (X, t) = \sum_{i=1}^{p} u_i(P_i, 1) + \sum_{j=1}^{q} v_j(Q_j, 0);$$

$$\text{all } u_i \geqq 0, \quad \text{all } v_j \geqq 0.$$

Since

$$S = \{X \mid (X, 1) \in C^{n+1}(S)\},$$

S consists of all vectors of the form

$$X = \sum_{i=1}^{p} u_i P_i + \sum_{j=1}^{q} v_j Q_j; \quad \text{all } u_i \geqq 0, \ \Sigma u_i = 1, \quad \text{all } v_j \geqq 0;$$

i.e.,

$$S = P^{\Delta} + Q^{\angle} .$$

(b) If we begin with a set $P^{\Delta} + Q^{\angle}$, then we can construct in $\bar{X}$-space the polyhedral convex cone D^{n+1} consisting of all vectors of the form

$$\bar{X} = (X, t) = \sum_{i=1}^{p} u_i (P_i, 1) + \sum_{j=1}^{q} v_j (Q_j, 0);$$

$$\text{all } u_i \geqq 0, \quad \text{all } v_j \geqq 0.$$

Clearly $P^{\Delta} + Q^{\angle} = \{X \mid (X, 1) \in D^{n+1}\}$. D^{n+1} lies in the halfspace $t \geqq 0$ and meets the hyperplane $t = 1$ (since $p > 0$); thus, by Lemma 1, $\{X \mid (X, 1) \in D^{n+1}\} = S(D^{n+1})$ is a nonvacuous polyhedral convex set.

(c) We must still prove that if

$$S = \{X \mid AX \leqq B\} = P^{\Delta} + Q^{\angle}$$

then

$$Q^{\angle} = \{X \mid AX \leqq 0\}.$$

The cone D^{n+1} constructed in (b) has the property

$$S = P^{\Delta} + Q^{\angle} = \{X \mid (X, 1) \in D^{n+1}\},$$

so $S = S(D^{n+1})$; by Lemma 1 it follows that

$$D^{n+1} = C^{n+1}(S) = \{\bar{X} \mid AX - Bt \leqq 0, \ - t \leqq 0\}.$$

Thus $Q^{\angle} = \{X \mid (X, 0) \in D^{n+1}\} = \{X \mid (X, 0) \in C^{n+1}(S)\} = \{X \mid AX \leqq 0\}$.

REMARK. As indicated at the end of Paper 2, Corollary 2A of that paper can be extended to the infinite case. It follows that the solution-set of an infinite system of nonhomogeneous linear inequalities also has a (possibly infinite) "basis". The converse of the Basis Theorem is not in general true in the infinite case, however; the set generated by an infinite basis need not be closed and therefore may not be expressible as the solution-set of a (finite or infinite) system of linear inequalities ($\leqq$).

We now define an <u>extreme vector</u> of a set S to be a vector X which lies in S but is not the mean of two other vectors of S; i.e.,

$$X = \frac{1}{2}(X_1 + X_2) \qquad (X_1, X_2 \in S)$$

implies

$$X = X_1 \text{ or } X = X_2 \text{ and thus } X = X_1 = X_2.$$

LEMMA 2. Let $S = \{X \mid AX \leqq B\}$ be a nonvacuous polyhedral convex set, where A is of rank n (i.e., $\{X \mid AX = 0\} = \{0\}$ so that $\{X \mid AX \leqq 0\}$ is a "pointed" cone). Then X is an extreme vector of S if, and only if, $(X, 1)$ lies on an edge of $C^{n+1} = C^{n+1}(S)$.

PROOF. (a) Because A is of rank n, the matrix

$$\begin{bmatrix} A & -B \\ 0 & -1 \end{bmatrix}$$

is of rank $n + 1$. Thus, using the language of Paper 2, the cone

$$C^{n+1} = \{\bar{X} \mid AX - Bt \leqq 0, \ -t \leqq 0\}$$

has $d = 0$ and so is "pointed". We recall also that

$$S = \{X \mid (X, 1) \in C^{n+1}\}.$$

(b) Suppose $(X, 1)$ lies on an edge F_H of C^{n+1}, but that X is <u>not</u> an extreme vector of S. Then

$$X = \frac{1}{2}(X_1 + X_2); \qquad X_1, X_2 \text{ in } S, \qquad X_1 \neq X_2.$$

Thus $(X, 1) = \frac{1}{2}(X_1, 1) + \frac{1}{2}(X_2, 1)$; $\frac{1}{2}(X_1, 1)$ and $\frac{1}{2}(X_2, 1)$ in C^{n+1}. The vectors $\frac{1}{2}(X_1, 1)$ and $\frac{1}{2}(X_2, 1)$ are nonzero and so neither of them lies in the unique subface of F_H (which consists of the single vector $(0, 0)$). As distinct vectors with equal last components, they cannot both lie in the edge F_H. Thus we have a contradiction to Lemma 4 of Paper 2.

(c) Suppose that X is an extreme vector of S, but that $(X, 1)$ is not on an edge of C^{n+1}. By Lemma 1 of Paper 2, we have

$$(X, 1) = (X_1, t_1) + (X_2, t_2)$$

where (X_1, t_1) and (X_2, t_2) lie in C^{n+1}, but not in the same face as $(X, 1)$. We may suppose $t_2 \leq t_1$; then $t_2 \leqq \frac{1}{2}$. Note that $t_1 + t_2 = 1$.

We write

$$(X, 1) = \frac{1}{2}(X_1/t_1, 1) + \frac{1}{2}((1 - 2t_2)(X_1/t_1, 1) + 2(X_2, t_2));$$

the second member of the "mean" is obtained geometrically by extending the line segment joining the tips of $(X, 1)$ and $(X_1/t_1, 1)$ its own length through the tip of $(X, 1)$. It is easy to verify that both members of the "mean" lie in the polyhedral convex cone C^{n+1} and have 1 as last component. So if we write

$$X = \frac{1}{2}(X_1/t_1) + \frac{1}{2}((1 - 2t_2)(X_1/t_1) + 2X_2)$$

and note that $X_1/t_1 \neq X$ (since otherwise (X_1, t_1) would be a positive multiple of $(X, 1)$, although the two lie in different faces of C^{n+1}), we have a contradiction to the fact that X is extreme.

COROLLARY 1A. Let $S = \{X \mid AX \leq B\}$ be a nonvacuous polyhedral convex set with A of rank n. Then S has a minimal basis $\{P_1, \ldots, P_p; Q_1, \ldots, Q_q\}$ which is unique (up to positive multiples of the Q_j's). Here $\{P_1, \ldots, P_p\}$ is the set of extreme vectors of S.

PROOF. It is clear from the proof of Theorem 1 that a minimal basis of S comes from a minimal set spanning $C^{n+1}(S)$. Because A is of rank n, it follows (as in the proof of Lemma 2) that $C^{n+1}(S)$ has $d = 0$; furthermore, $C^{n+1}(S)$ meets the hyperplane $t = 1$ and therefore does not consist of $(0, 0)$ alone. By Theorem 7 of Paper 2, $C^{n+1}(S)$ has a minimal spanning set, unique up to positive multiples, such that any other spanning set contains it; it is obtained by choosing a vector (P_i, t_i) with $t_i > 0$ on each edge of $C^{n+1}(S)$ not in the hyperplane $t = 0$ and a vector $(Q_j, 0)$ on each edge of $C^{n+1}(S)$ which lies in the hyperplane $t = 0$. We can normalize so that $t_i = 1$; then, by Lemma 2, $P = \{P_1, \ldots, P_p\}$ is the set of extreme vectors of S.

COROLLARY 1B. A nonvacuous polyhedral convex set

$$S = \{X \mid AX \leqq B\}$$

is bounded if, and only if, $Q^{\angle} = \{X \mid AX \leqq 0\} = \{0\}$. In this case S is a bounded convex polyhedron and is the convex hull of its finite set of extreme vectors. Furthermore, any set of vectors of which S is the convex hull must include all the extreme vectors of S.

PROOF. (a) According to Theorem 1, we can write

$$S = P^{\Delta} + Q^{\angle}.$$

If $Q^{\angle} = \{X \mid AX \leqq 0\} = \{0\}$, then $S = P^{\Delta}$, a bounded convex polyhedron. But if $\{X \mid AX \leqq 0\}$ contains a nonzero vector X_0, then S contains the infinite ray $\{X \mid X = X_1 + \lambda X_0, \lambda > 0\}$ (where X_1 is a fixed vector in S) and is therefore unbounded.

(b) If $\{X \mid AX \leqq 0\} = \{0\}$, then $S = P^{\Delta}$, as we saw in (a). Furthermore, $\{X \mid AX = 0\} = \{0\}$, so that A has rank n; by Corollary 1A, we can take P to be the set of extreme vectors of S. If T is a set of vectors with $S = P^{\Delta}$ as its convex hull, then T is a "basis" for S and so, by Corollary 1A, T must include all the extreme vectors of S.

Our next topic is the separation of two disjoint polyhedral sets by a hyperplane. We first show that a single vector and a polyhedral convex cone can be so separated (Lemma 3) and use this to prove that a polyhedral convex set and a polyhedral convex cone can be separated (Theorem 2). The algebraic counterpart of a "separation theorem" is a "transposition theorem" (see remarks following Corollary 2A of Paper 1 in this Study).

LEMMA 3. Either a given vector X_0 lies in a given polyhedral convex cone $Q^{\angle} = \{X \mid X = QV, V \geqq 0\}$, or there exists a hyperplane $YX = 0$ which separates X_0 from $Q^{\angle}$ in the sense that X_0 lies in the open halfspace $YX > 0$ but $Q^{\angle}$ lies in the closed halfspace $YX \leqq 0$.

PROOF. By Theorem 3 of Paper 2

$$Q^{\angle} = \{X \mid X = QV, V \geqq 0\} = \{X \mid YX \leqq 0, \text{ all } Y \text{ in } Q^*\} = Q^{**}$$

Thus X_0 fails to lie in $Q^{\angle}$ if and only if there is some vector Y in $Q^* = \{Y \mid YQ \leqq 0\}$ such that $YX_0 > 0$; clearly $YX \leqq 0$ for all X in $Q^{\angle} = Q^{**}$.

THEOREM 2. Let $P^{\Delta} = \{X \mid X = PU,\ U \geqq 0,\ \Sigma u_i = 1\}$ be a given bounded convex polyhedron and $Q^{\angle} = \{X \mid X = QV,\ V \geqq 0\}$ a given polyhedral convex cone. Either P^{Δ} and $Q^{\angle}$ intersect, or there exists a hyperplane $YX = 0$ which separates P^{Δ} and $Q^{\angle}$ in the sense that P^{Δ} lies in the open halfspace $YX > 0$ but $Q^{\angle}$ lies in the closed halfspace $YX \leqq 0$.

PROOF. It is clear that the alternatives are mutually exclusive. Let $P = \{P_1, \ldots, P_p\}$; if $p = 1$ then the desired result follows from Lemma 3, so we assume $p > 1$. We shall suppose that P^{Δ} and $Q^{\angle}$ do not intersect (i.e., that the first alternative does not hold) and prove that the second alternative holds.

We first observe that for $i \leqq i \leqq p$, P_i does not lie in $\{-P_1, \ldots, -P_{i-1}, -P_{i+1}, \ldots, -P_p, Q_1, \ldots, Q_q\}^{\angle}$. For if

$$P_i = \sum_{k \neq i} \bar{u}_k(-P_k) + \Sigma \bar{v}_j Q_j;\ \bar{u}_k \geqq 0,\ \bar{v}_j \geqq 0$$

then

$$\sum_{k \neq i} \bar{u}_k P_k + P_i = \Sigma \bar{v}_j Q_j,$$

and if we set

$$a = 1 + \sum_{k \neq i} \bar{u}_k > 0,\ u_k = \bar{u}_k / a \quad \text{for} \quad k \neq i,$$

$$u_i = 1/a, \quad \text{and} \quad v_j = \bar{v}_j / a$$

we obtain

$$\sum_k u_k P_k = \Sigma v_j Q_j;\ u_k \geqq 0,\ \Sigma u_k = 1,\ v_j \geqq 0,$$

which contradicts the disjointness of P^{Δ} and $Q^{\angle}$.

By Lemma 3, for each i $(1 \leqq i \leqq p)$ there is a vector Y_i

such that $Y_iP_i > 0$ and $Y_iX \leqq 0$ for each vector X in $\{-P_1, \ldots, -P_{i-1}, -P_{i+1}, \ldots, -P_p, Q_1, \ldots, Q_k\}$. Thus $Y_iP_i > 0$, $Y_iP_k \geqq 0$ for $k \neq i$ and $Y_iX \leqq 0$ for all X in $Q^{\angle}$. It follows easily that the second alternative of the theorem holds with $Y = Y_1 + \ldots + Y_p$.

References

[1] DAVIS, C., "The intersection of a linear subspace with the positive orthant," Michigan Mathematical Journal 1 (1952), pp. 163-168.

[2] DAVIS, C., "Remarks on a previous paper," Michigan Mathematical Journal 2 (1953-4), pp. 23-25.

[3] DAVIS, C., "The theory of positive linear dependence," American Journal of Math. 76 (1954), pp. 733-746.

[4] FARKAS, J., "Über die theorie der einfachen Ungleichungen," Journal fur reine und angewandte Mathematik 124 (1902), pp. 1-27.

[5] GOLDMAN, A. J., and TUCKER, A. W., "Polyhedral convex cones," Paper 2 in this Study.

[6] MINKOWSKI, H., Geometrie der Zahlen, Teubner, Leipzig (1910).

[7] MOTZKIN, T. S., "Beiträge zur theorie der linearen Ungleichungen," (Dissertation, Basel, 1933) Jerusalem, 1936.

[8] MOTZKIN, T. S., RAIFFA, H., THOMPSON, G. L., THRALL, R. M., "The double description method," Annals of Mathematics Study 28, pp. 51-74. See [12].

[9] TUCKER, A. W., "Dual systems of homogeneous linear relations," Paper 1 in this Study.

[10] WEYL, H., "The elementary theory of convex polyhedra," Annals of Mathematics Study 24, Princeton (1950, pp. 3-18. See [11].

[11] Contributions to the Theory of Games (Vol. 1), ed. by H. W. Kuhn and A. W. Tucker, Annals of Mathematics Study 24, Princeton, 1950.

[12] Contributions to the Theory of Games (Vol. 2), ed. by H. W. Kuhn and A. W. Tucker, Annals of Mathematics Study 28, Princeton, 1953.

Princeton University A. J. Goldman

THEORY OF LINEAR PROGRAMMING*

A. J. Goldman and A. W. Tucker

Foreword

The aim of this paper is a systematic presentation of theoretical properties of dual linear programs. The main results in Parts 1, 2, and 4 are already well established, but most of the remaining material has not been published previously. At the end of the paper there is a brief bibliography, to which references are made in the text by means of numbers in square brackets.

Contents

* This paper was written for the Office of Naval Research Logistics Project in the Department of Mathematics at Princeton University.

PART 1: Dual Linear Programs

The following constitute a pair of <u>dual linear programs</u> (or dual linear programming problems):

I. To maximize

$$c_1x_1 + \cdots + c_nx_n,$$

subject to the $m + n$ constraints

$$(1)\qquad \begin{array}{ccc} a_{11}x_1 + \cdots + a_{1n}x_n & \leqq & b_1 \\ \vdots & & \vdots \\ a_{m1}x_1 + \cdots + a_{mn}x_n & \leqq & b_m \end{array}$$

$$(2)\qquad x_1 \geqq 0, \quad x_2 \geqq 0, \ldots, x_n \geqq 0.$$

II. To minimize

$$u_1b_1 + \cdots + u_mb_m$$

subject to the $n + m$ constraints

$$(3)\qquad \begin{array}{ccc} u_1a_{11} + \cdots + u_ma_{m1} & \geqq & c_1 \\ \vdots & & \vdots \\ u_1a_{1n} + \cdots + u_ma_{mn} & \geqq & c_n \end{array}$$

$$(4)\qquad u_1 \geqq 0, \quad u_2 \geqq 0, \ldots, u_m \geqq 0.$$

Here the a_{ij}, b_i, and c_j are given real numbers. (But the results of this paper hold equally for numbers drawn from any ordered field.) The inequalities of (1) are called <u>row constraints</u> (since they involve the rows of the matrix of a_{ij}'s); those of (3) are <u>column constraints</u>.

These problems may be represented jointly by the following convenient scheme

$(\geqq 0)$	x_1	x_2	$\cdots$	x_n	$(\leqq)$
u_1	a_{11}	a_{12}	$\cdots$	a_{1n}	b_1
u_2	a_{21}	a_{22}	$\cdots$	a_{2n}	b_2
$\vdots$	$\vdots$	$\vdots$		$\vdots$	$\vdots$
u_m	a_{m1}	a_{m2}	$\cdots$	a_{mn}	b_m
$(\geqq)$	c_1	c_2	$\cdots$	c_n	

An interpretation may be given in terms of Activity Analysis. (See [19].) Let there be n "activities"; i.e., ways of making a single desired commodity from available stocks of m primary commodities ("materials"). Let a_{ij} be the amount of the i-th material used in one unit of the j-th activity, b_i the available stock of the i-th material, c_j the quantity of the desired commodity made by one unit of the j-th activity, and x_j the number of units of the j-th activity to be undertaken. The maximization problem is then a search for an "activity vector" $(x_1, \ldots, x_n)$ which will yield the greatest possible total output $\Sigma c_j x_j$ of the desired commodity, subject to the constraints (1) set by the available stocks of the m materials and by the natural impossibility (2) of negative "activity levels".

The dual problem pertains to accounting (fictitious or "shadow") prices attached to the m materials, on a scale whose unit is the price of the desired commodity. One seeks a "price vector" $(u_1, \ldots, u_m)$ that minimizes the total accounting value $\Sigma u_i b_i$ of the available stocks of materials, subject to the "one-can't-get-something-for-nothing" requirement (3) that the accounting value of the quantity of the desired commodity made by one unit of an activity can never exceed the total accounting value of the materials used in that unit, and to the natural requirement (4) that all accounting prices be non-negative.

These may be summarized schematically as follows:

		activity levels				
	$(\geqq 0)$	x_1	$\cdots\cdots$	x_n	$(\leqq)$	
	u_1	a_{11}	$\cdots\cdots$	a_{1n}	b_1	
accounting prices of materials	$\vdots$	$\vdots$	materials used per activity unit	$\vdots$	$\vdots$	available stocks of materials
	u_m	a_{m1}	$\cdots\cdots$	a_{mn}	b_m	
	$(\geqq)$	c_1	$\cdots\cdots$	c_n		
		outputs per activity unit				

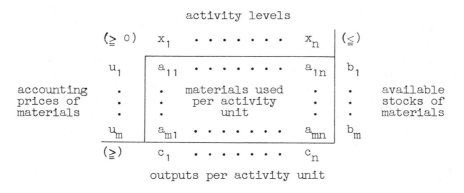

Returning to the mathematical discussion, we give a more compact notation for the problems. If we form the row vectors

$$U = (u_1, \ldots, u_m),$$
$$C = (c_1, \ldots, c_n),$$

and also the column vectors

$$X = \begin{bmatrix} x_1 \\ \cdot \\ \cdot \\ \cdot \\ x_n \end{bmatrix}, \qquad B = \begin{bmatrix} b_1 \\ \cdot \\ \cdot \\ \cdot \\ b_m \end{bmatrix},$$

then we may use matrix symbolism to write the problems as:

I. To maximize CX, subject to

(1) $AX \leqq B$

(2) $X \geqq 0$

II. To minimize UB, subject to

(3) $UA \geqq C$

(4) $U \geqq 0$.

Joint scheme:

($\geqq 0$)	X^T	($\leqq$)
U^T	A	B
($\geqq$)	C	

U^T and X^T (a column and a row vector, respectively) are the transposes of U and X. The vector inequalities written here hold component by component, just as the equality of two vectors holds componentwise. Strict inequality between vectors is also defined componentwise. We write $Y_1 \leq Y_2$ to indicate that $Y_1 \leqq Y_2$ but $Y_1 \neq Y_2$.

We say that the $m + n$ constraints (1) and (2) are feasible if there exists some vector X satisfying them; we then call the maximization problem feasible, and call such an X a feasible vector for it. A feasible X^0 which provides the desired maximum for CX is called an optimal vector for the maximization problem. The terms "feasible" and "optimal" are defined analogously for the minimization problem.

At this point we prove the following lemmas.

LEMMA 1. If X and U are feasible, then $CX \leqq UB$.

PROOF. $CX \leqq (UA)X = U(AX) \leqq UB$.

LEMMA 2. If X^o and U^o are feasible, and $CX^o = U^oB$ (or merely $CX^o \geqq U^oB$), then X^o and U^o are optimal.

PROOF. If $CX^o = UB^o$, then by Lemma 1 $U^o B = CX^o \leqq UB$ for all feasible U. Thus U^o is optimal, and a similar argument shows X^o is optimal. The parenthetical insertion is justified by Lemma 1.

According to Lemma 2, the assertion that X^o and U^o are a pair of optimal vectors can be checked directly and simply in the schematic form of the dual programs:

1. One checks the feasibility of X^o by making sure that all its components are non-negative and that the inner product of each row of the scheme with X^o is not greater than the corresponding b_i.

2. One checks the feasibility of U^o by making sure that all its components are non-negative and that its inner product with each column of the scheme is not less than the corresponding c_j.

3. Finally, one checks the equality of the inner product of C and X^o with that of U^o and B.

LEMMA 3. If all b_i are non-negative, then the maximization problem has feasible constraints. If all a_{ij} are non-negative and some a_{ij} is positive for each j, then the minimization problem has feasible constraints.

PROOF. The first statement is immediately proved by noting that the zero vector is feasible for the maximization problem. The second statement is proved by noting that under our hypotheses any U will be feasible if all its components are sufficiently large.

The following two examples illustrate the possibility that the constraints in one or both problems may be infeasible:

EXAMPLE 1.

$(\geqq 0)$	x	y	$(\leqq)$
u	- 1	- 2	- 3
v	1	3	2
$(\geqq)$	0	0	

Here $U = (0, 0)$ is feasible, but the requirements

$$\begin{aligned} -x - 2y &\leqq -3 \\ x + 3y &\leqq 2 \\ y &\geqq 0 \end{aligned}$$

clearly cannot be met, so the maximization problem has no feasible vector.

EXAMPLE 2.

($\geqq 0$)	x	y	($\leqq$)
u	0	1	− 1
v	0	4	3
($\geqq$)	1	2	

Here neither the requirements

$$\begin{aligned} 0x + y &\leqq -1 \\ y &\geqq 0 \end{aligned}$$

nor the requirement

$$0u + 0v \geqq 1$$

can be met, so neither problem has a feasible vector.

It will be shown in the "Existence Theorem" of Part 2 that both problems possess optimal vectors if they both possess feasible vectors.

PART 2: Duality and Existence Theorems

In this part we derive the two basic theorems of linear programming theory, together with several corollaries. The essential step in the analysis is the application of Theorem 5 of the preceding paper ("Dual Systems of Homogeneous Linear Relations") to the skew-symmetric matrix

$$K = \begin{bmatrix} 0 & A & -B \\ -A^T & 0 & C^T \\ B^T & -C & 0 \end{bmatrix}$$

to obtain a column vector $(U_o^T, X_o, t_o) \geq 0$ such that

(i) $Bt_o \geqq AX_o$

(ii) $U_oA \geqq Ct_o$

(iii) $CX_o \geqq U_oB$

(iv) $CX_o + t_o > U_oB$

(v) $U_o^T + Bt_o > AX_o$

(vi) $U_oA + X_o^T > Ct_o$.

Throughout Part 2 the symbols "X_o", "U_o", "t_o" will be reserved for these particular X_o, U_o, t_o, and the numbering (i) through (vi) will be reserved for the inequalities just listed. The cases $t_o > 0$ and $t_o = 0$ will be investigated separately.

LEMMA 4. Suppose $t_o > 0$. Then there are optimal vectors X^o and U^o for the dual programs such that

$$CX^o = U^oB, \quad (U^o)^T + B > AX^o, \quad U^oA + (X^o)^T > C.$$

PROOF. Since $t_o > 0$, the non-negative vector (U_o^T, X_o, t_o) can be "normalized" so that $t_o = 1$ without affecting the validity of the homogeneous inequalities (i) through (vi). Then (i) and (ii) (with $t_o = 1$) show that X_o and U_o are feasible; (iii) and Lemma 2 show that X_o and U_o are optimal, and Lemma 1 shows that $CX_o = U_oB$. The relations $U_o^T + B > AX_o$ and $U_oA + X_o^T > C$ follow from (v) and (vi) (with $t_o = 1$). Thus we can choose the normalized X_o and U_o to be the desired X^o and U^o.

LEMMA 5. Suppose $t_o = 0$.

(a) At least one of the dual programs has no feasible vector.

(b) If the maximization problem has a feasible vector, then the set of its feasible vectors is unbounded and CX is unbounded on this set. Dually for the minimization problem.

(c) Neither problem has an optimal vector.

PROOF. Suppose X is a feasible vector for the maximization problem. Using (ii) with $t_o = 0$ and the non-negativity of X, we obtain $U_oAX \geqq 0$. This last inequality, together with (iv) (with $t_o = 0$) and the feasibility of X, yields

(*) $$0 \leqq U_oAX \leqq U_oB < CX_o.$$

To prove (a), we note that if the minimization problem had a feasible vector $\bar{U}$, then we could obtain the "duals" of the first two inequalities in (*):

$$0 \geqq UAX_o \geqq CX_o.$$

This clearly contradicts (*), and so (a) is proved.

To prove (b), we examine the infinite ray consisting of the vectors

$$X + \lambda X_o \qquad \text{(all } \lambda \geqq 0).$$

Clearly $X + \lambda X_o \geqq 0$; using (i) with $t_o = 0$, we see that $A(X + \lambda X_o) \leqq AX \leqq B$. Thus the entire infinite ray consists of feasible vectors, which proves the first assertion of (b). Furthermore, since $CX_o > 0$ (by (*)), we see that

$$C(X + \lambda X_o) = CX + \lambda CX_o$$

can be made arbitrarily large by choosing λ large enough. So the second assertion of (b) is proved. Finally, (c) is an immediate consequence of (b). This completes the proof of the lemma.

COROLLARY 1A. Either both the maximization and minimization problems have optimal vectors, or neither does. In the first case the (attained) maximum and minimum are equal; their common magnitude is called the <u>optimal value</u> of the dual programs.

PROOF. If one problem has optimal vectors then (c) of Lemma 5 shows that $t_o > 0$ and Lemma 4 shows that both problems have optimal vectors X^o, U^o, such that the "maximum" CX^o is equal to the "minimum" U^oB.

COROLLARY 1B. A necessary and sufficient condition that either (and thus both) of the dual programs have optimal vectors is that either CX or UB be bounded on the corresponding nonvacuous set of feasible vectors.

PROOF. The necessity of the condition is clear. To prove its sufficiency, suppose that the maximization problem has a nonvacuous set of feasible vectors and that CX is bounded on this set. By (b) of Lemma 5 we must have $t_o > 0$, and by Lemma 4 both problems have optimal vectors.

THEOREM 1 (Duality Theorem). A feasible X^o is optimal if and only if there is a feasible U^o with $U^oB = CX^o$. A feasible U^o is optimal if and only if there is a feasible X^o with $CX^o = U^oB$.

PROOF. We shall demonstrate only the first statement, since the second clearly has an analogous proof. Lemma 2 immediately yields the sufficiency of the condition. To prove its necessity, suppose that X^o is optimal. By (c) of Lemma 5 we must have $t_o > 0$, by Lemma 4 the minimization problem also has an optimal vector U^o, and by Corollary 1A the attained maximum CX^o and minimum U^oB are equal.

THEOREM 2 (Existence Theorem). A necessary and sufficient condition that one (and thus both) of the dual problems have optimal vectors is that both have feasible vectors.

PROOF. The necessity of the condition is clear. To prove its sufficiency, suppose that both problems have feasible vectors. By (a) of Lemma 5 we have $t_o > 0$, and by Lemma 4 both problems have optimal vectors. This completes the proof.

The Duality and Existence Theorems were first proved by Gale, Kuhn, and Tucker in [7].

The next pair of corollaries deal with the way in which a pair X^o, U^o of optimal vectors satisfy the $2m + 2n$ feasibility constraints

$$X \geqq 0, \quad AX \leqq B, \quad U \geqq 0, \quad UA \geqq C.$$

Corollary 2B will imply that any such pair X^o, U^o satisfies <u>at least</u> $m + n$ of these constraints as equations, while Corollary 2A will imply the existence of a particular pair which satisfies at most $m + n$ (and thus <u>exactly</u> $m + n$) of the constraints as equations.

There is a convenient way to pair off the constraints associated with the two problems. The i-th relations summarized in the matrix statements $AX \leqq B$, $U \geqq 0$, are called a pair of <u>dual constraints</u>, as are the j-th relations given by $UA \geqq C$, $X \geqq 0$.

COROLLARY 2A. If both problems have feasible vectors, then they have optimal vectors X^o, U^o, such that:

(1) If X^o satisfies a row constraint as an EQUATION, then U^o satisfies the dual constraint as a STRICT INEQUALITY.

(2) If U^o satisfies a column constraint as an EQUATION, then X^o satisfies the dual constraint as a STRICT INEQUALITY.

PROOF. By Theorem 2 both problems have optimal vectors, so (c) of Lemma 5 yields $t_o > 0$. By Lemma 4 there are optimal vectors X^o, U^o such that

$$(U^o)^T + B > AX^o, \quad U^oA + (X^o)^T > C.$$

This X^o and U^o clearly have the desired properties.

In the statement and proof of the next corollary, it is convenient to use the notation $(Y)_k$ for the k-th component of a vector Y.

COROLLARY 2B. If both problems are feasible, then for any i <u>either</u> $(AX^o)_i < b_i$ for some optimal X^o and $u_i = 0$ for every optimal U, <u>or</u> $(AX)_i = b_i$ for every optimal X and $u_i^o > 0$ for some optimal U^o. (Of course the dual statement holds for $(U^oA)_j > c_j$, etc.)

PROOF. By Theorem 2 both problems have optimal vectors, so the alternatives are meaningful. Corollary 2A implies that if $(AX)_i = b_i$ for every optimal X, <u>then</u> $u_i^o > 0$ for some optimal U^o; thus it suffices to prove that <u>if</u> $(AX^o)_i < b_i$ for some optimal X^o, <u>then</u> $u_i = 0$ for every optimal U.

To see this, note that $(AX^o)_i < b_i$ and $u_i > 0$ together imply $u_i(AX^o)_i < u_ib_i$. For $r \neq i$ we have $u_r(AX^o)_r \leqq u_rb_r$, and so, adding together the summands of the scalar products $U(AX^o)$ and UB, we have (using the feasibility of U)

$$CX^o \leqq UAX^o < UB.$$

Since X^o and U are optimal, Corollary 1A asserts that $CX^o = UB$, and thus a contradiction is reached.

A constraint is said to be <u>tight</u> if every optimal vector satisfies it as an equation; otherwise the constraint is <u>loose</u>. We restate Corollary 2B in this language: The dual of a tight constraint is loose, and vice versa.

PART 3: Dual Problems with Mixed Constraints

Let N be the set of indices $[1, 2, \ldots, n]$, while M is the corresponding set $[1, 2, \ldots, m]$. Suppose N_1 and N_2 are complementary subsets of N with n_1 and n_2 elements respectively, while M_1 and M_2 are complementary subsets of M with m_1 and m_2 elements respectively. We are concerned here with problem-pairs of the following sort:

I. To maximize

$$c_1x_1 + \dots + c_nx_n$$

subject to the constraints

$$a_{i1}x_1 + \dots + a_{in}x_n \begin{cases} \leqq b_i & \text{for each } i \text{ in } M_1 \\ = b_i & \text{for each } i \text{ in } M_2 \end{cases}$$

$$x_j \begin{cases} \text{non-negative for each } j \text{ in } N_1 \\ \text{unrestricted for each } j \text{ in } N_2 \end{cases}$$

II. To minimize

$$u_1b_1 + \dots + u_mb_m$$

subject to the constraints

$$u_1a_{1j} + \dots + u_ma_{mj} \begin{cases} \geqq c_j & \text{for each } j \text{ in } N_1 \\ = c_j & \text{for each } j \text{ in } N_2 \end{cases}$$

$$u_i \begin{cases} \text{non-negative for each } i \text{ in } M_1 \\ \text{unrestricted for each } i \text{ in } M_2 \end{cases}$$

Note that the constraints which are equations correspond to the variables which are unrestricted.

We may adopt the previous terminology, and speak of X or U as <u>feasible</u> if it satisfies the constraints and as <u>optimal</u> if it is feasible and achieves the desired maximization or minimization.

If we decompose the matrix A and the vectors B, C, X and U into blocks corresponding to the decompositions of M and N into $M_1 + M_2$ and $N_1 + N_2$ respectively, then the problems take the following forms:

I. To maximize

$$C_1X_1 + C_2X_2$$

subject to the constraints

$$A_{11}X_1 + A_{12}X_2 \leqq B_1$$

$$A_{21}X_1 + A_{22}X_2 = B_2$$

$$X_1 \geqq 0, \quad (X_2 \text{ unrestricted}).$$

II. To minimize

$$U_1B_1 + U_2B_2$$

subject to the constraints

$$U_1A_{11} + U_2A_{21} \geqq C_1$$
$$U_1A_{12} + U_2A_{22} = C_2$$
$$U_1 \geqq 0, \quad (U_2 \text{ unrestricted}).$$

Joint Scheme:

	$X_1^T \geqq 0$	X_2^T		
$U_1^T \geqq 0$	A_{11}	A_{12}	$\leqq B_1$	(M_1)
U_2^T	A_{21}	A_{22}	$= B_2$	(M_2)
	$\geqq C_1$	$= C_2$		
	(N_1)	(N_2)		

We point out at once that such problem-pairs are essentially no more general than the "canonical" ones defined in Part 1, for which $m_2 = n_2 = 0$; thus in the remaining parts of this report we shall confine ourselves to the canonical forms. The lack of extra generality is most easily seen by applying to the constraint equations the principle that <u>any</u> equation $f = 0$ can be replaced by the equivalent pair of inequalities $f \geqq 0$ and $-f \geqq 0$.

To effect this formally, set

$$X_2' = \max(0, X_2) \qquad U_2' = \max(0, U_2)$$
$$X_2'' = \max(0, -X_2) \quad U_2'' = \max(0, -U_2)$$

where $\max(Y^1, Y^2)$ is the vector Z whose components are $z_i = \max(y_i^1, y_i^2)$. The new problems, which are of canonical type, are:

I'. To maximize

$$C_1X_1 + C_2X_2' + (-C_2)X_2''$$

subject to the constraints

$$A_{11}X_1 + A_{12}X_2' + (-A_{12})X_2'' \leqq B_1$$
$$A_{21}X_1 + A_{22}X_2' + (-A_{22})X_2'' \leqq B_2$$
$$(-A_{21})X_1 + (-A_{22}X_2') + A_{22}X_2'' \leqq -B_2$$
$$X_1 \geqq 0,\ X_2' \geqq 0,\ X_2'' \geqq 0.$$

II'. To minimize

$$U_1B_1 + U_2'B_2 + U_2''(-B_2)$$

subject to the constraints

$$U_1A_{11} + U_2'A_{21} + U_2''(-A_{21}) \geqq C_1$$
$$U_1A_{12} + U_2'A_{22} + U_2''(-A_{22}) \geqq C_2$$
$$U_1(-A_{12}) + U_2'(-A_{22}) + U_2''A_{22} \geqq -C_2$$
$$U_1 \geqq 0,\ U_2' \geqq 0,\ U_2'' \geqq 0.$$

The new problem-pair is equivalent to the old in the sense that (U_1, U_2', U_2'') is feasible (optimal) if and only if (U_1, U_2) is feasible (optimal), and similarly for

$$\begin{bmatrix} X_1 \\ X_2' \\ X_2'' \end{bmatrix} \quad \text{and} \quad \begin{bmatrix} X_1 \\ X_2 \end{bmatrix}$$

(Because of this equivalence, the Duality and Existence Theorems of Part 2, which are certainly valid for the "canonical" problems I' and II', also hold for the problems I and II with mixed constraints.) Furthermore, the old problems may be regained from the new (i.e., the process can be reversed) by setting

$$X_2 = X_2' - X_2''$$
$$U_2 = U_2' - U_2''$$

Unfortunately the matrix for the new problems, which is given by

$$\begin{bmatrix} A_{11} & A_{12} & -A_{12} \\ A_{21} & A_{22} & -A_{22} \\ -A_{21} & -A_{22} & A_{22} \end{bmatrix}$$

is larger than the original

$$A = \begin{bmatrix} A_{11} & A_{12} \\ A_{21} & A_{22} \end{bmatrix}$$

We shall next describe two methods for bringing a pair of problems with mixed constraints into canonical form, which are free from this disadvantage.

METHOD 1: Here we use the fact that a constraint equation can be employed to eliminate any variable appearing in it with non-zero coefficient; after this is done the equation of course appears as a defining relation rather than as a constraint. Suppose, for instance, that we had as a "row constraint" the equation

$$a_{m1}x_1 + \cdots + a_{mn}x_n = b_m,$$

with $a_{mn} \neq 0$. Then x_n can be eliminated by

(1) $$x_n = \frac{1}{a_{mn}} (b_m - a_{m1}x_1 - \cdots - a_{m,n-1}x_{n-1}).$$

Let

$$\bar{a}_{ij} = a_{ij} - \frac{a_{mj}a_{in}}{a_{mn}}$$

$$\bar{b}_i = b_i - \frac{b_m a_{in}}{a_{mn}} \qquad \text{for } i = 1, \ldots, n-1 \text{ and } j = 1, \ldots, n-1.$$

$$\bar{c}_j = c_j - \frac{a_{mj}c_n}{a_{mn}}$$

If, on the one hand, n is in N_2, then the unrestricted variable u_m may be eliminated by

(2) $$u_m = \frac{1}{a_{mn}} (c_n - u_1 a_{1n} - \cdots - u_{m-1}a_{m-1,n}).$$

The dual problems given by the matrix of the $\bar{a}_{ij}$'s and the vectors of the $\bar{b}_i$'s and $\bar{c}_j$'s are then equivalent to the previous ones, in that $(x_1, \ldots, x_n)$ or $(u_1, \ldots, u_m)$ is feasible (optimal) for the old problem if and only if $(x_1, \ldots, x_{n-1})$ or $(u_1, \ldots, u_{m-1})$ is feasible (optimal) for the new. Note that we have eliminated the variables x_n and u_m, the m-th row constraint, and the n-th column constraint. In reversing the operation (i.e., in regaining the original problems from the transformed ones), (1) and (2) are used to define x_n and u_m.

If, on the other hand, n is in N_1, then we also set

$$\bar{a}_{mj} = \frac{a_{mj}}{a_{mn}} \quad \text{for } j = 1, \ldots, n-1,$$

$$\bar{b}_m = \frac{b_m}{a_{mn}} ,$$

replace the unrestricted variable u_m by the non-negative variable

(3) $$\bar{u}_m = u_1 a_{1n} + \cdots + u_m a_{mn} - c_n ,$$

and form as new m-th row constraint

$$\bar{a}_{m1} x_1 + \cdots + \bar{a}_{m,n-1} x_{n-1} \leqq \bar{b}_m .$$

Note that we have eliminated the variable x_n and the n-th column constraint, and have changed the m-th row constraint from an equation to an inequality. Again we obtain an equivalent pair of problems, with $(x_1, \ldots, x_n)$ and $(u_1, \ldots, u_m)$ corresponding to $(x_1, \ldots, x_{n-1})$ and $(u_1, \ldots, u_{m-1}, \bar{u}_m)$ respectively, and (1) and (3) are used to define x_n and u_m in reversing the operation. In either case (n in N_1 or in N_2) the method changes the forms CX and UB only by the constant $b_m c_n / a_{mn}$.

Here we have dealt with a "row constraint" equation; of course a similar operation applies to a "column constraint" equation. After a finite sequence of such operations (applied to both rows and columns), we clearly reach a situation in which all constraint equations (if any exist) have only zero coefficients. If all the constant terms (b_i's or c_j's) in these equations are zero, then we may delete the associated rows and columns of zeros (cf. the inverses of Types 5 and 10 in Method 2 below), yielding a problem-pair of canonical form $(m_2 = n_2 = 0)$; if any of the constant terms is non-zero, then the corresponding member of the problem-pair (and thus the corresponding member of the original problem-pair) is exhibited as unfeasible.

METHOD 2: We begin by listing eleven types of elementary transformations on dual linear programs.

Type 1. Multiply a row constraint equation through by a non-zero quantity. Suppose, for instance, that the equation is

(4) $$a_{m1} x_1 + \cdots + a_{mn} x_n = b_m .$$

Then for any $k \neq 0$, we can replace a_{mj} $(j = 1, \ldots, n)$, b_m, and the unrestricted variable u_m, by

$$\bar{a}_{mj} = ka_{mj}$$

$$\bar{b}_m = kb_a$$

$$\bar{u}_m = \frac{u_m}{k} .$$

$(x_1, \ldots, x_n)$ or $(u_1, \ldots, u_m)$ is feasible (optimal) in the old situation if and only if $(x_1, \ldots, x_n)$ or $(u_1, \ldots, u_{m-1}, \bar{u}_m)$ is feasible (optimal) in the new one. The operation is clearly reversible, and leaves the values of CX and UB unchanged.

Type 2. Add a multiple of a row constraint equation to another row constraint. Suppose, for instance, that the equation is (4), and that the other constraint is associated with the first row. Then, for any λ, we can replace a_{1j} $(j = 1, \ldots, n)$, b_1, and the unrestricted variable u_m, by

$$\bar{a}_{1j} = a_{1j} + \lambda a_{mj}$$

$$\bar{b}_1 = b_1 + \lambda b_m$$

$$\bar{u}_m = u_m - \lambda u_1 .$$

The new problems are equivalent to the old in the same sense as for Type 1, and the operation is reversible. Again the values of CX and UB are unchanged.

Type 3. Add to C a multiple of the i-th row vector of A, where i is in M_2. Suppose, for instance, that $i = m$, so that the constraint equation is (4); then for any μ we can replace c_j $(j = 1, \ldots, n)$ and the unrestricted variable u_m by

$$\bar{c}_j = c_j + \mu a_{mj}$$

$$\bar{u}_m = u_m + \mu .$$

The new problems are equivalent to the old in the same sense as for Type 1, and the operation is reversible. The values of CX and UB are both changed by μb_m.

Type 4. If m is in M_1, then adjoin to the matrix A an (n+1)-st column $(0, \ldots, 0, 1)$, to the vector C an (n+1)-st component $c_{n+1} = 0$, and to the vector X an (n+1)-st component x_{n+1} (a new non-negative variable) defined by

$$a_{m1}x_1 + \cdots + a_{mn}x_n + x_{n+1} = b_m. \tag{5}$$

The result is a new problem-pair in which (5) appears as the m-th row constraint. Note that u_m was a non-negative variable in the old problems; in the new ones u_m is (formally) unrestricted but is subjected to the new (n+1)-st column constraint $u_m \geqq 0$. Thus m_2 and n_1 are increased by one and m_1 is reduced by one. $(x_1, \ldots, x_n)$ or $(u_1, \ldots, u_m)$ is feasible (optimal) in the old situation if and only if $(x_1, \ldots, x_n, x_{n+1})$ or $(u_1, \ldots, u_m)$ is feasible (optimal) in the new. The operation is reversible; the values of CX and UB are unchanged.

Type 5. Adjoin an (m+1)-st row of zero entries to A, an (m+1)-st component $b_{m+1} = 0$ to B, and an (m+1)-st component u_{m+1} (a new unrestricted variable) to U, together with the (m+1)-st row constraint

$$0x_1 + \cdots + 0x_n = 0.$$

$(x_1, \ldots, x_n)$ or $(u_1, \ldots, u_m)$ is feasible (optimal) in the old situation if and only if $(x_1, \ldots, x_n)$ or $(u_1, \ldots, u_m, u_{m+1})$ is feasible (optimal) in the new one. The operation is reversible, and does not change the values of CX and UB.

Types 6, 7, 8, 9, 10 are the respective analogues of Types 1, 2, 3, 4, 5 for columns instead of rows. In Type 9, the (m+1)-st row to be adjoined to A is $(0, \ldots, 0, -1)$.

Type 11. Border the matrix A with an (m+1)-st row $(0, \ldots, 0, \pm 1)$ and an (n+1)-st column $(0, \ldots, 0, \pm 1)$, intersecting in the entry (± 1). Also adjoin components $b_{m+1} = 0$ and $c_{n+1} = 0$ to B and C, and adjoin components u_{m+1} and x_{n+1} (new unrestricted variables) to U and X, together with the (m+1)-st row constraint

$$0x_1 + \cdots + 0x_n \pm x_{n+1} = 0$$

and the (n+1)-st column constraint

$$u_1 0 + \cdots + u_m 0 \pm u_{m+1} = 0.$$

A feasible vector for either new problem has zero as its last component; $(x_1, \ldots, x_n)$ or $(u_1, \ldots, u_m)$ is feasible (optimal) in the old situation if and only if $(x_1, \ldots, x_n, 0)$ or $(u_1, \ldots, u_m, 0)$ is feasible (optimal) in the new one. The operation is reversible, and does not change the values of CX and UB.

To see how these elementary transformations are used, suppose we have a row constraint equation with a non-zero coefficient. By renumbering, we may suppose the equation is

$$a_{m1}x_1 + \dots + a_{mn}x_n - b_m = 0$$

with $a_{mn} \neq 0$. Applying Type 1 with $k = 1/a_{mn}$, we can "make $a_{mn} = 1$." Using Type 2 to multiply the new m-th row constraint by $-a_{in}$ and add the result to the i-th row constraint (for $i = 1, 2, \dots, m-1$), we reach a situation in which the last column of A is $(0, \dots, 0, 1)$. By applying Type 3 with $i = m$ and $\mu = -c_n$, we can also make the last component of C equal to 0. So far we have not changed any of m_1, m_2, n_1, n_2. If n is in N_1 (so that the last component of X is a non-negative variable), then we can apply the inverse of Type 4; this reduces m_2 and n_1 by one, increases m_1 by one, and leaves n_2 unchanged. If n is in N_2, we first apply Types 7 and 8 to make the last row of A take the form $(0, \dots, 0, 1)$ and the last component of B equal to 0; then we can apply the inverse of Type 11, thus reducing m_2 and n_2 by one without changing m_1 or n_1. In either case (n in N_1 or N_2) we have eliminated the row constraint equation with which we began, without increasing n_2 or changing $m_1 + n_1$.

It is clear that the elementary transformations can be used similarly to eliminate a <u>column</u> constraint equation with a non-zero coefficient. Thus, after finitely many applications of these transformations, we reach dual problems for which the constraint equations have only zero coefficients. If the constant terms (b_i's and c_j's) in these equations are all zero, then we may apply the inverses of Types 5 and 10 to "eliminate" the associated rows and columns of zeros, thus reaching a problem-pair of canonical form. If any of the constant terms is non-zero, then it is clear that the corresponding problem is unfeasible.

The results of this Part can be summarized as follows: In finitely many steps one can either display the unfeasibility of one or both components of a problem-pair with associated $m \times n$ matrix, or else can reduce the problems to an "equivalent" pair in canonical form with an $m' \times n'$ matrix, where $m' \leq m$, $n' \leq n$, and $m' + n' = m_1 + n_1$.

PART 4: Linear Programming and Matrix Games

In this Part we discuss some relationships between the theory of linear programming and that of matrix games. First we describe briefly the fundamental concepts of the latter field, beginning with the notion of <u>matrix game</u>.

Let there be two players, I and II, with m and n possible courses of action respectively. Each player chooses his course of action without knowing the other player's choice. If I chooses his i-th alternative and II chooses his j-th, then II must pay I an amount p_{ij} (which may be positive, negative or zero) determined by the rules of the game; equivalently we could say that I must pay II an amount $-p_{ij}$. It is assumed that the players are concerned solely with maximizing their expected payoffs; thus the payoff matrix P, whose (i,j)-th entry is p_{ij}, contains all the information relevant to a rational analysis of the game, and so we may speak simply of "the game P". Furthermore, any matrix P can be interpreted as the payoff matrix of the game in which I acts by choosing a row of P, II acts by choosing a column of P, and p_{ij} is the payoff to I if the i-th row and j-th column are chosen. We point out in passing that our "matrix games" are precisely the "rectangular games" of McKinsey and the "zero-sum two-person games in normalized form" of von Neumann and Morgenstern.

A probability vector is a vector whose components are non-negative and sum to 1 (i.e., it is a discrete probability "distribution"). By a mixed strategy for I we mean a (row) probability vector $W = (w_1, \ldots, w_m)$, while a mixed strategy for II is a (column) probability vector $Z = (z_1, \ldots, z_n)$. Here w_i is interpreted as the probability (or relative frequency) with which I employs his i-th course of action, and z_j is interpreted similarly relative to II's j-th alternative. The symbol "i", which has already appeared as an index, may also be used without fear of ambiguity to designate the i-th unit vector of m-space; similarly "j" denotes the j-th unit vector of n-space. In view of the foregoing interpretation of mixed strategies, it is natural to define

$$E(W, Z) = \sum_{i,j} w_i p_{ij} z_j = WPZ \tag{1}$$

as the expected payoff to I if W and Z are used; that to II is of course $-E(W, Z)$.

Suppose there existed a number v and mixed strategies W^o and Z^o such that

$$E(W, Z^o) \leqq v \leqq E(W^o, Z) \quad \text{for all} \quad W, Z. \tag{2}$$

By employing W^o, I could ensure that his expected payoff is at least v (and that II's is at most $-v$) no matter what mixed strategy II employs, while by choosing Z^o, II could ensure that his expected payoff is at least $-v$ (and that I's is at most v) no matter what mixed strategy I employs. Thus I and II might as well settle for expected payoffs of v and $-v$ respectively, and might as well assure these by employing mixed strategies W^o and Z^o satisfying (2). The number v is called a <u>value</u> of the game P, and W^o and Z^o are <u>optimal strategies</u> (called "good strategies" by von Neumann and Morgenstern).

It is clear that (2) implies the statement

(3) $$E(i, Z^o) \leqq v \leqq E(W^o, j) \quad \text{for all} \quad i, j.$$

Conversely (3) implies (2), for by (3) we have

$$E(W, Z^o) = \Sigma w_i E(i, Z^o) \leqq (\Sigma w_i)v = v = v(\Sigma z_j)$$

$$\leqq \Sigma E(W^o, j)z_j = E(W^o, Z)$$

for any W, Z. We note finally that (3) is equivalent to the two conditions

(4) $$W^oP \geqq V^n,$$

(5) $$PZ^o \leqq V^m,$$

where V^n and V^m are n-dimensional and m-dimensional vectors with all components equal to v.

LEMMA 6. A matrix game has at most one value.

PROOF. Suppose the triples (v, W^o, Z^o) and (v^1, W^1, Z^1) both satisfy (2). Then we have

$$v \leqq E(W^o, Z^1) \leqq v^1 \leqq E(W^1, Z^o) \leqq v,$$

and so $v = v^1$. This completes the proof.

Two matrix games are here called <u>strategically equivalent</u> if they have the same sets of optimal strategies for both players. Using this terminology, we may prove the following result:

LEMMA 7. If matrix Q is obtained by adding a constant increment k to every entry of matrix P, then the games P and Q are strategically equivalent. If game P has value v, then game Q has value $v + k$.

PROOF. Let $E(W, Z)$ be the expected payoff function for game P;

then that for game Q is given by

$$\sum_{i,j} w_i (p_{ij} + k) z_j = \sum_{i,j} w_i p_{ij} z_j + \left(\sum w_i\right) k \left(\sum z_j\right) = E(W, Z) + k.$$

From this it is clear that v, W^o, and Z^o obey (2) for game P if and only if $v + k$, W^o, and Z^o obey (2) for game Q. This completes the proof.

The following theorem of von Neumann is the basic result in the theory of matrix games:

THEOREM 3. Every matrix game has a value and optimal strategies.

PROOF. By Lemma 7, we may arrange that the matrix P of the game has all its entries positive. By applying Lemma 3 and Theorem 2 to the pair of dual programs with $A = P$, $B = (1, \ldots, 1)$, and $C = (1, \ldots, 1)$, we obtain vectors $X^o \geqq 0$ and $U^o \geqq 0$ such that

$$\begin{aligned} &(i) \quad U^oP \geqq (1, \ldots, 1) \\ &(ii) \quad PX^o \leqq (1, \ldots, 1)^T \\ &(iii) \quad \sum x_j^o = \sum u_i^o . \end{aligned}$$

(Here (iii) is just the statement "$CX^o = U^oB$".) From (i) we know $U^o \neq 0$, and so we may define

$$\begin{aligned} v &= 1/\sum u_i^o = 1/\sum x_j^o \\ w_i^o &= vu_i \\ z_j^o &= vx_j . \end{aligned}$$

Then (i) and (ii) imply (4) and (5), and so W^o and Z^o are optimal strategies and v is the value of the game P. This completes the proof.

COROLLARY 3A. Any matrix game with value v has optimal strategies W^o and Z^o such that $w_i^o > 0$ for all i with $E(i, Z^o) = v$, and $z_j^o > 0$ for all j with $E(W^o, j) = v$.

COROLLARY 3B. Let P be a matrix game with value v. Then for any i, <u>either</u> $E(i, Z^o) < v$ for some optimal strategy Z^o and $w_i = 0$ for all optimal strategies W, <u>or</u> $E(i, Z) = v$ for all optimal strategies Z and $w_j^o > 0$ for some optimal strategy W^o. (Of course the dual statement also holds for $E(W^o, j) > v$, etc.)

PROOFS. From the statement and proof of Lemma 7, we see that adding any k to all elements of P leads to a strategically equivalent game and adds k to both the expected payoff function and the value. Thus we may assume that all the entries of P are positive. By passing to the (feasible) dual programs considered in the proof of Theorem 3 and applying Corollaries 2A and 2B to these programs, we obtain the desired results.

We note, in connection with the device employed in the last few proofs, that the process converts any matrix game P with positive value into "equivalent" dual programs with $A = P$, $B = (1, \ldots, 1)$, and $C = (1, \ldots, 1)$. Conversely, consider any pair of feasible dual programs with $A \geqq 0$, $B > 0$, and $C > 0$. The optimal value $\delta = U^oB$ of the programs must be <u>positive</u>, for this could fail to hold only if $U^o = 0$, and then constraint $U^oA \geqq C$ would be violated. The dual programs can be transformed by the substitution

$$p_{ij} = a_{ij}/b_ic_j$$

into a matrix game P whose value is $1/\delta$ and whose optimal strategies W^o and Z^o are related to the optimal vectors X^o, U^o of the programs by

$$w_i^o = u_i^ob_i/\delta \ ,$$

$$z_j^o = c_jx_j^o/\delta \ .$$

The following theorem, published in [4], is due to Dantzig and Brown.

THEOREM 4. The optimal vectors of the dual programs with matrix A and constraint vectors B and C, are precisely the vectors

$$X^o = X/t, \quad U^o = U/t,$$

where $(u_1, \ldots, u_m, x_1, \ldots, x_n, t)$ is an optimal strategy with positive last component t for the (symmetric) game

$$\begin{pmatrix} 0 & -A & B \\ A^T & 0 & -C^T \\ -B^T & C & 0 \end{pmatrix}$$

PROOF. We first note that the matrix is skew-symmetric, so that an optimal strategy for one player is also optimal for the other, and the value of the game must be 0. The mixed strategy $(u_1, \dots, u_m, x_1, \dots, x_n, t)$ is optimal if and only if

$$\text{(i)}\quad AX \leqq Bt$$
$$\text{(ii)}\quad UA \geqq tC$$
$$\text{(iii)}\quad UB \leqq CX.$$

If $t > 0$, then X/t and U/t are optimal vectors for the dual programs by Lemma 2.

Conversely, let $X^0 \geqq 0$ and $U^o \geqq 0$ be optimal vectors for the dual programs, so that

$$\text{(iv)}\quad AX^0 \leqq B$$
$$\text{(v)}\quad U^0A \geqq C$$
$$\text{(vi)}\quad U^0B \geqq CX^0.$$

Set $t = 1/(1 + \Sigma u_i^0 + \Sigma x_j^0) > 0$; then (iv), (v), and (vi) imply that $(tu_1^0, \dots, tu_m^0, tx_1^0, \dots, tx_n^0, t)$ satisfies (i), (ii), and (iii), and is thus an optimal mixed strategy. This completes the proof.

The earliest transformation of a pair of dual linear programs into a matrix game was given by Gale, Kuhn, and Tucker [7], and is presented in the next theorem.

THEOREM 5. The necessary and sufficient condition that X^0 and U^0 be optimal vectors for the dual program is that the matrix game

$$\begin{pmatrix} A & -B \\ -C & U^0AX^0 \end{pmatrix}$$

has value zero and optimal strategies (for the first and second players) proportional to $(U^0, 1)$ and $(X^0, 1)$ respectively.

PROOF. The matrix game has value zero and optimal strategies proportional to $(U^0, 1)$ and $(X^0, 1)$ if and only if

$$\text{(i)}\quad AX^0 - B \leqq 0$$
$$\text{(ii)}\quad -CX^o + U^oAX^o \leqq 0$$

$$\text{(iii)} \quad U^oA - C \geqq 0$$

$$\text{(iv)} \; - U^oB + U^oAX^o \geqq 0$$

$$\text{(v)} \quad X^o \geqq 0, \; U^o \geqq 0.$$

(i), (iii), and (v) are the necessary and sufficient conditions that X^o and U^o be feasible. (ii) and (iv) together are equivalent to

$$\text{(vi)} \quad U^oB \leqq U^oAX^o \leqq CX^o,$$

which (by Lemma 2, Theorem 2, and the feasibility of X^o and U^o) is seen to be a necessary and sufficient condition that X^o and U^o be optimal. This completes the proof.

Some of the results to be established later in this report are closely connected with theorems on matrix games, and we shall point out such correspondences as they arise.

PART 5: Lagrange Multipliers

We begin this Part by recalling to the reader the method of Lagrange multipliers traditionally used in the calculus for finding constrained extrema. If $G(x_1, \ldots, x_n) = G(X)$ is to be maximized or minimized subject to the constraints

$$F_1(X) = 0, \; \ldots, \; F_m(X) = 0,$$

then we form the Lagrangian function

$$H(X, u_1, \ldots, u_m) = H(X, U) = G(X) + \sum_{i=1}^{m} u_i F_i(X)$$

using the Lagrange multipliers u_i. The necessary conditions that $H(X, U)$ have an extreme value (viz., the vanishing of the first derivatives of H) are also necessary conditions that $G(X)$ have its constrained maximum or minimum, so that instead of seeking a constrained extremum for G we may seek an unconstrained extremum for the more complicated function H.

A similar situation arises in linear programming, where the object is the maximization or minimization of a linear function subject to constraints which are linear inequalities. We introduce the <u>Lagrangian Function</u>

$$\begin{aligned} L(X, U) &= CX + UB - UAX \\ &= CX + u_1(b_1 - \Sigma a_{1j}x_j) + \ldots + u_m(b_m - \Sigma a_{mj}x_j) \qquad (1) \\ &= UB + x_1(c_1 - \Sigma u_i a_{i1}) + \ldots + x_n(c_n - \Sigma u_i a_{in}). \end{aligned}$$

If, keeping the maximization problem in mind, we write $G(X) = CX$, $F_i(X) = (b_i - \Sigma a_{ij}x_j)$, and regard the u_i as "multipliers", then the formal analogy with the technique described above is exhibited by the second form for $L(X, U)$; if the roles of X and U are interchanged then the third form for $L(X, U)$ exhibits the analogy for the minimization problem. In the next theorem we shall show that the analogy has more than formal validity.

THEOREM 6. The necessary and sufficient condition that $X^o \geqq 0$ and $U^o \geqq 0$ be optimal vectors for the dual programs is that (X^o, U^o) be a saddle-point for $L(X, U)$ in the sense that

$$L(X, U^o) \leqq L(X^o, U^o) \leqq L(X^o, U)$$

for all $X \geqq 0$, $U \geqq 0$. If X^o and U^o are optimal, then $L(X^o, U^o)$ is the optimal value of the dual programs.

PROOF. (a) Suppose X^o and U^o are optimal. By Theorem 2 we have $CX^o = U^oB$. Since $CX^o \leqq U^oAX^o \leqq U^oB$, we have

$$L(X^o, U^o) = CX^o = U^oB,$$

as desired. For any $X \geqq 0$, $U \geqq 0$, we have

$$L(X, U^o) = U^oB + (C - U^oA)X \leqq U^oB = L(X^o, U^o),$$

$$L(X^o, U) = CX^o + U(B - AX^o) \geqq CX^o = L(X^o, U^o),$$

so (X^o, U^o) is a saddle-point.

(b) Now suppose (X^o, U^o) is a saddle-point, with $X^o \geqq 0$ and $U^o \geqq 0$. For any $X \geqq 0$, we have

$$U^oB - (U^oA - C)X = L(X, U^o) \leqq L(X^o, U^o) = U^oB - (U^oA - C)X^o,$$

or

$$(U^oA - C)(X - X^o) \geqq 0.$$

If we choose $X = X^o + E_j$, where E_j is the j-th unit vector, then the last relation yields $(U^oA - C)_j \geqq 0$. Taking $j = 1, \ldots, n$, we have $U^oA \geqq C$, and so U^o is feasible. Using the other half of the saddle-point statement similarly, we see that X^o is also feasible. From

$$L(0, U^o) \leqq L(X^o, U^o) \leqq L(X^o, 0)$$

we have $U^oB \leqq CX^o$, and so by Lemma 2 X^o and U^o are optimal. This completes the proof.

For comparison with relation (2) of Part 4 (which defines "optimal strategy") we restate Theorem 5 in the following form:

$$X^{o} \geqq 0 \quad \text{and} \quad U^{o} \geqq 0 \quad \text{are optimal if and only if}$$

$$L(X, U^{o}) \leqq U^{o}AX^{o} \leqq L(X^{o}, U)$$

for all $X \geqq 0$, $U \geqq 0$.

We note that the "Lagrange multiplier" situation for dual linear programs differs from that in the calculus in that (a) the fact that we are dealing simultaneously with a maximum problem and a minimum problem leads to consideration of a saddle-point (rather than an extremum) for $L(X, U)$, (b) the conditions involved are not only necessary but also sufficient, and (c) after passing to the Lagrangian Function, we are still left with the (simple) constraints $X \geqq 0$, $U \geqq 0$. Lagrange multipliers also play a similar role in Non-Linear Programming (see [12]).

The method of Lagrange multipliers can also be applied to the "problems with mixed constraints" considered in Part 3. In this case the multipliers which are dual to constraint equations are not required to be non-negative; we omit further details.

PART 6: Systems of Equated Constraints

Many of the results to be presented in this section stem from the work of Shapley and Snow [15] on matrix games. We will reverse the historical development by proving the linear-programming versions of the theorems first, and then deriving the (original) game-theoretic results as consequences.

We begin by sketching informally the geometric ideas behind the next few definitions and theorems. The set of feasible vectors for the maximization problem is defined by a finite system of linear inequalities and is therefore a (possibly unbounded) convex polyhedral set; the system (I) of equated constraints defined below determines a linear subspace (of the space of vectors X) whose intersection with this polyhedral set, if nonvacuous, is a (closed) face of the latter. Similarly the system (II) (see below) defines a face of the convex polyhedral set of feasible vectors for the minimization problem (again if the corresponding "intersection" is nonvacuous). If systems (I) and (II) are dual (in the sense described below), we will say they define dual faces of the two polyhedral sets in question. Theorem 7, when translated into this geometric language, asserts that feasible X, U are optimal if and only if they lie in dual faces. Theorem 8 says that (a) the optimal vectors for each problem form a face of the corresponding polyhedral set of feasible vectors, and (b) these two "optimal faces" are dual, and are the only pair of dual faces which consist entirely of optimal vectors. A nonsingular square system of equated constraints leads to zero-dimensional faces or "vertices", and Theorem 9 shows that the notion of "vertex" is essentially the same as that of "extreme vector" for the sets of feasible vectors. Theorem 10 studies the extreme vectors of the sets of optimal vectors; feasible nonzero X and U are of this type if and only if they are dual vertices of the sets of feasible vectors.

Now we proceed to the definitions and theorems. Let M_1 and M_2 be arbitrary subsets of the set M of indices $[1, \ldots, m]$, while N_1 and N_2 are arbitrary subsets of the set N of indices $[1, \ldots, n]$. Then each of

$$\text{(I)} \quad \begin{cases} (AX)_i = b_i & \text{all } i \text{ in } M_1 \\ x_j = 0 & \text{all } j \text{ in } N_2 \end{cases}$$

and

$$\text{(II)} \quad \begin{cases} (UA)_j = c_j & \text{all } j \text{ in } N_1 \\ u_i = 0 & \text{all } i \text{ in } M_2 \end{cases}$$

is a system of equated constraints. Systems (I) and (II) are dual if $M_2 = M - M_1$ and $N_2 = N - N_1$; in this case we renumber so that $M_1 = [1, \ldots, p]$ and $N_1 = [1, \ldots, q]$, and the systems may be written as

$$\text{(I)} \begin{cases} a_{11}x_1 + \cdots + a_{1q}x_q = b_1 \\ \vdots \qquad\qquad \vdots \qquad\quad \vdots \\ a_{p1}x_1 + \cdots + a_{pq}x_q = b_p \\ x_{q+1} = 0, \ldots, x_n = 0 . \end{cases} \qquad \text{(II)} \begin{cases} u_1a_{11} + \cdots + u_pa_{p1} = c_1 \\ \vdots \qquad\qquad \vdots \qquad\quad \vdots \\ u_1a_{1q} + \cdots + u_pa_{pq} = c_q \\ u_{p+1} = 0, \ldots, u_m = 0 . \end{cases}$$

If a system of equated constraints is written in one of these last forms after a renumbering, and if the matrix

$$A_1 = \begin{pmatrix} a_{11} & \cdots & a_{1q} \\ \vdots & & \vdots \\ a_{p1} & \cdots & a_{pq} \end{pmatrix}$$

is square and nonsingular, then the system is a nonsingular square system.

THEOREM 7. Feasible vectors X and U are optimal if and only if they satisfy dual systems of equated constraints.

PROOF. To prove the necessity of the condition, suppose that X and U are optimal; let M_1 be the set of i's such that $(AX)_i = b_i$, and let $M_2 = M - M_1$. Then Corollary 2B ensures that $u_i = 0$ for all i in M_2. We define N_1 and N_2 analogously, and find that $x_j = 0$ for all j in N_2. Thus X and U satisfy the dual systems of equated constraints associated with M_1, M_2, N_1 and N_2.

To prove the sufficiency, suppose that X and U satisfy the dual systems (I) and (II). Then

$$UB = \sum^{p} u_i b_i = \sum^{p} u_i \left(\sum^{q} a_{ij} x_j \right) = \sum^{q} \left(\sum^{p} u_i a_{ij} \right) x_j = \sum^{q} c_j x_j = CX,$$

and so by Lemma 2 X and U are optimal. This completes the proof.

THEOREM 8. There is a unique pair of dual systems of equated constraints such that each is the maximal system of equated constraints satisfied by all optimal vectors.

PROOF. Consider the i's such that $(AX)_i = b_i$ for all optimal X, and the j's such that $(UA)_j = c_j$ for all optimal U. By Corollary 2B, the row and column constraints corresponding to these indices determine dual systems of equated constraints which clearly have the desired property; uniqueness is also clear.

We now turn to the study of <u>extreme</u> feasible or optimal vectors; these are feasible or optimal vectors which are not the mean $\frac{1}{2}(X^1 + X^2)$ or $\frac{1}{2}(U^1 + U^2)$ of two other feasible or optimal vectors.

THEOREM 9. A feasible non-zero X (or U) is an extreme feasible vector if and only if it satisfies a nonsingular square system of equated constraints.

PROOF. (a) Suppose feasible X satisfies the nonsingular square system with associated matrix A_1. For any n-dimensional vector Y, set $\bar{Y} = (y_1, \ldots, y_q)$. Suppose $X = \frac{1}{2}(X^1 + X^2)$, where X^1 and X^2 are feasible. For $j > q$ we would have $x_j = \frac{1}{2}(x_j^1 + x_j^2) = 0$, and so, since $x_j^1 \geqq 0$ and $x_j^2 \geqq 0$, we would have $x_j^1 = x_j^2 = 0$. It would also be true that

$$A_1\bar{X}^1 \leqq B_1, \quad A_1\bar{X}^2 \leqq B_1, \quad \frac{1}{2} A_1\left(\bar{X}^1 + \bar{X}^2\right) = B_1,$$

where $B_1 = (b_1, \ldots, b_p)$. From these relations it would follow that $A_1\bar{X}^1 = A_1\bar{X}^2 = B_1$, and so (since A_1 is nonsingular) $\bar{X}^1 = \bar{X}^2$. Thus

$X^1 = X^2$. From this we may conclude that X is extreme.

(b) Suppose non-zero X is an extreme feasible vector. Let M' be the set of i's for which $(AX)_i = b_i$. We prove first that M' is not void. Since $X \neq 0$, some x_j is > 0. The vectors X^1 and X^2 obtained from X by replacing x_j with $x_j + \epsilon$ and $x_j - \epsilon$ respectively have X as their mean; if M' were void (i.e., if $(AX)_i < b_i$ for all i), then X^1 and X^2 would be feasible for sufficiently small $\epsilon > 0$, contradicting the fact that X is extreme.

Now let N_2 be the set of j's for which $x_j = 0$. Delete from A the rows which are <u>not</u> "in M'" and the columns which <u>are</u> "in N_2". Since M' is not void and $N_1 = N - N_2$ is not void (because $X \neq 0$), we actually have a submatrix $\bar{A}$ left, and it is clear that

$$\bar{A}\bar{X} = \bar{B},$$

where the components of $\bar{X}$ are the positive components of X and the components of $\bar{B}$ are the appropriate components of B.

We next assert that the columns of $\bar{A}$ are linearly independent. If this were not so then there would exist $\bar{X}' \neq 0$ such that $\bar{A}\bar{X}' = 0$, and if we first set $\bar{X}^1 = \bar{X} + \epsilon\,\bar{X}'$, $\bar{X}^2 = \bar{X} - \epsilon\,\bar{X}'$, and then adjoined appropriate zero components to $\bar{X}^1$ and $\bar{X}^2$ to obtain n-dimensional vectors X^1 and X^2, we would find that X^1 and X^2 have X as their mean and are feasible for sufficiently small $\epsilon > 0$, contradicting the fact that X is extreme.

Since the columns of $\bar{A}$ are linearly independent, we can delete suitable rows of $\bar{A}$ to obtain a nonsingular square submatrix A_2, and X clearly satisfies the system of equated constraints associated with A_2. This completes the proof.

The restriction to non-zero vectors in the last theorem is unimportant, since clearly the zero vector is an extreme feasible vector if it is feasible.

THEOREM 10. Feasible non-zero X and U are extreme optimal vectors if and only if they satisfy dual nonsingular square systems of equated constraints.

PROOF. The sufficiency of the condition follows immediately from Theorem 7 and Theorem 9. To prove its necessity, suppose that X and U are extreme optimal vectors. Renumber so that $(AX)_i = b_i$ for $1 \leqq i \leqq p$, $(AX)_i < b_i$ for $i > p$, $(UA)_j = c_j$ for $1 \leqq j \leqq q$, $(UA)_j > c_j$ for $j > q$. By Corollary 2B, $x_j = 0$ for $j > q$ and $u_i = 0$ for $i > p$. Since some x_j with $j \leqq q$ or some u_i with $i \leqq p$ can also vanish, we further renumber using $\bar{p} \leqq p$ and $\bar{q} \leqq q$ so that $x_j > 0$ for $1 \leqq j \leqq \bar{q}$, $x_j = 0$ for $j > \bar{q}$, $u_i > 0$ for $1 \leqq i \leqq \bar{p}$, and $u_i = 0$ for $i > \bar{p}$. The hypotheses $X \neq 0$, $U \neq 0$ ensure that $\bar{p} > 0$ and $\bar{q} > 0$; therefore $p > 0$ and $q > 0$. Let $\bar{A}$ be the matrix obtained as the intersection of the first p rows and first q columns of A.

The first $\bar{q}$ columns of $\bar{A}$ are linearly independent; the proof of this fact parallels the argument used in (b) of the proof of Theorem 9 to show that the matrix $\bar{A}$ considered there had linearly independent columns, except that here (in order to obtain a contradiction to the hypothesis that X is an extreme optimal vector) we must also show that if X^1 and X^2 are feasible vectors with $X = \frac{1}{2}(X^1 + X^2)$, then X^1 and X^2 are optimal. This follows since the relations

$$CX^1 \leqq UB$$

$$CX^2 \leqq UB$$

$$\tfrac{1}{2}C(X^1 + X^2) = UB$$

(which hold since X^1, X^2 are feasible and X, U are optimal) imply $CX^1 = CX^2 = UB$, so that X^1 and X^2 are optimal by Lemma 2.

Similarly, the first $\bar{p}$ rows of $\bar{A}$ are linearly independent. We now renumber in the intervals $\bar{p} \leqq i \leqq p$ and $\bar{q} \leqq j \leqq q$ so that the first p' rows of $\bar{A}$ $(p' \geqq \bar{p})$ are a maximal linearly independent subset of the rows of $\bar{A}$ and the first q' columns of $\bar{A}$ $(q' \geqq \bar{q})$ are a maximal linearly independent subset of the columns of $\bar{A}$.

The intersection of the first p' rows and the first q' columns of $\bar{A}$ is a matrix A_1. Because the last $q - q'$ columns of $\bar{A}$ are dependent on the first q' columns, any linear relationship between the p' rows of A_1 can be extended to a relationship between the first p' rows of $\bar{A}$. The latter, however, are independent, and so the rows of A_1 are linearly independent; similarly, the columns of A_1 are linearly independent, and so A_1 is a nonsingular square matrix. Clearly X and U satisfy the dual nonsingular square systems of equated constraints associated with A_1; this completes the proof.

COROLLARY 10A. The sets of feasible and optimal vectors of linear programs have finitely many extreme vectors.

PROOF. This is an immediate consequence of Theorems 9 and 10.

Theorem 10 provides a systematic method for finding extreme

optimal vectors; one examines all square systems of equated constraints, discards those with singular associated matrices, and lists those solutions of the remaining systems which are feasible vectors. This process, however, usually requires a prohibitively great amount of work.

A system of equated constraints for a matrix game P has (by definition) one of the forms

$$(\mathrm{I}') \quad \begin{cases} p_{i1}z_1 + \cdots + p_{in}z_n - t = 0 & \text{all } i \text{ in } M_1 \\ z_j = 0 & \text{all } j \text{ in } N_2 \\ z_1 + \cdots + z_n = 1 \end{cases}$$

$$(\mathrm{II}') \quad \begin{cases} w_1p_{1j} + \cdots + w_mp_{mj} - s = 0 & \text{all } j \text{ in } N_1 \\ w_i = 0 & \text{all } i \text{ in } M_2 \\ w_1 + \cdots + w_m = 1 \end{cases}$$

Dual systems and square systems are defined as for linear programs; a square system is nonsingular if it has a unique solution $(z_1, \ldots, z_n, t)$ or $(w_1, \ldots, w_m, s)$. An extreme optimal strategy for P is an optimal strategy which is not the mean of two other optimal strategies.

Before deriving the matrix-game analogues of Theorems 9 and 10, two preliminary remarks are in order. We note first that if matrix Q is obtained from P by adding a constant k to each entry of P, then $(z_1, \ldots, z_n, t)$ or $(w_1, \ldots, w_m, s)$ satisfies a system (I') or (II') for P if and only if $(z_1, \ldots, z_n, t + k)$ or $(w_1, \ldots, w_m, s + k)$ satisfies the corresponding system for Q. Second, we recall from Part 4 that with any matrix game P with positive value v we may associate a feasible pair of dual linear programs with $A = P$, $B = (1, \ldots, 1)$, and $C = (1, \ldots, 1)$; the optimal strategies of P are put into one-one correspondence with the optimal vectors of the dual programs by the relations

$$(\mathrm{R}) \qquad W^o = vU^o, \quad Z^o = vX^o.$$

It is clear that (R) also gives a one-one correspondence between the extreme optimal strategies of P and the extreme optimal vectors of the dual programs. We can set up a one-one correspondence between the systems of equated constraints; (I) and (I') correspond if and only if they have the same M_1 and N_2, while (II) and (II') correspond if and only if they have the same N_1 and M_2.

LEMMA 8. Let P be a matrix game with positive value v. If W^o is an optimal strategy for P and (W^o, v)

is the (unique) solution of a nonsingular square system (II'), then the corresponding square system (II) for the associated dual programs is also nonsingular. Conversely, if optimal vector U^o is the (unique) solution of a nonsingular square system (II), then the corresponding square system (II') is also nonsingular. (Of course the dual statement for systems (I'), (I) also holds.)

PROOF. (a) Suppose W^o is an optimal strategy and (W^o, v) is the solution of nonsingular square system (II'). The U^o associated with W^o by (R) is a solution of (II), and $\Sigma u_i^o \neq 0$ (since $U^o \neq 0$, in view of the constraint $UA \geqq (1, \ldots, 1)$). If U is any solution of (II) with $\Sigma u_i \neq 0$, then $(U/\Sigma u_i, 1/\Sigma u_i)$ is a solution of (II'); thus $U/\Sigma u_i = W^o$ and $1/\Sigma u_i = v$, so $U = vW^o = U^o$. If U^1 is any solution of (II) with $\Sigma u_i^1 = 0$, then $U^2 = \frac{1}{2}(U^o + U^1)$ is a solution of II with $\Sigma u_i^2 \neq 0$, and so $U^2 = U^o$; this implies $U^1 = U^o$, contradicting $\Sigma u_i^o \neq 0 = \Sigma u_i^1$. So (II) has U^o as unique solution, and is therefore nonsingular.

(b) Now suppose optimal vector U^o is the solution of nonsingular square system (II). If (W, s) is any solution of (II') with $s \neq 0$, then W/s is a solution of (II); clearly different choices of (W, s) yield different solutions of (II) in this way. Since (II) is nonsingular, only one such (W, s) can exist, and it must be (W^o, v) where W^o corresponds to U^o by (R). If (W^1, s^1) is any solution of (II') other than (W^o, v), then $s^1 = 0$; $(W^2, s^2) = (\frac{1}{2}(W^o + W^1), \frac{1}{2}(v + s^1))$ is a (W, s) of the type just mentioned, and so $(W^2, s^2) = (W^o, v)$. This implies $(W^1, s^1) = (W^o, v)$, a contradiction. So (II') has (W^o, v) as unique solution, and is thus nonsingular.

THEOREM 11 (Kuhn [11]). Let P be a matrix game with value v. Optimal strategy W^o is an extreme optimal strategy if and only if (W^o, v) is the solution of a nonsingular square system of equated constraints for P. (Of course the dual statement for optimal strategy Z^o also holds.)

PROOF. In view of Lemma 7 and the first preliminary remark above, we may arrange that $v > 0$. Note that the relations (R) effect a one-one correspondence between extreme optimal strategies and extreme optimal vectors for the associated dual programs.

If W^o is an extreme optimal strategy, then the U^o corresponding to W^o by (R) is an extreme optimal vector for the associated minimization problem. U^o is also an extreme feasible vector, for if U^1 and U^2 are feasible and $U^o = \frac{1}{2}(U^1 + U^2)$, then $U^1B \leqq U^oB$, $U^2B \leqq U^oB$ and $\frac{1}{2}(U^1B + U^2B) = U^oB$, so that $U^1B = U^2B = U^oB$ and U^1, U^2 are optimal, a contradiction unless $U^1 = U^2 = U^o$. By Theorem 9, U^o satisfies a nonsingular square system (II) of equated constraints for the minimization problem; Lemma 8 ensures that the corresponding system (II') is also nonsingular, and it is clear that (W^o, v) satisfies (II').

Conversely, suppose (W^o, v) is the solution of a nonsingular square system (II'). By Lemma 8, the corresponding system (II) is also nonsingular. The U^o corresponding to W^o by (R) is clearly the solution of (II); by Theorem 9 U^o is an extreme optimal vector, and so W^o is an extreme optimal strategy. This completes the proof.

THEOREM 12. Let P be a matrix game with value v different from zero. Optimal strategies W^o and Z^o are extreme optimal strategies if and only if (W^o, v) and (Z^o, v) satisfy dual nonsingular square systems of equated constraints for P.

PROOF. If $v > 0$, then the necessity and sufficiency of the condition follows immediately from Theorem 10, Lemma 8, and the fact that the relations (R) make extreme optimal strategies of P correspond to extreme optimal vectors of the associated dual programs.

The case $v < 0$ can be reduced to the previous one by noting that Players I and II (for P) can be considered to be the second and first players, respectively, in the game $-P^T$ with value $-v > 0$. This completes the proof.

In the statement and proof of the next result, we shall employ the symbol $\dot{\underline{1}}$ as an abbreviation for the row vector $(1, \ldots, 1)$ of appropriate dimension; adj Q will denote the adjoint of matrix Q. If Q is a submatrix of P and W, Z are mixed strategies for P, then $\dot{W}$, $\dot{Z}$ will denote the vectors obtained by deleting from W and Z the components corresponding to the rows and columns of P which must be deleted to obtain Q.

THEOREM 13 (Shapley-Snow [15]). Let P be a matrix game with value v. Optimal strategies W and Z for P are extreme optimal strategies if and only if there is a square submatrix Q of P with $\dot{1}\ \mathrm{adj}\ (Q)\ \dot{1}^T \neq 0$ and

$$v = \frac{|Q|}{\dot{1}\ (\mathrm{adj}\ Q)\ \dot{1}^T}$$

$$\dot{W} = \frac{\dot{1} \text{ adj } Q}{\dot{1} \text{ (adj } Q) \dot{1}^T}$$

$$\dot{Z} = \frac{(\text{adj } Q) \dot{1}^T}{\dot{1} \text{ (adj } Q) \dot{1}^T}$$

PROOF. (a) Suppose the condition holds and v is different from zero. We have the identity

(Adj) $$Q(\text{adj } Q) = |Q| \, I,$$

where I is the identity matrix; since $v \neq 0$, we have $|Q| \neq 0$, and so Q is nonsingular and Q^{-1} exists and is given by $Q^{-1} = (\text{adj } Q)/|Q|$. Thus the hypotheses may be rewritten as

$$v = 1/\dot{1}Q^{-1}\dot{1}^T$$

$$\dot{W} = v\dot{1}Q^{-1}$$

$$\dot{Z} = vQ^{-1}\dot{1}^T .$$

Therefore $\dot{W}Q = v\dot{1}$ and $Q\dot{Z} = v\dot{1}^T$; furthermore $\dot{W}\dot{1}^T = \dot{1}\dot{Z} = 1$, so that $\dot{W}$ and $\dot{Z}$ are probability vectors and the components of W and Z not in $\dot{W}$ and $\dot{Z}$ must all vanish. We have shown that W and Z satisfy the dual square systems of equated constraints with associated nonsingular matrix Q; by Theorem 12, W and Z are extreme optimal strategies.

(b) Suppose W and Z are extreme optimal strategies and $v \neq 0$. By Theorem 12, W and Z satisfy dual nonsingular square systems of equated constraints, with some associated square matrix Q. Thus we have

$$\dot{W}Q = v\dot{1}, \quad Q\dot{Z} = v\dot{1}^T, \quad \dot{1}\dot{Z} = \dot{W}\dot{1}^T = 1$$

or

$$\dot{W} = v\dot{1}Q^{-1}, \quad \dot{Z} = vQ^{-1}\dot{1}^T, \quad \dot{1}\dot{Z} = \dot{W}\dot{1}^T = 1,$$

which implies

$$v\dot{1}Q^{-1}\dot{1}^T = \dot{1}\dot{Z} = 1;$$

so that

$$v = 1/\dot{1}Q^{-1}\dot{1}^T .$$

The relations $\dot{W} = v\dot{1}Q^{-1}$, $\dot{Z} = vQ^{-1}\dot{1}^T$, $v = 1/\dot{1}Q^{-1}\dot{1}^T$, together with (Adj), imply that W and Z satisfy the condition.

(c) Suppose $v = 0$; add a positive quantity k to each entry of P, obtaining a strategically equivalent game $P(k)$ with positive value k.

By (a) and (b), W and Z are extreme optimal strategies for P(k) (and thus for P) if and only if there is a square submatrix Q(k) of P(k) with $\dot{1}\,(\text{adj } Q(k))\, \dot{1}^T \neq 0$ and

$$k = \frac{|Q(k)|}{\dot{1}\,(\text{adj } Q(k))\, \dot{1}^T}$$

$$\dot{W} = \frac{\dot{1} \text{ adj } Q(k)}{\dot{1}\,(\text{adj } Q(k))\, \dot{1}^T}$$

$$\dot{Z} = \frac{(\text{adj } Q(k))\, \dot{1}^T}{\dot{1}\,(\text{adj } Q(k))\, \dot{1}^T}$$

With each submatrix Q(k) of P(k) is associated a submatrix Q of P obtained by subtracting k from each entry of Q(k). In view of the identities

$$\dot{1} \text{ adj } Q(k) = \dot{1} \text{ adj } Q,$$

$$|Q(k)| = |Q| + k\dot{1}\,(\text{adj } Q)\, \dot{1}^T,$$

it is clear that Q(k) has the properties just stated if and only if Q has the properties stated in the theorem (with $v = 0$). This completes the proof.

PART 7: Optimal Rays

An <u>optimal ray</u> $[X^o; X]$ for the maximization problem is a set of optimal vectors of the form

$$X^o + \lambda X,$$

where λ runs through all non-negative numbers, X^o is a fixed optimal vector, and X is a fixed vector whose components sum to 1. (This last condition serves only as a normalization.) Optimal rays for the minimization problem are defined analogously. In the next lemma we characterize the <u>directions</u> X of the optimal rays.

LEMMA 9. Suppose the components of X sum to 1. Then $[X^o; X]$ is an optimal ray (for optimal X^o) if and only if

(1) X is a probability vector.

(2) $AX \leqq 0$.

(3) $CX = 0$.

The dual statement holds for the minimization problem; (2) becomes $UA \geqq 0$.

PROOF. We give the proof only for X, since that for U is analogous. $[X^0; X]$ is an optimal ray if and only if

$$\text{(i)} \quad AX^0 + \lambda AX \leqq B$$

$$\text{(ii)} \quad CX^0 + \lambda CX = CX^0$$

$$\text{(iii)} \quad X^0 + \lambda X \geqq 0$$

for all $\lambda \geqq 0$. Clearly these conditions are satisfied if and only if (1), (2), and (3) hold. This completes the proof.

In studying the existence of optimal rays, it is useful to introduce the notion of an <u>admissible number</u> μ, which is a number such that the matrix game

$$\begin{pmatrix} A & -B \\ -C & \mu \end{pmatrix}$$

has value zero. If the dual linear programs are feasible, then Theorem 5 asserts that their optimal value μ^0 is admissible.

THEOREM 14. For a feasible pair of dual linear programs, statements (1) and (2) are equivalent and statements (3) and (4) are equivalent:

(1) The maximization problem has an optimal ray.

(2) Some $\mu > \mu^0$ is admissible.

(3) The minimization problem has an optimal ray.

(4) Some $\mu < \mu^0$ is admissible.

Furthermore, if (1) or (2) holds then <u>every</u> $\mu > \mu^0$ is admissible, while if (3) or (4) holds then <u>every</u> $\mu < \mu^0$ is admissible.

PROOF. It clearly suffices to deal only with (1) and (2). We note first that μ is admissible if and only if

$$\text{(i)} \quad AX - Bt \leqq 0$$

$$\text{(ii)} \quad UA - sC \geqq 0$$

$$\text{(iii)} \quad \mu t - CX \leqq 0$$

$$\text{(iv)} \quad s\mu - UB \geqq 0$$

for some probability vectors (X, t) and (U, s).

If (1) holds, then by Lemma 9 there is a probability vector X with $AX \leqq 0$ and $CX = 0$. Using this X and taking $t = 0$, we see that (i) and (iii) are satisfied. If U^o is any optimal vector for the minimization problem (here Theorem 2 is used), then the probability vector (U, s) proportional to $(U^o, 1)$ clearly satisfies

$$(\text{iv}') \quad s\mu^o - UB = 0.$$

Using the same (U, s), we see from (iv') that (iv) will be satisfied for any $\bar{\mu} > \mu^o$.

Now suppose (2) holds; then there is a probability vector $(\bar{X}, \bar{t})$ and a number $\bar{\mu} > \mu^o$ such that $A\bar{X} \leqq \bar{t}B$ and $C\bar{X} \geqq \bar{t}\bar{\mu}$. If $\bar{t} > 0$, then $\bar{X}/\bar{t}$ is feasible and $C(\bar{X}/\bar{t}) \geqq \bar{\mu} > \mu^o$, contradicting the fact that μ^o is the optimal value of the dual programs. Thus $\bar{t} = 0$, and so $\bar{X}$ is a probability vector obeying $A\bar{X} \leqq 0$ and $C\bar{X} \geqq 0$. Thus $C\bar{X} = 0$, for if $C\bar{X} > 0$ then for any optimal X^o we would have $X^o + \lambda\bar{X}$ feasible, while $C(X^o + \lambda\bar{X})$ would exceed the optimal value of the dual programs for $\lambda > 0$. So $A\bar{X} \leqq 0$ and $C\bar{X} = 0$; by Lemma 9 the maximization problem has an optimal ray. This completes the proof.

LEMMA 10. *The set of directions of optimal rays of a linear programming problem has finitely many extreme vectors.*

PROOF. According to Lemma 9, $\bar{X} \geqq 0$ is the direction of an optimal ray for the maximization problem if and only if

$$(\text{i}) \quad \Sigma x_j \leqq 1$$

$$(\text{ii}) \quad \Sigma\left(-x_j\right) \leqq 1$$

$$(\text{iii}) \quad AX \leqq 0$$

$$(\text{iv}) \quad CX \leqq 0$$

$$(\text{v}) \quad (-C)X \leqq 0.$$

(i) - (v) can be considered the row constraints of a suitable new maximization problem; the desired conclusion follows by applying Corollary 10A. Of course an analogous argument holds for the minimization problem. This completes the proof.

THEOREM 15. *Let $\{X^r\}$ be the (finite) set of extreme optimal vectors for the maximization problem and $\{X^s\}$ be the (finite) set of extreme directions* of optimal rays for the maximization problem. Then the set of all optimal vectors X is the set of all vectors of the form

$$X = \sum \lambda_r X^r + \sum \mu_s X^s ,$$

with all $\lambda_r \geqq 0$, all $\mu_s \geqq 0$, and $\Sigma\lambda_r = 1$. (Of course the dual statement holds for the minimization problem.)

PROOF. Let X^0 be a fixed optimal vector. The set of all optimal vectors X is the solution-set of the system (S):

$$\begin{aligned} -IX &\leqq 0 \\ AX &\leqq B \\ CX &\leqq CX^0 \\ (-C)X &\leqq -CX^o \end{aligned}$$

Here I is the identity matrix; the presence of $-I$ as a "block" in the coefficient matrix of (S) ensures that this matrix has linearly independent columns. Let (S') be the system obtained by making (S) homogeneous; Lemma 9 shows that the directions of optimal rays are precisely the solutions of (S') which obey the extra normalization condition $\Sigma x_j = 1$. We now apply Corollary 1A of [9] (in this Study) to obtain the desired result; the normalization condition serves to fix the vectors "Q_j" of the "basis", which that corollary had determined only to within a positive scalar factor.

PART 8: Analysis and Synthesis Theorems

The scheme

$(\geqq 0)$	X_1^T	X_2^T	X_3^T	$(\leqq)$
U_1^T	A_{11}	A_{12}	A_{13}	B_1
U_2^T	A_{21}	A_{22}	A_{23}	B_2
U_3^T	A_{31}	A_{32}	A_{33}	B_3
$(\geqq)$	C_1	C_2	C_3	

represents (for our first theorem) a feasible pair of dual linear programs partitioned (after a possible renumbering of rows and columns) so that

(1) $U_1^0 > 0$, $U_2^0 > 0$, $\sum U_i^o A_{i3} > C_3$ for some optimal U^0;

(2) $X_1^0 > 0$, $X_2^0 > 0$, $\sum A_{3j} X_j^0 < B_3$ for some optimal X^0;

(3) A_{22} is a maximal nonsingular square block in

$$\begin{bmatrix} A_{11} & A_{12} \\ A_{21} & A_{22} \end{bmatrix} .$$

Corollary 2A asserts that at least one such partition exists (with some blocks possibly vacuous), but no claim is made that finding one is practicable.

In this Part we shall use the scheme above to give an explicit description of the sets of optimal vectors for the dual programs, and shall then show how to construct dual programs with preassigned sets of optimal vectors. These two steps together will implicitly characterize the sets which appear as sets of all optimal vectors for some linear programming problem. Analogous investigations for matrix games have been made by Gale and Sherman [8] and by Bohnenblust, Karlin, and Shapley [1]; we shall not derive their results.

LEMMA 11. There are matrices R and S such that

$$A_{12} = RA_{22} \qquad B_1 = RB_2$$
$$A_{21} = A_{22}S \qquad C_1 = C_2S$$
$$A_{11} = RA_{22}S .$$

PROOF. By condition (3) above, each row of $(A_{11}A_{12})$ is a linear combination of the rows of $(A_{21}A_{22})$; clearly the coefficients of these linear combinations form a matrix R such that $A_{12} = RA_{22}$ and $A_{11} = RA_{21}$. The maximization problem has an optimal vector, and so, by condition (1) and Corollary 2B, the system of equations

$$A_{11}X_1 + A_{12}X_2 = R\left(A_{21}X_1 + A_{22}X_2\right) = B_1$$
$$A_{21}X_1 + A_{22}X_2 = B_2$$

has a solution. Thus $B_1 = RB_2$. Similarly we can find a matrix S such that $A_{21} = A_{22}S$, $C_1 = C_2S$, and $A_{11} = RA_{21} = RA_{22}S$.

THEOREM 16 (Analysis Theorem). The optimal vectors for the dual programs are precisely the vectors X, U, such that

$$
\text{(I)}\quad \begin{cases} X_1 \geqq 0 \\ A_{22}^{-1}\left(A_{21}X_1 - B_2\right) \leqq 0 \\ \left(A_{31} - A_{32}A_{22}^{-1}A_{21}\right)X_1 - \left(B_3 - A_{32}A_{22}^{-1}B_2\right) \leqq 0 \\ X_2 = A_{22}^{-1}\left(B_2 - A_{21}X_1\right) \\ X_3 = 0\ , \end{cases}
$$

$$
\text{(II)}\quad \begin{cases} U_1 \geqq 0 \\ \left(C_2 - U_1A_{12}\right)A_{22}^{-1} \geqq 0 \\ U_1\left(A_{13} - A_{12}A_{22}^{-1}A_{23}\right) - \left(C_3 - C_2A_{22}^{-1}A_{23}\right) \geqq 0 \\ U_2 = \left(C_2 - U_1A_{12}\right)A_{22}^{-1} \\ U_3 = 0\ . \end{cases}
$$

The optimal value of the programs is given by

$$
\text{(III)}\qquad \sum U_iB_i = C_2A_{22}^{-1}B_2 = \sum C_jX_j
$$

PROOF. (a) Suppose X is optimal. By condition (1) above and Corollary 2B we see that $X_3 = 0$ and that

$$
\begin{aligned} A_{11}X_1 + A_{12}X_2 &= B_1, \\ A_{21}X_1 + A_{22}X_2 &= B_2, \\ A_{31}X_1 + A_{32}X_2 &\leqq B_3. \end{aligned}
$$

The second of these equations yields a value for X_2,

$$
X_2 = A_{22}^{-1}\left(B_2 - A_{21}X_1\right),
$$

which may be substituted into the last inequality above, yielding

$$
\left(A_{31} - A_{32}A_{22}^{-1}A_{21}\right)X_1 - \left(B_3 - A_{32}A_{22}^{-1}B_2\right) \leqq 0.
$$

Since $X_2 \geqq 0$, we must also have

$$
A_{22}^{-1}\left(A_{21}X_1 - B_2\right) \leqq 0.
$$

X is optimal, and so $X_1 \geqq 0$; we have derived all the conditions (I). Similarly we can show that the conditions (II) are necessary.

(b) Suppose X satisfies (I). By reversing the steps in (a), we see that $X \geqq 0$ and that

$$A_{21}X_1 + A_{22}X_2 = B_2,$$

$$A_{31}X_1 + A_{32}X_2 \leqq B_3 .$$

Furthermore we have

$$A_{11}X_1 + A_{12}X_2 = \left(A_{11} - A_{12}A_{22}^{-1}A_{21}\right)X_1 + A_{12}A_{22}^{-1}B_2 ;$$

using Lemma 11, we see that the coefficient of X_1 in the last expression vanishes, while the remaining term is just B_1. Thus

$$A_{11}X_1 + A_{12}X_2 = B_1 ,$$

and so we have proved that X is feasible. Let U^0 be any optimal vector for the minimization problem; by (a) it must satisfy (II). Then

$$C_1X_1 + C_2X_2 = \left(C_1 - C_2A_{22}^{-1}A_{21}\right)X_1 + C_2A_{22}^{-1}B_2 ,$$

$$U_1^0B_1 + U_2^0B_2 = U_1^0\left(B_1 - A_{12}A_{22}^{-1}B_2\right) + C_2A_{22}^{-1}B_2 .$$

Applying Lemma 11 to these equations yields

$$\sum U_i^0B_i = C_2A_{22}^{-1}B_2 = \sum C_jX_j .$$

The last equation, together with Lemma 2, shows that X is optimal and that (III) holds. Thus the conditions (I) are sufficient conditions that X be optimal; similarly we can prove that the conditions (II) are sufficient. This completes the proof.

We note that B_1 and C_1 do not appear in (I) or (II); thus these terms play no part in determining the sets of optimal vectors. A_{22} is the only term to appear in <u>both</u> (I) and (II); this double appearance thus expresses the sole connection between the sets of optimal vectors for the two problems.

In the next theorem we let A_{21}^*, A_{31}^*, B_2^*, B_3^* be such that

(1*) $$A_{21}^*X_1^0 < B_2^*, \quad A_{31}^*X_1^0 < B_3^* \text{ for some } X_1^0 > 0,$$

and let A_{12}^*, A_{13}^*, C_2^*, C_3^* be such that

(2*) $$U_1^0A_{12}^* < C_2^*, \quad U_1^0A_{13}^* > C_3^* \text{ for some } U_1^0 > 0.$$

Furthermore, we permit <u>arbitrary</u> assignment of

$$\begin{bmatrix} A_{22} & A_{23} \\ A_{32} & A_{33} \end{bmatrix}$$

provided only that

(3*) A_{22} is a nonsingular square block,

and we assign the remaining parts as follows:

$$A_{12} = A^*_{12}A_{22}, \qquad A_{13} = A^*_{13} + A^*_{12}A_{23} ,$$

$$C_2 = C^*_2A_{22}, \qquad C_3 = C^*_3 + C^*_2A_{23} ,$$

$$A_{21} = A_{22}A^*_{21}, \qquad A_{31} = A^*_{31} + A_{32}A^*_{21} ,$$

$$B_2 = A_{22}B^*_2, \qquad B_3 = B^*_3 + A_{32}B^*_2 ,$$

$$A_{11} = A^*_{12}A_{22}A^*_{21}, \quad B_1 = A^*_{12}A_{22}B^*_2, \quad C_1 = C^*_2A_{22}A^*_{21} .$$

THEOREM 17 (Synthesis Theorem). The dual programs with the scheme shown at the beginning of Part 8 have as optimal vectors the vectors X and U satisfying

$$\text{(I*)} \quad \begin{cases} X_1 \geqq 0, \quad A^*_{21}X_1 \leqq B^*_2, \quad A^*_{31}X_1 \leqq B^*_3 , \\ X_2 = B^*_2 - A^*_{21}X_1 , \\ X_3 = 0 \end{cases}$$

$$\text{(II*)} \quad \begin{cases} U_1 \geqq 0, \quad U_1A^*_{12} \leqq C^*_2, \quad U_1A^*_{13} \geqq C^*_3 , \\ U_2 = C^*_2 - U_1A^*_{12} , \\ U_3 = 0 . \end{cases}$$

The optimal value of the dual programs is

$$\text{(III*)} \qquad \sum U_iB_i = C^*_2A_{22}B^*_2 = \sum C_jX_j .$$

PROOF. Straightforward substitution shows that (I*), (II*) and (III*) are equivalent to (I), (II), and (III). In view of Theorem 16, it suffices to prove that the dual programs satisfy (1), (2), and (3).

From $A_{11} = A^*_{12}A_{21}$ and $A_{12} = A^*_{12}A_{22}$, we see that each row of

$(A_{11}A_{12})$ is a linear combination of the rows of $(A_{21}A_{22})$ with the elements of a row of A_{12}^* as coefficients. Similarly, each column of

$$\begin{bmatrix} A_{11} \\ A_{21} \end{bmatrix}$$

is a linear combination of the columns of

$$\begin{bmatrix} A_{12} \\ A_{22} \end{bmatrix}$$

This verifies (3).

Define X_2^O and U_2^O in terms of X_1^O and U_1^O by (I*) and (II*), and set $X_3^O = 0$, $U_3^O = 0$. The first relations of (1*) and (2*) then assert that $X_2^O > 0$ and $U_2^O > 0$, while the second relations of (1*) and (2*) are equivalent to the third relations of (1) and (2). Since X^O satisfies (I*) and thus (I), we can show (as in (b) of the proof of Theorem 16) that X^O is feasible and that $\Sigma C_j X_j^O = C_2 A_{22}^{-1} B_2$. Similarly we can show that U^O is feasible and that $\Sigma U_i^O B_i = C_2 A_{22}^{-1} B_2$. An application of Lemma 2 shows that X^O and U^O are optimal; thus (1) and (2) are verified and the proof is complete.

We conclude with an example illustrating Theorem 17.

EXAMPLE 3.

	x_1	x_2	x_3	x_4	x_5	x_6	x_7	
u_1	3	2	2	1	0	1	1	15
u_2	2	1	1	0	1	1	2	9
u_3	3	4	0	1	2	1	1	17
u_4	1	0	1	0	0	0	0	4
u_5	1	2	0	1	0	0	0	7
u_6	1	1	0	0	1	0	0	5
u_7	0	1	0	0	0	0	0	3
	20	16	8	4	8	2	3	

Here A_{22} is the 3×3 identity matrix; clearly (3*) is satisfied, and it is easy to verify that (1*) and (2*) are satisfied, with

$$\left(x_1^O,\ x_2^O\right) = (1,\ 1) \quad \text{and} \quad \left(u_1^O,\ u_2^O,\ u_3^O\right) = (1,\ 1,\ 1).$$

By (III*) we find that the optimal value of the dual programs is 100. The conditions which (I*) and (II*) impose on x_1, x_2 and u_1, u_2, u_3 are

$$\begin{cases} x_1 \leqq 4 \\ x_1 + 2x_2 \leqq 7 \\ x_1 + x_2 \leqq 5 \\ x_1 \geqq 0,\ x_2 \geqq 0 \end{cases} \qquad \begin{cases} 2u_1 + u_2 \leqq 8 \\ u_1 + u_3 \leqq 4 \\ u_2 + 2u_3 \leqq 8 \\ u_1 + u_2 + u_3 \geqq 2 \\ u_1 + 2u_2 + u_3 \geqq 3 \\ u_1 \geqq 0,\ u_2 \geqq 0,\ u_3 \geqq 0 \end{cases}$$

Thus the set of optimal X's forms a hexagon, while the set of optimal U's forms an octohedron. The vertices of these figures can of course be found by using the technique described after the proof of Corollary 10A; for the hexagon it is simpler to proceed graphically.

References

[1] BOHNENBLUST, H. F., KARLIN, S., SHAPLEY, L. S., "Solutions of discrete, two-person games," Annals of Mathematics Studies 24, Princeton (1950), [18], pp. 51-72.

[2] DANTZIG, G. B., "Programming in a linear structure," Econometrica 17 (1949), pp. 73-74.

[3] DANTZIG, G. B., "Maximization of a linear function of variables subject to linear inequalities," Cowles Commission Monograph No. 13, [19], pp. 339-347.

[4] DANTZIG, G. B., "A proof of the equivalence of the programming problem and the game problem," Cowles Commission Monograph No. 13 [19], pp. 330-335.

[5] DANTZIG, G. B., and WOOD, M. K., "Programming of interdependent activities I," Econometrica 17 (1949), pp. 193-199.

[6] DANTZIG, G. B., "Programming of interdependent activities II," Econometrica 17 (1949), pp. 200-211.

[7] GALE, D., KUHN, H. W., and TUCKER, A. W., "Linear programming and the theory of games," Cowles Commission Monograph No. 13, [19], pp. 317-329.

[8] GALE, D., and SHERMAN, S., "Solutions of finite two-person games," Annals of Mathematics Studies 24, Princeton (1950), [18], pp. 37-49.

[9] GOLDMAN, A. J., "Resolution and separation theorems for polyhedral convex sets," this Study.

[10] HOFFMAN, A. J., "How to solve a linear programming problem," Proceedings of the Second Symposium in Linear Programming (National Bureau of Standards and U. S. Air Force) vol. 1 (1955), pp. 397-424. (This has an extensive bibliography.)

[11] KUHN, H. W., "Lectures on the theory of games," Notes of Lectures at Princeton University (1952).

[12] KUHN, H. W., and TUCKER, A. W., "Non-linear programming," Proc. Second Berkeley Symposium on Math. Stat. and Prob. (ed. J. Neyman) (Univ. of Calif. 1951), pp. 481-492.

[13] McKINSEY, J. C. C., Introduction to the Theory of Games, McGraw-Hill, New York (1952).

[14] von NEUMANN, J., MORGENSTERN, O., Theory of Games and Economic Behavior, Princeton (1953, 3rd ed.).

[15] SHAPLEY, L. S., and SNOW, R. N., "Basic solutions of discrete games," Annals of Mathematics Studies 24 (1950), [18], pp. 27-35.

[16] TUCKER, A. W., "Game theory and linear programming," Notes of Lectures at the National Science Foundation Summer Institute for Teachers of Collegiate Mathematics, Oklahoma A. and M. (1955).

[17] TUCKER, A. W., "Dual systems of homogeneous linear relations," this Study.

[18] Contributions to the Theory of Games (vol. I), ed. by H. W. Kuhn and A. W. Tucker, Annals of Mathematics Studies 24, Princeton (1950).

[19] Activity Analysis of Production and Allocation, ed. by T. C. Koopmans, Cowles Commission Monograph No. 13, John Wiley and Sons, New York (1951).

A. J. Goldman

A. W. Tucker

Princeton University

ON SYSTEMS OF LINEAR INEQUALITIES*

Ky Fan

INTRODUCTION

This paper is divided into four parts. In Part I, we treat the purely algebraic aspects of finite systems of linear inequalities. Neither metric (norm) nor topological structure is assumed in the linear space considered. Also the dimension of the linear space is arbitrary, finite or infinite. Most results in Part I are not new, but they usually appeared in the literature in a form which has meaning only for finite dimensional linear spaces.

Part II is devoted to those results concerning finite systems of linear inequalities, which require finite dimensionality of the linear space. As in Part I, no metric structure of the linear space is needed in Part II.

In Part III, we study linear inequalities from the point of view of Functional Analysis. There we deal with normed or topological linear spaces. Most results are valid for both finite or infinite systems of linear inequalities.

The linear spaces considered in all first three parts are real linear spaces. Part IV is devoted to systems of linear inequalities on a complex linear space. All inequalities considered there are inequalities concerning the absolute values of complex linear functionals.**

It is only natural in the subject that many results of this paper are based on separation of convex sets. For separation theorems of convex

* This paper was prepared under a National Bureau of Standards contract with The American University, sponsored by the Office of Scientific Research of the Air Research and Development Command, USAF. Part of the work was done at Numerical Analysis Research, University of California, Los Angeles, California.

** The first three parts were written in August 1954. Part IV was added in August 1955. The author wishes to thank Dr. Philip Davis for calling his attention to the interest of the complex case.

sets, we refer to N. Bourbaki ([3], p. 69, Théorème 1; p. 71, Proposition 1; p. 73, Proposition 4; p. 77, Ex. 8).

The list of references (at the end of the paper) includes only those which we have consulted during the preparation of this work. Other references can be found in S. N. Černikov [7] and T. Motzkin [22].

PART I

FINITE SYSTEMS OF LINEAR INEQUALITIES ON A LINEAR SPACE OF ARBITRARY DIMENSION

Throughout this Part I, X denotes a real linear space of arbitrary dimension, finite or infinite. We do not require that norm or topology be defined in the linear space. We shall study finite systems of linear inequalities of the form

$$f_i(x) \geq \alpha_i \qquad (1 \leq i \leq p), \tag{1}$$

where $f_1, f_2, \ldots, f_p$ are given linear functionals on X, and $\alpha_1, \alpha_2, \ldots, \alpha_p$ are given real numbers. The system (1) is said to be <u>consistent</u>, if there exists an element $x \in X$ satisfying (1); otherwise it is said to be <u>inconsistent</u>.

§1. CONSISTENCY CONDITION

THEOREM 1. The system (1) is consistent, if and only if, for any p non-negative numbers $\lambda_i \geq 0$ $(1 \leq i \leq p)$, the relation

$$\sum_{i=1}^{p} \lambda_i f_i = 0$$

implies

$$\sum_{i=1}^{p} \lambda_i \alpha_i \leq 0.$$

PROOF. The "only if" part being trivial, we only consider the "if" part. Assume that (1) is inconsistent, we shall find p non-negative numbers λ_i such that

$$\sum_{i=1}^{p} \lambda_i f_i = 0, \qquad \sum_{i=1}^{p} \lambda_i \alpha_i > 0.$$

In the Euclidean p-space E^p, let S denote the linear subspace formed by all points of the form $(f_1(x), f_2(x), \ldots, f_p(x))$, when x varies in X. Let P denote the set of all points in E^p with non-negative coordinates. Let α denote the point in E^p with coordinates $\alpha = (\alpha_1, \alpha_2, \ldots, \alpha_p)$. Then the inconsistency of (1) means that[1]

$$(S - \alpha) \cap P = \emptyset. \tag{2}$$

For the linear subspace S in E^p, we can find vectors $b_1, b_2, \ldots, b_q$ in E^p such that

$$S = \left\{ y \in E^p \;\middle|\; (b_j, y) = 0 \quad \text{for} \quad 1 \leq j \leq q \right\}, \tag{3}$$

where (b_j, y) denotes the inner product in E^p. Let

$$\beta_j = -(b_j, \alpha) \qquad (1 \leq j \leq q). \tag{4}$$

Then

$$S - \alpha = \left\{ z \in E^p \;\middle|\; (b_j, z) = \beta_j \quad \text{for} \quad 1 \leq j \leq q \right\}. \tag{5}$$

In the Euclidean q-space E^q, let Q denote the set of all points of the form $((b_1, y), (b_2, y), \ldots, (b_q, y))$, when y varies in P. Then Q is a closed convex cone[2] in E^q. Let β denote the point in E^q with coordinates $\beta = (\beta_1, \beta_2, \ldots, \beta_q)$. According to (5), the relation (2) means that no point $z \in P$ satisfies all q equations

$$(b_j, z) = \beta_j \qquad (1 \leq j \leq q).$$

In other words, the point β is not contained in the closed convex cone Q. Hence there exists a hyperplane in E^q separating Q and β strictly. It follows that there exist q real numbers $\mu_j (1 \leq j \leq q)$ satisfying

$$\sum_{j=1}^{q} \mu_j (b_j, z) > \sum_{j=1}^{q} \mu_j \beta_j \quad \text{for all} \quad z \in P.$$

By (4), this can be written

[1] Throughout this paper, $\emptyset$ denotes the empty set. $S - \alpha$ denotes the set of all differences $s - \alpha$ with $s \in S$.

[2] A set C in a real linear space is called a convex cone, if $C + C \subset C$ and $\lambda C \subset C$ for all real $\lambda \geq 0$.

$$\left(\sum_{j=1}^{q} \mu_j b_j, \; z + \alpha \right) > 0 \quad \text{for all} \quad z \in P. \tag{6}$$

Finally, let

$$b_j = (b_{j1}, b_{j2}, \ldots, b_{jp}) \qquad (1 \leq j \leq q),$$

and

$$\lambda_i = \sum_{j=1}^{q} \mu_j b_{ji} \qquad (1 \leq i \leq p).$$

Then (6) becomes

$$\sum_{i=1}^{p} \lambda_i (z_i + \alpha_i) > 0 \quad \text{whenever all} \quad z_i \geq 0.$$

This implies

$$\sum_{i=1}^{p} \lambda_i \alpha_i > 0$$

and $\lambda_i \geq 0$ $(1 \leq i \leq p)$. In fact, if $\lambda_{i_o} < 0$, then by taking z_{i_o} sufficiently large and by taking $z_i = 0$ for $i \neq i_o$, the sum

$$\sum_{i=1}^{p} \lambda_i (z_i + \alpha_i)$$

would be negative. Furthermore, by (3), we have

$$\sum_{i=1}^{p} b_{ji} f_i(x) = 0 \quad \text{for} \quad 1 \leq j \leq q \quad \text{and for all} \quad x \in X,$$

or

$$\sum_{i=1}^{p} b_{ji} f_i = 0 \qquad (1 \leq j \leq q).$$

Hence

$$\sum_{i=1}^{p} \lambda_i f_i = \sum_{i=1}^{p} \sum_{j=1}^{q} \mu_j b_{ji} f_i = 0.$$

We have thus found p non-negative numbers $\lambda_i (1 \leq i \leq p)$ such that

$$\sum_{i=1}^{p} \lambda_i f_i = 0 \quad \text{and} \quad \sum_{i=1}^{p} \lambda_i \alpha_i > 0.$$

This completes the proof.

COROLLARY 1. If the system (1) is inconsistent, then there exists an $\epsilon > 0$ such that for any real numbers δ_i satisfying $\delta_i \geq -\epsilon$ $(1 \leq i \leq p)$, the system

$$f_i(x) \geq \alpha_i + \delta_i \qquad (1 \leq i \leq p)$$

is inconsistent.

PROOF. When (1) is inconsistent, there exist $\lambda_i \geq 0$ $(1 \leq i \leq p)$ such that

$$\sum_{i=1}^{p} \lambda_i f_i = 0 \quad \text{and} \quad \sum_{i=1}^{p} \lambda_i \alpha_i > 0.$$

Then it suffices to choose $\epsilon > 0$ so small that

$$\epsilon \cdot \sum_{i=1}^{p} \lambda_i < \sum_{i=1}^{p} \lambda_i \alpha_i .$$

§2. PRINCIPLE OF BOUNDING SOLUTIONS

The main result (Theorem 2) of this paragraph may be called the principle of bounding solutions. Based on this principle, one can derive certain known consistency conditions, such as Černikov's generalization [6] of Kronecker-Capelli's theorem, and a consistency condition given by L. M. Blumenthal ([2], Theorem 3).

The following lemma will be needed in the proof of Theorem 2 and also later.

LEMMA 1. Let $f_1, f_2, \ldots, f_m, f_{m+1}$ be linear functionals on X, and let $\alpha_1, \alpha_2, \ldots, \alpha_m, \alpha_{m+1}$ be real numbers such that the system

$$(7) \qquad \begin{cases} f_i(x) = \alpha_i \\ f_{m+1}(x) \geq \alpha_{m+1} \end{cases} \qquad (i \leq i \leq m),$$

is consistent. Then every solution of the system

$$(8) \qquad f_i(x) = \alpha_i \qquad (1 \leq i \leq m)$$

is a solution of (7), if and only if f_{m+1} is a linear combination of $f_1, f_2, \ldots, f_m$.

PROOF. Assume that f_{m+1} is not a linear combination of $f_1, f_2, \ldots, f_m$. Then we can find an element $y_0 \in X$ such that

$$\begin{aligned} f_i(y_0) &= 0 \\ f_{m+1}(y_0) &\neq 0 \end{aligned} \qquad (1 \leq i \leq m).$$

Take a solution $x_0 \in X$ of (7). Then for any real number λ, $x = x_0 + \lambda y_0$ is a solution of (8). But

$$f_{m+1}(x) = f_{m+1}(x_0) + \lambda f_{m+1}(y_0)$$

can be made $< \alpha_{m+1}$ by choosing λ suitably. This proves the "only if" part.

Conversely, assume now

$$f_{m+1} = \sum_{i=1}^{m} c_i f_i.$$

Let x_0 be a solution of (7). Then for an arbitrary solution x of (8), we have

$$f_{m+1}(x) = \sum_{i=1}^{m} c_i f_i(x) = \sum_{i=1}^{m} c_i f_i(x_0)$$

$$= f_{m+1}(x_0) \geq \alpha_{m+1}.$$

Hence, every solution of (8) is a solution of (7).

THEOREM 2. Let the system (1) be consistent. If $r \geq 1$ is the maximum number of linearly independent linear functionals among $f_1, f_2, \ldots, f_p$, then there exist r linearly independent linear functionals $f_{\nu_1}, f_{\nu_2}, \ldots, f_{\nu_r}$ among them such that every solution of the system

(9) $$f_{\nu_k}(x) = \alpha_{\nu_k} \qquad (1 \leq k \leq r)$$

is a solution of (1).

PROOF. According to Lemma 1, the statement to be proved is equivalent to the following one:

"There exist r linearly independent linear functionals $f_{\nu_1}, f_{\nu_2}, \ldots, f_{\nu_r}$ among the f_i's such that the system

(10) $$\begin{cases} f_{\nu_k}(x) = \alpha_{\nu_k} & (1 \leq k \leq r) \\ f_i(x) \geq \alpha_i & (1 \leq i \leq p;\ i \neq \nu_1, \nu_2, \ldots, \nu_r), \end{cases}$$

is consistent."

We shall find these indices $\nu_1, \nu_2, \ldots, \nu_r$ by induction. Since $r \geq 1$, it is obvious that there exists an index ν_1 such that $f_{\nu_1} \neq 0$ and that the system

$$\begin{cases} f_{\nu_1}(x) = \alpha_{\nu_1} & \\ f_i(x) \geq \alpha_i & (1 \leq i \leq p;\ i \neq \nu_1), \end{cases}$$

is consistent. Assume that for some $m < r$, we have already chosen $\nu_1, \nu_2, \ldots, \nu_m$ such that $f_{\nu_1}, f_{\nu_2}, \ldots, f_{\nu_m}$ are linearly independent and that the system

(11) $$\begin{cases} f_{\nu_k}(x) = \alpha_{\nu_k} & (1 \leq k \leq m) \\ f_i(x) \geq \alpha_i & (1 \leq i \leq p;\ i \neq \nu_1, \nu_2, \ldots, \nu_m), \end{cases}$$

is consistent. As $m < r$, at least one f_i is not a linear combination of $f_{\nu_1}, f_{\nu_2}, \ldots, f_{\nu_m}$. By Lemma 1, the system

(12) $$f_{\nu_k}(x) = \alpha_{\nu_k} \qquad (1 \leq k \leq m)$$

has a solution x_1 which is not a solution of (11). Let x_0 be a solution of (11). Then for any real λ,

$$x_\lambda = x_0 + \lambda(x_1 - x_0)$$

is a solution of (12). Let $\sigma_1, \sigma_2, \ldots, \sigma_s$ be all those indices $i \neq \nu_1, \nu_2, \ldots, \nu_m$ such that f_i is a linear combination of $f_{\nu_1}, f_{\nu_2}, \ldots, f_{\nu_m}$. (s may be 0!). Then again by Lemma 1, we have

$$f_{\sigma_j}(x_\lambda) \geq \alpha_{\sigma_j} \qquad (1 \leq j \leq s)$$

for all real λ. Thus we have

$$\begin{cases} f_{\nu_k}(x_\lambda) = \alpha_{\nu_k} & (1 \leq k \leq m) \\ f_{\sigma_j}(x_\lambda) \geq \alpha_{\sigma_j} & (1 \leq j \leq s), \end{cases}$$

for all real λ. Since $m < r$, there is at least one index i different from $\nu_1, \nu_2, \ldots, \nu_m, \sigma_1, \sigma_2, \ldots, \sigma_s$. For each such i, let

$$\lambda_i = \sup\left\{\lambda \geq 0 \;\middle|\; f_i(x_\lambda) \geq \alpha_i\right\}.$$

Let

$$\lambda_0 = \operatorname{Min}\left\{\lambda_i \;\middle|\; i \neq \nu_1, \nu_2, \ldots, \nu_m, \sigma_1, \sigma_2, \ldots, \sigma_s\right\}.$$

Since x_1 is not a solution of (11), we have $0 \leq \lambda_0 < 1$. We choose as ν_{m+1} an index i such that $i \neq \nu_1, \nu_2, \ldots, \nu_m, \sigma_1, \sigma_2, \ldots, \sigma_s$ and such that $\lambda_i = \lambda_0$. Then it is clear that the system

$$\begin{cases} f_{\nu_k}(x) = \alpha_{\nu_k} & (1 \leq k \leq m+1) \\ f_i(x) \geq \alpha_i & (1 \leq i \leq p;\ i \neq \nu_1, \nu_2, \ldots, \nu_{m+1}), \end{cases}$$

has x_{λ_0} as a solution and therefore is consistent. Here the $m + 1$ linear functionals f_{ν_k} $(1 \leq k \leq m+1)$ are linearly independent.

By repeating this argument, we finally arrive at r linearly independent linear functionals $f_{\nu_1}, f_{\nu_2}, \ldots, f_{\nu_r}$ such that the system (10) is consistent.

In the above proof, we have actually established a result which is slightly stronger than Theorem 2. For its use in Part II, we state it here explicitly.

THEOREM 2'. Let $r \geq 1$ be the maximum number of linearly independent linear functionals among

$f_i (1 \leq i \leq p)$. If, for some $m(< r)$ indices $\nu_1, \nu_2, \ldots, \nu_m$ among $1, 2, \ldots, p$, the linear functionals $f_{\nu_1}, f_{\nu_2}, \ldots, f_{\nu_m}$ are linearly independent and the system (11) is consistent, then there exist $r - m$ indices $\nu_{m+1}, \nu_{m+2}, \ldots, \nu_r$ among the remaining ones such that $f_{\nu_1}, f_{\nu_2}, \ldots, f_{\nu_m}, f_{\nu_{m+1}}, \ldots, f_{\nu_r}$ are linearly independent and that every solution of (9) is a solution of (1).

§3. INEQUALITIES WHICH ARE CONSEQUENCES OF A SYSTEM OF INEQUALITIES

THEOREM 3. Let the system (1) be consistent, and let g be a linear functional on X, β a real number. If the inequality

$$g(x) \geq \beta \tag{13}$$

is a consequence of (1), but not a consequence of any proper subsystem of (1), then the linear functionals $f_1, f_2, \ldots, f_p$ are linearly independent.

PROOF. By hypothesis, for each $j = 1, 2, 3, \ldots, p$, there is an element $x(j) \in X$ such that

$$\begin{aligned} f_i(x(j)) &\geq \alpha_i \\ g(x(j)) &< \beta \end{aligned} \qquad (i \neq j).$$

Since (13) is a consequence of (1), we must have

$$f_j(x(j)) < \alpha_j.$$

For any two distinct indices j_1, j_2, we can construct a convex combination $x(j_1, j_2)$ of $x(j_1)$ and $x(j_2)$ such that

$$\begin{aligned} f_{j_1}(x(j_1, j_2)) &= \alpha_{j_1} \\ f_i(x(j_1, j_2)) &\geq \alpha_i \\ g(x(j_1, j_2)) &< \beta \end{aligned} \qquad (i \neq j_1, j_2).$$

Again since (1) implies (13), we must have

$$f_{j_2}(x(j_1, j_2)) < \alpha_{j_2}.$$

Similarly, for any three distinct indices j_1, j_2, j_3, we can construct a convex combination $x(j_1, j_2, j_3)$ of $x(j_1, j_2)$ and $x(j_1, j_3)$ such that

$$\begin{aligned} f_{j_1}(x(j_1, j_2, j_3)) &= \alpha_{j_1} \\ f_{j_2}(x(j_1, j_2, j_3)) &= \alpha_{j_2} \\ f_i(x(j_1, j_2, j_3)) &\geq \alpha_i \\ g(x(j_1, j_2, j_3)) &< \beta \end{aligned} \qquad (i \neq j_1, j_2, j_3);$$

which implies

$$f_{j_3}(x(j_1, j_2, j_3)) < \alpha_{j_3}.$$

Continuing this process, we finally obtain p elements of X

$$\begin{aligned} y_1 &= x(2, 3, 4, \ldots, p, 1), \\ y_2 &= x(1, 3, 4, \ldots, p, 2), \\ &\cdots\cdots\cdots\cdots \\ y_p &= x(1, 2, 3, \ldots, p-1, p) \end{aligned}$$

such that

$$(14) \qquad \begin{cases} f_i(y_j) = \alpha_i \\ f_j(y_j) < \alpha_j \end{cases} \qquad (i \neq j).$$

Using Theorem 2, it is easily seen from (14) that $f_1, f_2, \ldots, f_p$ are linearly independent.

THEOREM 4. In order that the inequality (13) be a consequence of a consistent system (1), it is necessary and sufficient that there exist p non-negative numbers $\lambda_i \geq 0$ $(1 \leq i \leq p)$ such that

$$(15) \qquad g = \sum_{i=1}^{p} \lambda_i f_i,$$

$$(16) \qquad \beta \leq \sum_{i=1}^{p} \lambda_i \alpha_i.$$

Theorem 4 is well-known and due to J. Farkas ([11], pp. 5-7). See also H. Weyl ([30], Theorem 3.)

PROOF. The sufficiency of the condition is trivial. In the case $p = 1$, also the necessity is clear. To prove the necessity by induction on p, we shall assume that (13) is not a consequence of any proper subsystem of (1), for otherwise we can refer to the induction assumption.

Take an arbitrary $\epsilon > 0$. Since (13) is a consequence of (1), the system

$$\begin{cases} f_i(x) \geq \alpha_i \\ -g(x) \geq -\beta + \epsilon \end{cases} \qquad (1 \leq i \leq p),$$

is inconsistent. By Theorem 1, there exist $p + 1$ non-negative numbers $\mu_1, \mu_2, \ldots, \mu_p, \mu$ such that

$$\sum_{i=1}^{p} \mu_i f_i - \mu g = 0,$$

$$\sum_{i=1}^{p} \mu_i \alpha_i - \mu(\beta - \epsilon) > 0.$$

As (1) is consistent, we have $\mu > 0$. If we take $\lambda_i = \frac{\mu_i}{\mu}$ $(1 \leq i \leq p)$, then $\lambda_i \geq 0$ and (15) is satisfied.

Since we assume that (13) is not a consequence of any proper subsystem of (1), $f_1, f_2, \ldots, f_p$ are linearly independent (by Theorem 3). Then there exists $x_o \in X$ such that

(17) $$f_i(x_o) = \alpha_i \qquad (1 \leq i \leq p).$$

This implies $g(x_o) \geq \beta$, which, by virtue of (15), (17), is precisely (16).

COROLLARY 2. Let K be the set of all solutions of a consistent system (1), and let g be a linear functional on X. Then the infimum

(18) $$\inf \left\{ g(x) \,\middle|\, x \in K \right\}$$

is finite, if and only if g is a linear combination of $f_1, f_2, \ldots, f_p$ with non-negative coefficients. Furthermore, when this condition is satisfied, then

$$\text{Max}\left\{ \sum_{i=1}^{p} \lambda_i \alpha_i \;\middle|\; \lambda_i \geq 0, \quad g = \sum_{i=1}^{p} \lambda_i f_i \right\} \tag{19}$$

exists and has the same value as the infimum (18).

Corollary 2 is a special case of a more general theorem of D. Gale, H. W. Kuhn and A. W. Tucker [16].

PROOF. The infimum (18) is finite, if and only if there exists a real number β such that the inequality $g(x) \geq \beta$ is a consequence of (1). By Theorem 4, such β exists, if and only if g is a linear combination of $f_1, f_2, \ldots, f_p$ with non-negative coefficients.

Assume now that the infimum (18) is finite and its value is γ. This means: (i) For any $\epsilon > 0$, there is an $x_\epsilon \in K$ such that $g(x_\epsilon) < \gamma + \epsilon$; (ii) the inequality $g(x) \geq \gamma$ is a consequence of (1). Let $\lambda_i \geq 0$ be such that

$$g = \sum_{i=1}^{p} \lambda_i f_i.$$

Then by (i), for any $\epsilon > 0$, we have

$$\gamma + \epsilon > g(x_\epsilon) = \sum_{i=1}^{p} \lambda_i f_i(x_\epsilon) \geq \sum_{i=1}^{p} \lambda_i \alpha_i.$$

It follows that

$$\sum_{i=1}^{p} \lambda_i \alpha_i \leq \gamma$$

for any $\lambda_i \geq 0$ satisfying

$$g = \sum_{i=1}^{p} \lambda_i f_i.$$

According to Theorem 4, (ii) implies the existence of $\hat{\lambda}_i \geq 0$ such that

$$g = \sum_{i=1}^{p} \hat{\lambda}_i f_i, \qquad \gamma \leq \sum_{i=1}^{p} \hat{\lambda}_i \alpha_i.$$

Hence γ is the maximum (19).

COROLLARY 3. A consistent system (1) has a solution $x \in X$ which does not satisfy all p equations

$$f_i(x) = \alpha_i \qquad (1 \leq i \leq p), \tag{20}$$

if and only if, for any p positive numbers $\lambda_i > 0$, the relation

$$\sum_{i=1}^{p} \lambda_i f_i = 0$$

implies

$$\sum_{i=1}^{p} \lambda_i \alpha_i < 0.$$

PROOF. The necessity of the condition is trivial. To prove the sufficiency, assume that every solution of (1) satisfies (20). This means that each of the p inequalities

$$- f_j(x) \geq - \alpha_j \qquad (1 \leq j \leq p)$$

is a consequence of (1). By Theorem 4, for each $j = 1, 2, \ldots, p$, there exist p non-negative numbers $\lambda_i^{(j)} \geq 0$ $(1 \leq i \leq p)$ such that

$$- f_j = \sum_{i=1}^{p} \lambda_i^{(j)} f_i,$$

$$- \alpha_j \leq \sum_{i=1}^{p} \lambda_i^{(j)} \alpha_i.$$

It follows that

$$\sum_{i=1}^{p} \left(1 + \sum_{j=1}^{p} \lambda_i^{(j)} \right) f_i = 0,$$

$$\sum_{i=1}^{p} \left(1 + \sum_{j=1}^{p} \lambda_i^{(j)} \right) \alpha_i \geq 0.$$

If we put

$$\lambda_i = 1 + \sum_{j=1}^{p} \lambda_i^{(j)} \qquad (1 \leq i \leq p),$$

then $\lambda_i > 0$ $(1 \leq i \leq p)$ and

$$\sum_{i=1}^{p} \lambda_i f_i = 0, \qquad \sum_{i=1}^{p} \lambda_i \alpha_i \geq 0.$$

Hence the condition is sufficient.

COROLLARY 4. The system

$$f_i(x) \geq 0 \qquad (1 \leq i \leq p)$$

has a solution $x \in X$ which does not satisfy all p equations

$$f_i(x) = 0 \qquad (1 \leq i \leq p),$$

if and only if

$$\sum_{i=1}^{p} \lambda_i f_i \neq 0$$

holds for any p positive numbers $\lambda_i > 0$.

This result which is a special case of Corollary 3, is due to R. W. Stokes ([28], p. 805, Theorem 17). The question treated in Corollary 4 has been recently studied by L. M. Blumenthal ([2], Theorem 2), and J. W. Gaddum [15]. Their conditions are different from the one in Corollary 4.

§4. IRREDUCIBLY INCONSISTENT SYSTEMS

The system (1) is said to be irreducibly inconsistent, if the system itself is inconsistent and if every proper subsystem is consistent. This concept has been studied by W. B. Carver [5] for systems of strict inequalities (like (25) below). It has also been investigated by T. Motzkin ([22], §11).

THEOREM 5. The system (1) is irreducibly inconsistent, if and only if the following two conditions are simultaneously fulfilled:

(i) Any $p - 1$ of the linear functionals $f_1, f_2, \ldots, f_p$ are linearly independent.

(ii) There exist p positive numbers $\lambda_i > 0$ such that

(21)
$$\sum_{i=1}^{p} \lambda_i f_i = 0,$$

(22)
$$\sum_{i=1}^{p} \lambda_i \alpha_i > 0.$$

PROOF. Sufficiency. (i) implies that every proper subsystem of (1) is consistent. By Theorem 1, (ii) implies the inconsistency of (1).

Necessity. The system (1) being inconsistent, we can choose $\epsilon > 0$ such that the system

$$\begin{cases} f_i(x) \geq \alpha_i \\ f_p(x) \geq \alpha_p - \epsilon \end{cases} \qquad (1 \leq i \leq p - 1),$$

remains inconsistent (see Corollary 1). Then the inequality

(23)
$$- f_p(x) \geq - \alpha_p + \epsilon$$

is a consequence of the consistent system

(24)
$$f_i(x) \geq \alpha_i \qquad (1 \leq i \leq p - 1).$$

We observe that (23) is not a consequence of any proper subsystem of (24). Suppose, for instance, that (23) is a consequence of

$$f_i(x) \geq \alpha_i \qquad (1 \leq i \leq p - 2),$$

then the system

$$f_i(x) \geq \alpha_i \qquad (1 \leq i \leq p, \ i \neq p - 1)$$

would be inconsistent, against our hypothesis. Hence, by Theorem 3, $f_1, f_2, \ldots, f_{p-1}$ are linearly independent. This proves (i).

As (1) is inconsistent, by Theorem 1, there exist p non-negative numbers $\lambda_i \geq 0$ satisfying (21), (22). Since every proper subsystem of (1) is consistent, we must have $\lambda_i > 0$ $(1 \leq i \leq p)$.

§5. SYSTEMS OF STRICT INEQUALITIES

Before closing this Part I, we add a fundamental theorem of W. B.

Carver [5] concerning the system of strict inequalities:

$$(25) \qquad f_i(x) > \alpha_i \qquad (1 \leq i \leq p),$$

where f_i are given linear functionals on X, and α_i are given real numbers.

THEOREM 6. The system (25) is consistent, if and only if, for any p non-negative numbers $\lambda_i \geq 0$, not all zero, the relation

$$\sum_{i=1}^{p} \lambda_i f_i = 0$$

implies

$$\sum_{i=1}^{p} \lambda_i \alpha_i < 0.$$

PROOF. The "only if" part is trivial. To prove the "if" part, let us assume that (25) is inconsistent. Then for each positive integer n, the system

$$f_i(x) \geq \alpha_i + \frac{1}{n} \qquad (1 \leq i \leq p)$$

is inconsistent. By Theorem 1, there exist p non-negative numbers $\lambda_i^{(n)} \geq 0$ $(1 \leq i \leq p)$ such that

$$\sum_{i=1}^{p} \lambda_i^{(n)} f_i = 0, \qquad \sum_{i=1}^{p} \lambda_i^{(n)} \left(\alpha_i + \frac{1}{n} \right) > 0.$$

As $\lambda_i^{(n)}$ $(1 \leq i \leq p)$ cannot be all zero, we may assume that

$$\sum_{i=1}^{p} \lambda_i^{(n)} = 1.$$

Then we can pick an increasing sequence of positive integers $k_1 < k_2 < \cdots < k_n < \cdots$ such that the p limits

$$\lim_{n \to \infty} \lambda_i^{(k_n)} = \lambda_i \qquad (1 \leq i \leq p)$$

exist. We have $\lambda_i \geq 0$,

$$\sum_{i=1}^{p} \lambda_i = 1$$

and

$$\sum_{i=1}^{p} \lambda_i f_i = 0, \qquad \sum_{i=1}^{p} \lambda_i \alpha_i \geq 0.$$

COROLLARY 5. The system

$$f_i(x) > 0 \qquad (1 \leq i \leq p)$$

is consistent, if and only if the zero-functional is not in the convex hull of $f_1, f_2, \dots, f_p$.

PART II

FINITE SYSTEMS OF LINEAR INEQUALITIES ON A LINEAR SPACE OF FINITE DIMENSION

The linear spaces considered in this Part II are assumed to be of finite dimension. But the linear space is not required to be normed. A real linear space of dimension n will be denoted by X^n. We shall be concerned with finite systems of linear inequalities of the form

$$(26) \qquad f_i(x) \geq \alpha_i \qquad (1 \leq i \leq p)$$

where $f_1, f_2, \dots, f_p$ are given linear functionals on X^n; $\alpha_1, \alpha_2, \dots, \alpha_p$ are given real numbers; and the unknown x is an element of X^n. For the sake of geometric interpretation, we assume that all $f_i \neq 0$.

§6. LINEAR MANIFOLDS CONTAINED IN THE SET OF SOLUTIONS

THEOREM 7. Let K be the set of all solutions of a consistent system (26) on X^n. Let r be the maximum number of linearly independent linear functionals among the f_i's, and let q be the maximum dimension of linear manifolds contained in K. Then $q + r = n$.

PROOF. First, by Theorem 2, we have $q \geq n - r$. Consider now a q-dimensional linear manifold M contained in K. Let M be the set of all solutions of the system of linear equations

$$(27) \qquad g_j(x) = \beta_j \qquad (1 \le j \le n - q),$$

where $g_1, g_2, \ldots, g_{n-q}$ are $n - q$ linearly independent linear functionals on X^n. As $M \subset K$, every solution of (27) is a solution of (26). Then by Lemma 1, each f_i is a linear combination of $g_1, g_2, \ldots, g_{n-q}$. Hence $r \le n - q$ and therefore $q + r = n$.

THEOREM 8. Let K be the set of all solutions of a consistent system (26) on X^n. Let M be an m-dimensional linear manifold in X^n such that $M \cap K \ne \emptyset$. If q is the maximum dimension of linear manifolds contained in $M \cap K$, then $M \cap K$ contains a q-dimensional linear manifold which is contained in the intersection of at least $m - q$ linearly independent hyperplanes among the p hyperplanes

$$(28) \qquad H_i = \left\{ x \in X^n \;\middle|\; f_i(x) = \alpha_i \right\} \qquad (1 \le i \le p).$$

PROOF. Consider first the case $m = n$. Then $M \cap K = K$ and q is the maximum dimension of linear manifolds contained in K. By Theorem 7, $n - q$ is the maximum number of linearly independent linear functionals among the f_i's. Then the present theorem follows from Theorem 2.

Assume now $m < n$. We shall also assume $q < m$, since the theorem becomes trivial for $q = m$. Let M be the set of all solutions of the system

$$(29) \qquad g_j(x) = \beta_j \qquad (1 \le j \le n - m),$$

where $g_1, g_2, \ldots, g_{n-m}$ are $n - m$ linearly independent linear functionals on X^n. $M \cap K$ is the set of all solutions of the system

$$(30) \qquad \begin{cases} g_j(x) = \beta_j & (1 \le j \le n - m), \\ f_i(x) \ge \alpha_i & (1 \le i \le p) \end{cases}$$

which can be written

$$\begin{cases} g_j(x) \ge \beta_j & (1 \le j \le n - m), \\ -g_j(x) \ge -\beta_j & (1 \le j \le n - m), \\ f_i(x) \ge \alpha_i & (1 \le i \le p) . \end{cases}$$

Since q is the maximum dimension of linear manifolds contained in $M \cap K$, by Theorem 7, $n - q$ is the maximum number of linearly independent linear functionals among

$$g_1, g_2, \ldots, g_{n-m}, -g_1, -g_2, \ldots, -g_{n-m}, f_1, f_2, \ldots, f_p.$$

Hence $n - q$ is also the maximum number of linearly independent linear functionals among

$$g_1, g_2, \ldots, g_{n-m}, f_1, f_2, \ldots, f_p. \tag{31}$$

By Theorem 2', there exist $(n-q) - (n-m) = m - q$ linear functionals $f_{\nu_1}, f_{\nu_2}, \ldots, f_{\nu_{m-q}}$ among the f_i's such that

$$g_1, g_2, \ldots, g_{n-m}, f_{\nu_1}, f_{\nu_2}, \ldots, f_{\nu_{m-q}} \tag{32}$$

are linearly independent and that every solution of the system

$$\begin{cases} g_j(x) = \beta_j & (1 \leq j \leq n - m), \\ f_{\nu_k}(x) = \alpha_{\nu_k} & (1 \leq k \leq m - q) \end{cases} \tag{33}$$

is a solution of (30). The solutions of (33) form a q-dimensional linear manifold N. We have $N \subset M \cap K$, and N is contained in each of the linearly independent hyperplanes H_{ν_k} $(1 \leq k \leq m - q)$.

THEOREM 9. Let K be the set of all solutions of a consistent system (26) on X^n, and let M be an m-dimensional linear manifold in X^n such that $M \cap K \neq \emptyset$. Let q be the maximum dimension of linear manifolds contained in $M \cap K$. If no point of M satisfies all p strict inequalities

$$f_i(x) > \alpha_i \qquad (1 \leq i \leq p),$$

then there exist a q-dimensional linear manifold N and $m - q + 1$ hyperplanes H_{ν_k} $(1 \leq k \leq m - q + 1)$ among the p hyperplanes (28) such that:

(i) $N \subset M \cap K$;

(ii) $N \subset \bigcap_{k=1}^{m-q+1} H_{\nu_k}$;

(iii) Among the $m - q + 1$ hyperplanes H_{ν_k} $(1 \leq k \leq m - q + 1)$, there are at least $m - q$ linearly independent ones.

PROOF. We shall assume $m < n$ in this proof, which can be easily modified for the case $m = n$.

As $m < n$, we may regard M as the set of all solutions of the system (29), where the linear functionals $g_1, g_2, \cdots, g_{n-m}$ are linearly independent. By hypothesis, system (30) is consistent, but the system

$$(34) \qquad \begin{cases} g_j(x) = \beta_j & (1 \leq j \leq n - m), \\ f_i(x) > \alpha_i & (1 \leq i \leq p) \end{cases}$$

is inconsistent. By Theorem 7, $n - q$ is the maximum number of linearly independent linear functionals among (31). We discuss two separate cases according as whether $q = m$ or $q < m$.

(Case 1) $q = m$.

In this case, $M \subset K$. It is clear that we have to take $N = M$. We have to show that M is contained in at least one of the hyperplanes $H_i (1 \leq i \leq p)$.

Let x_0 be a solution of (30). Since (34) is inconsistent, we have $f_i(x_0) = \alpha_i$ for at least one index i, say for $i = \nu_1$. Then the system

$$(35) \qquad \begin{cases} g_j(x) = \beta_j \\ f_{\nu_1}(x) = \alpha_{\nu_1} \end{cases} \qquad (1 \leq j \leq n - m),$$

is consistent. As $q = m$, the maximum number of linearly independent linear functionals among (31) is $n - q = n - m$, so that f_{ν_1} is a linear combination of $g_1, g_2, \cdots, g_{n-m}$. Hence every solution of (29) is a solution of (35); i.e., $M \subset H_{\nu_1}$.

(Case 2) $q < m$.

By Theorem 2', there exist $(n-q) - (n-m) = m - q$ linear functionals $f_{\nu_1}, f_{\nu_2}, \cdots, f_{\nu_{m-q}}$ among the f_i's such that the linear functionals in (32) are linearly independent and that every solution of (33) is a solution of (30).

Let x_0 be a solution of (33). Then

$$\begin{cases} g_j(x_o) = \beta_j & (1 \leq j \leq n - m), \\ f_{\nu_k}(x_o) = \alpha_{\nu_k} & (1 \leq k \leq m - q), \\ f_i(x_o) \geq \alpha_i & (i \neq \nu_1, \nu_2, \ldots, \nu_{m-q}). \end{cases}$$

We claim that $f_i(x_o) = \alpha_i$ for at least one index $i \neq \nu_1, \nu_2, \ldots, \nu_{m-q}$. Suppose the contrary:

(36) $$f_i(x_o) > \alpha_i \qquad (i \neq \nu_1, \nu_2, \ldots, \nu_{m-q}).$$

We choose q linear functionals $h_1, h_2, \ldots, h_q$ on X^n such that

$$g_1, g_2, \ldots, g_{n-m}, f_{\nu_1}, f_{\nu_2}, \ldots, f_{\nu_{m-q}}, h_1, h_2, \ldots, h_q$$

are linearly independent. (In case $q = 0$, we do not introduce $h_1, h_2, \ldots, h_q$.) Let

$$\gamma_\ell = h_\ell(x_o) \qquad (1 \leq \ell \leq q).$$

Then for any real ϵ, the system

(37) $$\begin{cases} g_j(x) = \beta_j & (1 \leq j \leq n - m), \\ f_{\nu_k}(x) = \alpha_{\nu_k} + \epsilon & (1 \leq k \leq m - q), \\ h_\ell(x) = \gamma_\ell & (1 \leq \ell \leq q) \end{cases}$$

has a unique solution $x = x(\epsilon)$. For $\epsilon = 0$, we have $x(0) = x_o$. If we regard the linear space X^n as topologized with the usual Euclidean topology, then $x(\epsilon)$ varies continuously with ϵ. From this fact and the strict inequality in (36), we can choose $\epsilon > 0$ so small that the unique solution $x(\epsilon)$ of (37) satisfies

$$f_i(x(\epsilon)) > \alpha_i \qquad (i \neq \nu_1, \nu_2, \ldots, \nu_{m-q}).$$

Then for this $\epsilon > 0$, $x(\epsilon)$ would be a solution of (34). This is absurd, since (34) is inconsistent.

We have thus proved that $f_i(x_o) = \alpha_i$ for at least one $i \neq \nu_1, \nu_2, \ldots, \nu_{m-q}$. Take one such index i as ν_{m-q+1}. Then the system

$$(38)\quad \begin{cases} g_j(x) = \beta_j & (1 \le j \le n - m), \\ f_{\nu_k}(x) = \alpha_{\nu_k} & (1 \le k \le m - q + 1), \\ f_i(x) \ge \alpha_i & (i \ne \nu_1, \nu_2, \ldots, \nu_{m-q+1}) \end{cases}$$

is consistent. As each f_i is a linear combination of the linear functionals in (32), it follows (by Lemma 1) that every solution of

$$(39)\quad \begin{cases} g_j(x) = \beta_j & (1 \le j \le n - m), \\ f_{\nu_k}(x) = \alpha_{\nu_k} & (1 \le k \le m - q + 1) \end{cases}$$

is a solution of (38). This system (39) defines a q-dimensional linear manifold N which has the desired properties (i), (ii), (iii).

§7. A DETERMINANTAL FORM OF CONSISTENCY CONDITION

If coordinates are introduced in the n-dimensional linear space X^n, then the system (26) takes the form

$$(40)\quad \sum_{j=1}^{n} a_{ij}x_j \ge \alpha_i \qquad (1 \le i \le p),$$

where the coefficient matrix

$$(41)\quad A = \begin{pmatrix} a_{11} & a_{12} & \cdots & a_{1n} \\ a_{21} & a_{22} & \cdots & a_{2n} \\ \cdot & \cdot & \cdots & \cdot \\ a_{p1} & a_{p2} & \cdots & a_{pn} \end{pmatrix}$$

and the real numbers $\alpha_1, \alpha_2, \ldots, \alpha_p$ are given. We assume that no row in A contains 0 only.

THEOREM 10. Let the rank of the matrix A be $p - 1$. Suppose that the first $p - 1$ columns of A are linearly independent, and let

$$(42)\quad \hat{A} = \begin{pmatrix} a_{11} & a_{12} & \cdots & a_{1,p-1} \\ a_{21} & a_{22} & \cdots & a_{2,p-1} \\ \cdot & \cdot & \cdots & \cdot \\ a_{p1} & a_{p2} & \cdots & a_{p,p-1} \end{pmatrix}$$

be the submatrix of A formed by its first $p - 1$ columns. For each $i = 1, 2, \ldots, p$, let M_i denote the determinant of order $p - 1$ obtained from $\hat{A}$ by deleting its i-th row. Then the system (40) is irreducibly inconsistent, if and only if the following two conditions are both fulfilled:

(43) $$M_i M_{i+1} < 0 \qquad (1 \leq i \leq p - 1),$$

(44) $$\sum_{i=1}^{p} \alpha_i \left| M_i \right| > 0.$$

PROOF. Necessity. Let (40) be irreducibly inconsistent. By Theorem 5, there exist p positive numbers $\lambda_i > 0$ such that

(45) $$\sum_{i=1}^{p} \lambda_i a_{ij} = 0 \qquad (1 \leq j \leq n),$$

(46) $$\sum_{i=1}^{p} \lambda_i \alpha_i > 0.$$

Since the rank of $\hat{A}$ is $p - 1$, it follows from the first $p - 1$ equations of (45) that

(47) $$\lambda_i = (-1)^{i-1} \rho M_i \qquad (1 \leq i \leq p),$$

where ρ is some constant $\neq 0$. Then (43) follows from the fact that $\lambda_i > 0$. (44) follows from (46).

Sufficiency. From (43), we have $M_i \neq 0$ $(1 \leq i \leq p)$. So any $p - 1$ rows in $\hat{A}$ are linearly independent. Therefore any $p - 1$ rows in A are also linearly independent. This means that the system (40) satisfies condition (i) of Theorem 5.

Let

(48) $$\lambda_i = \left| M_i \right| \qquad (1 \leq i \leq p).$$

Then $\lambda_i > 0$ and (44) becomes (46). Since the rank of A is $p - 1$, (47) gives the general solution of (45). Therefore, using (43), we infer that the λ_i's defined by (48) satisfy (45). This proves that the system (40) satisfies condition (ii) of Theorem 5. Hence, (40) is irreducibly inconsistent.

Clearly a system (40) of linear inequalities is inconsistent, if and only if it contains a subsystem which is irreducibly inconsistent. Hence the following theorem follows directly from Theorem 10.

THEOREM 11. The system (40) is inconsistent, if and only if certain q linearly dependent rows of the matrix (41) contain a $q \times (q-1)$ submatrix

$$B = \begin{pmatrix} a_{i_1 j_1} & a_{i_1 j_2} & \cdots & a_{i_1 j_{q-1}} \\ a_{i_2 j_1} & a_{i_2 j_2} & \cdots & a_{i_2 j_{q-1}} \\ \cdot & \cdot & \cdots & \cdot \\ a_{i_q j_1} & a_{i_q j_2} & \cdots & a_{i_q j_{q-1}} \end{pmatrix} \tag{49}$$

such that

$$N_k N_{k+1} < 0 \qquad (1 \leq k \leq q-1), \tag{50}$$

$$\sum_{k=1}^{q} \alpha_{i_k} \left| N_k \right| > 0; \tag{51}$$

where N_k $(1 \leq k \leq q)$ denotes the determinant of order $q - 1$ obtained from B by deleting its k-th row.

We add a remark concerning systems of strict inequalities.

Theorem 11 remains valid, if the system (40) is replaced by a system of strict inequalities

$$\sum_{j=1}^{n} a_{ij} x_j > \alpha_i \qquad (1 \leq i \leq p), \tag{40'}$$

and if (51) is replaced by

$$\sum_{k=1}^{q} \alpha_{i_k} \left| N_k \right| \geq 0. \tag{51'}$$

To see this, it suffices to observe that the inconsistency of (40') is equivalent to the fact that for any $\epsilon > 0$, the system

$$\sum_{j=1}^{n} a_{ij}x_j \geq \alpha_i + \epsilon \qquad (1 \leq i \leq p)$$

is inconsistent.

This result concerning system (40') generalizes the following theorem of T. Motzkin ([22], p. 49, Satz D3; p. 48, Satz B1):

The system of homogeneous strict inequalities

$$\sum_{j=1}^{n} a_{ij}x_j > 0 \qquad (1 \leq i \leq p)$$

is inconsistent, if and only if certain q linearly dependent rows of the matrix (41) contain a $q \times (q - 1)$ submatrix B such that

$$N_k N_{k+1} < 0 \qquad (1 \leq k \leq q - 1),$$

where N_k $(1 \leq k \leq q)$ denotes the determinant of order $q - 1$ obtained from B by deleting its k-th row.

PART III

LINEAR INEQUALITIES ON A NORMED OR TOPOLOGICAL LINEAR SPACE

§8. CONSISTENCY CONDITION. MINIMUM NORM OF SOLUTIONS

We begin with two consistency theorems for an arbitrary system (52), finite or infinite, of linear inequalities on a real normed linear space X. In this system (52), x_ν are given elements of X, and α_ν are given real numbers. The unknown is the continuous linear functional f on X. The reason for this interchange of the rôles played by elements of X and by linear functionals on X lies in a topological property of the conjugate space of a normed linear space (See the proof of Theorem 12, especially footnote 3.)

THEOREM 12. Let $\{x_\nu\}_{\nu \in I}$ be a family, finite or infinite, of elements in a real normed linear space X, and let $\{\alpha_\nu\}_{\nu \in I}$ be a corresponding family of real numbers. Then for any $\rho \geq 0$, the following two conditions are equivalent:

(i) There exists a continuous linear functional f on X with $\|f\| \leq \rho$ such that

$$f(x_\nu) \geq \alpha_\nu \qquad (\nu \in I). \tag{52}$$

(ii) For any finite number n of indices $\nu_1, \nu_2, \ldots, \nu_n$ of I and for any n positive numbers $\lambda_1, \lambda_2, \ldots, \lambda_n$, the inequality

$$\rho \left\| \sum_{i=1}^{n} \lambda_i x_{\nu_i} \right\| \geq \sum_{i=1}^{n} \lambda_i \alpha_{\nu_i} \tag{53}$$

holds.

PROOF. That (i) implies (ii) is clear. We need only prove that (ii) implies (i).

Assuming (ii), we shall first prove that, given any finite number of indices $\nu_1, \nu_2, \ldots, \nu_n$ of I, there exists a continuous linear functional f on X satisfying $\|f\| \leq \rho$ and

$$f\left(x_{\nu_i}\right) \geq \alpha_{\nu_i} \qquad (1 \leq i \leq n). \tag{54}$$

Given the indices $\nu_1, \nu_2, \ldots, \nu_n$, we shall consider the Euclidean n-space E^n. Let α denote the point in E^n with coordinates $\left(\alpha_{\nu_1}, \alpha_{\nu_2}, \ldots, \alpha_{\nu_n}\right)$. Let P denote the set of all points in E^n with non-negative coordinates. As usual, the conjugate space of X will be designated by X^*. Let

$$S_\rho^* = \left\{f \in X^* \middle| \ \|f\| \leq \rho \right\}.$$

Let K denote the set of all points in E^n with coordinates $(f(x_{\nu_1}), f(x_{\nu_2}), \ldots, f(x_{\nu_n}))$, when f varies in S_ρ^*. As S_ρ^* is compact[3] with respect to the w^*-topology of X^* (i.e., the weak topology of X^* induced by X), K is a compact set in E^n. Now, suppose that no $f \in S_\rho^*$ satisfies

[3] "Compact" in this paper means "bicompact" of Alexandroff-Hopf. It is a well-known theorem of Banach-Bourbaki that S_ρ^* is compact with respect to the w^*-topology of X^*. (See [8], p. 128, Théorème 22.)

all n inequalities of (54). This means that the compact convex set K is disjoint from the closed convex set $P + \alpha$. Then these two convex sets can be separated strictly by a hyperplane in E^n. Hence there exist $n + 1$ real numbers $\lambda_1, \lambda_2, \ldots, \lambda_n$ and β such that

$$\sum_{i=1}^{n} \lambda_i f\left(x_{\nu_i}\right) < \beta \qquad \text{for} \qquad \|f\| \leq \rho;$$

and

$$\sum_{i=1}^{n} \lambda_i \left(y_i + \alpha_{\nu_i}\right) > \beta \qquad \text{whenever} \qquad y_i \geq 0.$$

The first inequality implies

$$\rho \left\| \sum_{i=1}^{n} \lambda_i x_{\nu_i} \right\| \leq \beta.$$

The second one implies

$$\sum_{i=1}^{n} \lambda_i \alpha_{\nu_i} > \beta$$

and

$$\lambda_i \geq 0 \qquad (1 \leq i \leq n).$$

Thus these non-negative numbers λ_i satisfy the strict reversed inequality of (53), which contradicts condition (ii). This proves that any finite subsystem (54) of (52) has a solution $f \in X^*$ with $\|f\| \leq \rho$.

For each non-empty finite subset J of I, let

$$A_J^* = \left\{ f \in S_\rho^* \;\middle|\; f(x_\nu) \geq \alpha_\nu \qquad \text{for} \qquad \nu \in J \right\}.$$

Let $\mathcal{A}^*$ denote the family of all sets A_J^*, when J varies over all non-empty finite subsets of I. With respect to the w^*-topology of X^*, each A_J^* is a closed subset of S_ρ^*. From what we have just proved, any finite number of sets of $\mathcal{A}^*$ have a non-empty intersection. Therefore by the compactness of S_ρ^* (with respect to the w^*-topology), the intersection of all sets of $\mathcal{A}^*$ is non-empty. This proves the existence of an $f \in S_\rho^*$ satisfying (52).

The above theorem may be regarded as a generalization of a classical theorem due to Hahn and Banach ([1], p. 55, Théorème 4) concerning linear equations.

COROLLARY 6. Let K_ρ^* denote the set of all $f \in X^*$ satisfying (52) and $\|f\| \leq \rho$. If $K_\rho^* \neq \emptyset$, then for any element $y \in X$,

$$\mathrm{Min}\left\{f(y) \;\middle|\; f \in K_\rho^*\right\}$$

is equal to the supremum of the expression

$$\sum_{i=1}^{n} \lambda_i \alpha_{\nu_i} - \rho \left\| y - \sum_{i=1}^{n} \lambda_i x_{\nu_i} \right\|,$$

when $n = 1, 2, 3, \ldots$; $\nu_i \in I$ and $\lambda_i \geq 0$ vary.

PROOF. With respect to the w^*-topology, K_ρ^* being a closed subset of the compact set S_ρ^*, is compact. Therefore the minimum of $f(y)$ exists, when f varies in K_ρ^*. Next, the equation

$$\beta = \mathrm{Min}\left\{f(y) \;\middle|\; f \in K_\rho^*\right\}$$

means that β has the following two properties: (i) The system

$$\begin{cases} \|f\| \leq \rho \\ f(x_\nu) \geq \alpha_\nu & (\nu \in I), \\ f(-y) \geq -\beta \end{cases}$$

is consistent. (ii) For any $\epsilon > 0$, the system

$$\begin{cases} \|f\| \leq \rho \\ f(x_\nu) \geq \alpha_\nu & (\nu \in I), \\ f(-y) \geq -\beta + \epsilon \end{cases}$$

is inconsistent. Then, using Theorem 12, these two properties (i), (ii) of β means that β is the supremum in question.

THEOREM 13. Let $\{x_\nu\}_{\nu \in I}$ be a family of elements, not all 0, in a real normed linear space X, and let $\{\alpha_\nu\}_{\nu \in I}$ be a corresponding family of real numbers. Let

(55) $$\sigma = \sup \sum_{i=1}^{n} \lambda_i \alpha_{\nu_i} ,$$

when $n = 1, 2, 3, \ldots$; $\nu_i \in I$ and λ_i vary under the conditions

(56) $$\lambda_i > 0 \ (1 \leq i \leq n); \qquad \left\| \sum_{i=1}^{n} \lambda_i x_{\nu_i} \right\| = 1.$$

Then:

(i) The system (52) of linear inequalities has a solution $f \in X^*$, if and only if σ is finite.

(ii) If the system (52) has solutions $f \in X^*$, and if the zero-functional is not a solution of (52), then σ is equal to the minimum of the norms of all solutions f of (52).

PROOF. (i) If the system (52) has solutions $f \in X^*$, then by Theorem 12, it is clear that σ must be finite. To derive the converse from Theorem 12, it suffices to observe that, if σ is finite, then for any finite number n of indices $\nu_1, \nu_2, \ldots, \nu_n$ of I and for any n positive numbers $\lambda_1, \lambda_2, \ldots, \lambda_n$, the relation

(57) $$\sum_{i=1}^{n} \lambda_i x_{\nu_i} = 0$$

implies

(58) $$\sum_{i=1}^{n} \lambda_i \alpha_{\nu_i} \leq 0.$$

(One can also see this by using Theorem 1.) In fact, suppose, if possible, that we have

$$\sum_{i=1}^{n} \lambda_i x_{\nu_i} = 0, \qquad \sum_{i=1}^{n} \lambda_i \alpha_{\nu_i} = \beta > 0, \qquad \lambda_i > 0.$$

Then if we choose $\nu_{n+1} \in I$ and $\lambda_{n+1} > 0$ such that $\| \lambda_{n+1} x_{\nu_{n+1}} \| = 1$, we would have

$$\left\| \mu \cdot \sum_{i=1}^{n} \lambda_i x_{\nu_i} + \lambda_{n+1} x_{\nu_{n+1}} \right\| = 1$$

for any real number μ. But

$$\mu \sum_{i=1}^{n} \lambda_i \alpha_{\nu_i} + \lambda_{n+1}\alpha_{\nu_{n+1}} = \mu\beta + \lambda_{n+1}\alpha_{\nu_{n+1}}$$

can be made arbitrarily large by choosing $\mu > 0$ sufficiently large. This is against our hypothesis that σ is finite.

(ii) Let K^* denote the set of all solutions $f \in X^*$ of (52). Let

$$\sigma' = \inf \left\{ \|f\| \;\middle|\; f \in K^* \right\}.$$

From Theorem 12, it is clear that $\sigma \leq \sigma'$.

Since the zero-functional is not a solution of (52), we have $\sigma > 0$. We have seen in the above that for $\nu_i \in I$, $\lambda_i > 0$, the relation (57) implies (58). Using this fact and our definition of σ, the inequality

$$\sum_{i=1}^{n} \lambda_i \alpha_{\nu_i} \leq \sigma \left\| \sum_{i=1}^{n} \lambda_i x_{\nu_i} \right\|$$

holds for any finite number of indices $\nu_1, \nu_2, \ldots, \nu_n$ and for any positive numbers $\lambda_1, \lambda_2, \ldots, \lambda_n$. Then since $\sigma > 0$, Theorem 12 asserts the existence of an $f_0 \in K^*$ with $\|f_0\| \leq \sigma$. This together with $\sigma \leq \sigma'$ proves that

$$\sigma = \sigma' = \operatorname{Min} \left\{ \|f\| \;\middle|\; f \in K^* \right\}.$$

§9. THE CASE OF EUCLIDEAN OR HILBERT SPACE

Theorem 13 can be strengthened in the case when the system (52) is finite and when X is either a Euclidean n-space E^n or a real Hilbert space. In this special case, we have a finite system

$$(59) \qquad (x, a_i) \geq \alpha_i \qquad (1 \leq i \leq p),$$

where (x, a_i) denotes the inner product in E^n or in Hilbert space, and where a_i are given elements (not all 0) in the space.

THEOREM 14. Let K be the (closed convex) set of all solutions of a consistent system (59) on a Euclidean n-space E^n or on a real Hilbert space. Assume that $0 \notin K$, and let

(60) $$\sigma = \text{Min}\left\{ \|x\| \;\middle|\; x \in K \right\}.$$

Let x_0 be the point (necessarily unique) of K with minimum norm[4]: $\|x_0\| = \sigma$. Then x_0 is the only point in the space which can be expressed in the form

(61) $$x_0 = \sigma \sum_{i=1}^{p} \lambda_i a_i$$

with p non-negative numbers λ_i satisfying

(62) $$\left\| \sum_{i=1}^{p} \lambda_i a_i \right\| = 1, \qquad \sum_{i=1}^{p} \lambda_i \alpha_i = \sigma.$$

Furthermore, when x_0 is expressed in the form (61) with p non-negative numbers λ_i satisfying (62), then $(x_0, a_i) = \alpha_i$ holds for all those indices i for which $\lambda_i > 0$.

PROOF. Since $x_0 \in K$ and

$$\left\| x_0 \right\| = \sigma = \text{Min}\left\{ \|x\| \;\middle|\; x \in K \right\},$$

we have

(63) $$(x, x_0) \geq \sigma^2 \quad \text{for all} \quad x \in K.$$

In fact, suppose, if possible, there exists a point $y \in K$ such that $(y, x_0) = \sigma^2 - \epsilon$ with $\epsilon > 0$. Then, as $y \in K$ and $y \neq x_0$, we have $\|y\|^2 = \sigma^2 + \delta$ with $\delta > 0$. If we choose α, β such that $\alpha > 0$, $\beta > 0$, $\alpha + \beta = 1$, and $\beta\delta < 2\alpha\epsilon$, and if we take $z = \alpha x_0 + \beta y$, then $\|z\|^2 = \alpha^2\|x_0\|^2 + \beta^2\|y\|^2 + 2\alpha\beta(x_0, y) = (\alpha + \beta)^2\sigma^2 + \beta(\beta\delta - 2\alpha\epsilon) < \sigma^2$, which is absurd, since $z \in K$. This proves (63).

---

[4] Since X is either a Euclidean n-space E^n or a real Hilbert space, every non-empty closed convex set in X has a unique point of minimum norm.

Inequality (63) means that the inequality

$$\left(x, \frac{x_o}{\sigma}\right) \geq \sigma$$

is a consequence of (59). By Theorem 4, there exist p non-negative numbers λ_i such that

$$\frac{x_o}{\sigma} = \sum_{i=1}^{p} \lambda_i a_i, \qquad \sigma \leq \sum_{i=1}^{p} \lambda_i \alpha_i .$$

As $\| x_o \| = \sigma$, we have

$$\left\| \sum_{i=1}^{p} \lambda_i a_i \right\| = 1.$$

By Theorem 13, σ defined as minimum in (60), is equal to

$$\sup\left\{ \sum_{i=1}^{p} \mu_i \alpha_i \;\middle|\; \mu_i \geq 0, \quad \left\| \sum_{i=1}^{p} \mu_i a_i \right\| = 1 \right\}.$$

(Actually this supremum is a maximum.) So we must have

$$\sigma = \sum_{i=1}^{p} \lambda_i \alpha_i .$$

This shows that x_o has the desired expression (61).

Next, assume that a point x_1 in the space can be expressed as

(64) $$x_1 = \sigma \sum_{i=1}^{p} \mu_i a_i ,$$

where $\mu_i \geq 0$ and

(65) $$\left\| \sum_{i=1}^{p} \mu_i a_i \right\| = 1, \qquad \sum_{i=1}^{p} \mu_i \alpha_i = \sigma.$$

We shall prove that $x_1 = x_o$. First, as $x_o \in K$, we have

$$(x_0, a_i) \geq \alpha_i \qquad (1 \leq i \leq p),$$

and therefore

$$\sigma \sum_{i=1}^{p} \mu_i (x_0, a_i) \geq \sigma \sum_{i=1}^{p} \mu_i \alpha_i ,$$

or by (64) and (65),

$$(x_0, x_1) \geq \sigma^2 .$$

From (64) and (65), we also have $\|x_1\| = \sigma$. Therefore

$$\|x_1 - x_0\|^2 = \|x_0\|^2 + \|x_1\|^2 - 2(x_0, x_1) \leq 2\sigma^2 - 2\sigma^2 = 0$$

and $x_1 = x_0$. Thus x_0 is the only point in the space which can be expressed in the form (61) with p non-negative numbers λ_i satisfying (62).

Consider now such an expression (61) of x_0. We want to prove that $\lambda_i > 0$ implies $(x_0, a_i) = \alpha_i$. Suppose, if possible, that for some index i_0, we have

$$\lambda_{i_0} > 0, \qquad \left(x_0, a_{i_0}\right) = \alpha'_{i_0} > \alpha_{i_0} .$$

Let K' denote the set of all solutions of the system

$$\begin{cases} \left(x, a_i\right) \geq \alpha_i & (1 \leq i \leq p,\ i \neq i_0); \\ \left(x, a_{i_0}\right) \geq \alpha'_{i_0} \end{cases}$$

and let

$$\sigma' = \operatorname{Min} \left\{ \|x\| \;\middle|\; x \in K' \right\} .$$

As $K' \subset K$, we have $\sigma' \geq \sigma$. But $x_0 \in K'$, so $\sigma' = \sigma$. On the other hand, by Theorem 13,

$$\sigma' \geq \lambda_{i_0} \alpha'_{i_0} + \sum_{i \neq i_0} \lambda_i \alpha_i .$$

As $\lambda_{i_0} > 0$ and $\alpha'_{i_0} > \alpha_{i_0}$, the right-hand side is

$$> \sum_{i=1}^{p} \lambda_i \alpha_i = \sigma .$$

We have then $\sigma' > \sigma$, which is a contradiction. This completes the proof.

In Theorem 14, we could have considered any point $y \notin K$ instead of 0. The necessary modification is clear. In fact, for any $y \notin K$, we can apply Theorem 14 to the system

$$(x, a_i) \geq \alpha_i - (y, a_i) \qquad (1 \leq i \leq p),$$

for which the set of solutions is precisely $K - y$.

Theorem 14 is related to a result of P. C. Rosenbloom ([26], p. 14, Lemma 4) and also to a theorem of A. J. Hoffman [20]. Their results estimate upper bounds for the distance to K from a point outside K.

§10. FORMULATION IN TERMS OF LINEAR TRANSFORMATIONS AND CONVEX CONES

A more general formulation for systems of linear inequalities is that in terms of linear transformations and convex cones. Let P be a convex cone in a real normed linear space X, and let

$$P^* = \left\{ f \in X^* \;\middle|\; f(x) \geq 0 \quad \text{for all} \quad x \in P \right\}.$$

Then P^* is clearly a convex cone in X^*. It is called the conjugate convex cone of P. The following theorem is stated without proof, which is a simple application of the separation theorem of convex sets.

THEOREM 15. Let X, Y be two real normed linear spaces. Let A be a continuous linear transformation from X into Y, and let A^* denote the adjoint of A.[5] Let $y_0 \in Y$, let Q be a convex cone in Y with[5] Int $Q \neq \emptyset$, and let Q^* denote the conjugate convex cone of Q. Then there exists an $x \in X$ such that $Ax - y_0 \in$ Int Q, if and only if $g \in Q^*$, $A^*g = 0$, and $g \neq 0$ imply $g(y_0) < 0$.

Let X, Y be two real normed linear spaces. For any $\rho \geq 0$, let

$$S_\rho = \left\{ x \in X \;\middle|\; \|x\| \leq \rho \right\}.$$

A continuous linear transformation A from X into Y is said to be compact, if $A(S_\rho)$ is compact for every $\rho \geq 0$ (or, what is equivalent, if $A(S_1)$ is compact).

---

[5] The adjoint A^* of A is the linear transformation from Y^* into X^* for which $f = A^*g (g \in Y^*)$ is determined by $f(x) = g(Ax)$ (for all $x \in X$). Int Q denotes the interior of Q.

THEOREM 16. Let X, Y be two real normed linear spaces, and let A be a compact continuous linear transformation from X into Y. Let $\rho \geq 0$, $y_0 \in Y$ and let Q be a closed convex cone in Y. Then there exists an $x \in X$ satisfying $Ax - y_0 \in Q$ and $\|x\| \leq \rho$, if and only if $g(y_0) \leq \rho\|A^*g\|$ holds for every $g \in Q^*$. (Here A^* denotes the adjoint of A, Q^* denotes the conjugate convex cone of Q.)

PROOF. If $x_0 \in X$ satisfies $Ax - y_0 \in Q$ and $\|x\| \leq \rho$, then for any $g \in Q^*$, we have $g(Ax_0 - y_0) \geq 0$ and therefore $g(y_0) \leq g(Ax_0) = (A^*g)(x_0) \leq \|A^*g\| \cdot \|x_0\| \leq \rho \|A^*g\|$.

To prove the converse, assume that no element $x \in X$ satisfies both $Ax - y_0 \in Q$ and $\|x\| \leq \rho$. Then $A(S_\rho) \cap (Q + y_0) = \emptyset$, where

$$S_\rho = \left\{ x \in X \;\middle|\; \|x\| \leq \rho \right\}.$$

As A is a compact continuous linear transformation, $A(S_\rho)$ is a compact convex set. $Q + y_0$ is, like Q, a closed convex set. Hence by separation theorem of convex sets, there exist $g \in Y^*$ and a real number c such that

$$g(Ax) < c \quad \text{for} \quad \|x\| \leq \rho$$
$$g(y + y_0) > c \quad \text{for} \quad y \in Q.$$

Since $g(Ax) = (A^*g)(x)$, the first relation implies $\rho\|A^*g\| \leq c$. From the second relation, we have $g(y_0) > c$ and $g(y) > c - g(y_0)$ for $y \in Q$. Since Q is a convex cone, the last inequality implies that $g(y) \geq 0$ for $y \in Q$. So we have $g \in Q^*$ and $g(y_0) > c \geq \rho\|A^*g\|$. This proves the sufficiency of our condition.

§11. A MOMENT PROBLEM IN TOPOLOGICAL LINEAR SPACES

Our next result is concerned with a "moment problem" in real topological linear spaces.[6]

THEOREM 17. Let X be a real topological linear space, and P be a convex cone in X with Int $P \neq \emptyset$. Let $\left\{x_\nu\right\}_{\nu \in I}$ be a family of elements of X and

[6] A real topological linear space is a real linear space which is so topologized that the vector operations are continuous.

$\{\alpha_\nu\}_{\nu \in I}$ a corresponding family of real numbers. If there is an index $\nu_0 \in I$ such that

(66) $$x_{\nu_0} \in \text{Int } P, \qquad \alpha_{\nu_0} > 0,$$

then the following two conditions are equivalent:

(i) There exists a continuous linear functional f on X such that

(67) $$f(x) \geq 0 \quad \text{for} \quad x \in P,$$

(68) $$f(x_\nu) = \alpha_\nu \quad \text{for} \quad \nu \in I.$$

(ii) For any finite number n of indices $\nu_1, \nu_2, \ldots, \nu_n$ of I and for any n real numbers $\lambda_1, \lambda_2, \ldots, \lambda_n$ satisfying

$$\sum_{i=1}^{n} \lambda_i \alpha_{\nu_i} = 0,$$

the linear combination

$$\sum_{i=1}^{n} \lambda_i x_{\nu_i}$$

is not in Int P.

PROOF. Assume that (i) is satisfied. Then the case $\nu = \nu_0$ of (68) implies that $f \neq 0$. Hence from (67) we have

$$f(x) > 0 \quad \text{for} \quad x \in \text{Int } P.$$

If

$$\sum_{i=1}^{n} \lambda_i \alpha_{\nu_i} = 0,$$

then by (68)

$$f\left(\sum_{i=1}^{n} \lambda_i x_{\nu_i}\right) = 0$$

and therefore

$$\sum_{i=1}^{n} \lambda_i x_{\nu_i}$$

is not in Int P.

To prove that (ii) implies (i), we consider the set M of all elements of the form

$$\sum_{i=1}^{n} \lambda_i x_{\nu_i} ,$$

where $\nu_1, \nu_2, \ldots, \nu_n$ are any finite number of indices of I and where $\lambda_1, \lambda_2, \ldots, \lambda_n$ are real numbers satisfying

$$\sum_{i=1}^{n} \lambda_i \alpha_{\nu_i} = 0.$$

M is a linear subspace of X. Condition (ii) means that $M \cap \text{Int } P = \emptyset$. Hence, by the separation theorem of convex sets, there exists a continuous linear functional $g \neq 0$ on X such that

$$g(x) \geq 0 \quad \text{for} \quad x \in P,$$
$$g(x) = 0 \quad \text{for} \quad x \in M.$$

Since $x_{\nu_0} \in \text{Int } P$, we have $g(x_{\nu_0}) > 0$. If we define f by

$$f(x) = \alpha_{\nu_0} \cdot \frac{g(x)}{g(x_{\nu_0})} \qquad (x \in X),$$

then it can be easily seen that f satisfies (67), (68).

We state below two special cases of Theorem 17:

Let S be a compact Hausdorff space. Let $\{x_\nu(s)\}_{\nu \in I}$ be a family of real-valued continuous functions on S, and $\{\alpha_\nu\}_{\nu \in I}$ a corresponding family of real numbers. If, for at least one index $\nu \in I$, the function $x_\nu(s)$ remains > 0 throughout S and the corresponding $\alpha_\nu > 0$, then the following two conditions are equivalent:

(i) There exists a regular Borel measure[7] μ on S such that

$$\int_S x_\nu(s)\, d\mu(s) = \alpha_\nu \qquad (\nu \in I).$$

(ii) For any finite number of indices $\nu_1, \nu_2, \dots, \nu_n$ of I and for any real numbers $\lambda_1, \lambda_2, \dots, \lambda_n$ satisfying

$$\sum_{i=1}^{n} \lambda_i \alpha_{\nu_i} = 0,$$

the function

$$\sum_{i=1}^{n} \lambda_i x_{\nu_i}(s)$$

does not remain > 0 throughout S.

If the compact Hausdorff space S is connected, then the sentence "the function

$$\sum_{i=1}^{n} \lambda_i x_{\nu_i}(s)$$

does not remain > 0 throughout S" in (ii) of the above result can be replaced by "the function

$$\sum_{i=1}^{n} \lambda_i x_{\nu_i}(s)$$

vanishes at least once in S." In this form the above result generalizes a theorem of I. J. Schoenberg ([27], p. 277) who considered a countable family of functions on a closed finite interval in the real line. Schoenberg's result is in its turn a generalization of a theorem due to J. Favard ([12], p. 244; [13], p. 23).

Another special case of Theorem 17 is the following result concerning Hermitian matrices. (For related results, see P. Finsler [14], M. R. Hestenes and E. J. McShane [19].)

Let $\{H_\nu\}_{\nu \in I}$ be a family of Hermitian matrices of order

7 See P. R. Halmos ([18], Chap. X).

n and let $\{\alpha_\nu\}_{\nu \in I}$ be a corresponding family of real numbers. Suppose that for at least one index $\nu \in I$, H_ν is positive definite and the corresponding $\alpha_\nu > 0$. Then in order that there exists a positive semi-definite Hermitian matrix A of order n such that the trace $tr(AH_\nu) = \alpha_\nu$ for each $\nu \in I$, it is necessary and sufficient that, for any finite number of indices $\nu_1, \nu_2, \ldots, \nu_m$ of I and for any real numbers $\lambda_1, \lambda_2, \ldots, \lambda_m$ satisfying

$$\sum_{i=1}^{m} \lambda_i \alpha_{\nu_i} = 0,$$

the matrix

$$\sum_{i=1}^{m} \lambda_i H_{\nu_i}$$

is not positive definite.

§12. A MINIMAX THEOREM

We shall now give a new proof of the following minimax theorem.

THEOREM 18. Let S, T be two compact Hausdorff spaces, and let φ be a real-valued continuous function on the product space $S \times T$. Let M^* and N^* be the sets of all regular Borel measures with total measure 1 on S and T respectively. Then

(69) $$\operatorname*{Max}_{\mu \in M^*} \operatorname*{Min}_{\nu \in N^*} \int_{S \times T} \varphi d(\mu \times \nu) = \operatorname*{Min}_{\nu \in N^*} \operatorname*{Max}_{\mu \in M^*} \int_{S \times T} \varphi d(\mu \times \nu).$$

In the case when each of S, T is a discrete space formed by a finite number of points, Theorem 18 was first given by J. von Neumann ([23]; [24], p. 153-155). In the case when both S, T are closed finite intervals in the real line, it was proved by J. Ville [29]. In its general form, Theorem 18 was proved independently by I. L. Glicksberg [17] and by the author [9], both using a fixed-point theorem in locally convex topological linear spaces. In another paper [10] by the author, it was pointed out that Theorem 18 can be derived from von Neumann's minimax theorem (i.e., the case of finite discrete spaces S, T of Theorem 18). Recently, H.

Nikaidô [25] gave a proof by using Brouwer's fixed-point theorem. The proof given below is based on separation of convex sets. In the case of discrete spaces S, T, the idea of using separation of convex sets is well-known and due to von Neumann. However for the general case, a proof based on separation of convex sets seems to be new.

PROOF of Theorem 18. Let $C(S)$ denote the Banach space of all real-valued continuous functions on S with the usual uniform norm. Let $C^*(S)$ denote the conjugate space of $C(S)$. With respect to the w^*-topology of $C^*(S)$, M^* may be identified with a compact set in $C^*(S)$. Moreover, it is easy to see that, with respect to the w^*-topology,

$$\int_{S\times T} \varphi d(\mu \times \nu)$$

is a continuous function on the compact set $M^* \times N^*$. Thus the expressions on both sides of (69) are meaningful.

For any real number α, let K_α denote the set of all functions on T of the form

$$\int_S \Big[\varphi(s, t) - \alpha\Big] d\mu(s),$$

when μ varies in M^*. K_α is a convex set in $C(T)$. Let P denote the convex cone in $C(T)$ formed by all non-negative functions. Then according to whether $K_\alpha \cap \text{Int } P \neq \emptyset$ or $= \emptyset$, we have the following alternatives: Either there exists a $\mu_0 \in M^*$ such that

$$\text{(70)} \qquad \int_S \Big[\varphi(s, t) - \alpha\Big] d\mu_0(s) > 0 \quad \text{for all} \quad t \in T;$$

or (by the separation theorem of convex sets) there exists a $\nu_0 \in N^*$ such that

$$\text{(71)} \qquad \int_T \left\{ \int_S \Big[\varphi(s, t) - \alpha\Big] d\mu(s) \right\} d\nu_0(t) \leq 0 \quad \text{for all} \quad \mu \in M^*.$$

Let

$$f(\mu, \nu) = \int_{S\times T} \varphi d(\mu \times \nu).$$

Now (70) implies $f(\mu_0, \nu) \geq \alpha$ for all $\nu \in N^*$, (71) means $f(\mu, \nu_0) \leq \alpha$ for all $\mu \in M^*$. Hence for any real number α, either there exists a

$\mu_o \in M^*$ such that

$$\operatorname*{Min}_{\nu \in N^*} f(\mu_o, \nu) \geq \alpha,$$

or there exists a $\nu_o \in N^*$ such that

$$\operatorname*{Max}_{\mu \in M^*} f(\mu, \nu_o) \leq \alpha.$$

In other words, any real number α satisfies at least one of the two inequalities

$$\operatorname*{Max}_{\mu \in M^*} \operatorname*{Min}_{\nu \in N^*} f(\mu, \nu) \geq \alpha,$$

$$\operatorname*{Min}_{\nu \in N^*} \operatorname*{Max}_{\mu \in M^*} f(\mu, \nu) \leq \alpha.$$

Hence

$$\operatorname*{Max}_{\mu \in M^*} \operatorname*{Min}_{\nu \in N^*} f(\mu, \nu) \geq \operatorname*{Min}_{\nu \in N^*} \operatorname*{Max}_{\mu \in M^*} f(\mu, \nu),$$

and therefore (69).

PART IV

LINEAR INEQUALITIES ON A COMPLEX LINEAR SPACE

The previous three parts are concerned with real linear functionals on a real linear space. In this Part IV, we shall study inequalities concerning the absolute values of complex linear functionals on a complex linear space. However all results in this part remain valid, if the complex linear space considered is replaced by a real linear space and if all scalars considered are restricted to be real.

§13. FINITE SYSTEMS ON AN ARBITRARY COMPLEX LINEAR SPACE

In this paragraph, X denotes a complex linear space of arbitrary dimension, finite or infinite. We do not require that norm or topology be defined in X. Let $f_1, f_2, \ldots, f_p$ be linear functionals on X. Let $\alpha_1, \alpha_2, \ldots, \alpha_p$ be complex numbers and $r_1, r_2, \ldots, r_p$ real non-negative numbers. The following theorem gives a necessary and sufficient condition in order that the system of inequalities

$$(72) \qquad \left| f_j(x) - \alpha_j \right| \leq r_j \qquad (1 \leq j \leq p)$$

have a solution $x \in X$.

THEOREM 19. The system (72) is consistent, if and only if, for any p complex numbers $\lambda_j (1 \leq j \leq p)$, the relation

$$\sum_{j=1}^{p} \lambda_j f_j = 0$$

implies

$$\left| \sum_{j=1}^{p} \lambda_j \alpha_j \right| \leq \sum_{j=1}^{p} |\lambda_j| r_j.$$

PROOF. The "only if" part is trivial. In fact, if $x_0 \in X$ is a solution of (72) and if

$$\sum_{j=1}^{p} \lambda_j f_j = 0,$$

then

$$\left| \sum_{j=1}^{p} \lambda_j \alpha_j \right| = \left| \sum_{j=1}^{p} \lambda_j \left(f_j(x_0) - \alpha_j \right) \right| \leq \sum_{j=1}^{p} |\lambda_j| r_j.$$

To prove the "if" part, we assume that (72) is inconsistent and we shall find p complex numbers λ_j such that

$$\sum_{j=1}^{p} \lambda_j f_j = 0$$

and

$$\left| \sum_{j=1}^{p} \lambda_j \alpha_j \right| > \sum_{j=1}^{p} |\lambda_j| r_j.$$

Denote by U^p the unitary p-space. Let M be the linear manifold in U^p formed by all points of the form $(f_1(x) - \alpha_1, f_2(x) - \alpha_2, \ldots, f_p(x) - \alpha_p)$, when x varies in X. Let R denote the set of all points $(z_1, z_2, \ldots, z_p) \in U^p$ such that $|z_j| \leq r_j$ $(1 \leq j \leq p)$. Since (72) is inconsistent, M and R are disjoint. Now we regard the unitary p-space U^p as a Euclidean (2p)-space E^{2p}, in which M is a closed convex set and R is a compact convex set. Applying the separation theorem for convex sets in the real linear space E^{2p}, M and R can be strictly separated by a hyperplane. Thus there exist p complex numbers $\lambda_j (1 \leq j \leq p)$ and a real number c such that

$$\text{Re} \sum_{j=1}^{p} \lambda_j \left[f_j(x) - \alpha_j \right] > c \quad \text{for all} \quad x \in X, \tag{73}$$

$$\text{Re} \sum_{j=1}^{p} \lambda_j z_j < c \quad \text{whenever each} \quad |z_j| \leq r_j. \tag{74}$$

(73) implies

$$\text{Re} \sum_{j=1}^{p} \lambda_j f_j(x) + \left| \sum_{j=1}^{p} \lambda_j \alpha_j \right| > c \quad \text{for all} \quad x \in X.$$

But the real part of the linear functional

$$\sum_{j=1}^{p} \lambda_j f_j$$

cannot remain bounded from below throughout the entire linear space X unless

$$\sum_{j=1}^{p} \lambda_j f_j = 0.$$

Hence we have

$$\sum_{j=1}^{p} \lambda_j f_j = 0$$

and

$$\left| \sum_{j=1}^{p} \lambda_j \alpha_j \right| > c.$$

On the other hand, (74) implies

$$\sum_{j=1}^{p} |\lambda_j| r_j < c,$$

whence

$$\left| \sum_{j=1}^{p} \lambda_j \alpha_j \right| > \sum_{j=1}^{p} |\lambda_j| r_j .$$

In the case when X is a finite dimensional complex linear space, S. N. Černikov [6] has given a consistency condition for system (72), a condition which is expressed in terms of determinants. Černikov's result is based on what we have called the "principle of bounding solutions" (See §2). It is different from Theorem 19 and has a quite complicated form.

COROLLARY 7. The system of strict inequalities

$$(75) \qquad |f_j(x) - \alpha_j| < r_j \qquad (1 \le j \le p)$$

(α_j complex; $r_j > 0$) is consistent, if and only if, for any p complex numbers λ_j, not all zero, the relation

$$\sum_{j=1}^{p} \lambda_j f_j = 0$$

implies

$$\left| \sum_{j=1}^{p} \lambda_j \alpha_j \right| < \sum_{j=1}^{p} |\lambda_j| r_j .$$

PROOF. This can be derived from Theorem 19 by an argument similar to the proof of Theorem 6.

THEOREM 20. Let K denote the set of all solutions of a consistent system (72). Let f be a linear functional on X and α a complex number. Then:

(i) The minimum

$$(76) \qquad \mu = \operatorname{Min} \left\{ |f(x) - \alpha| \;\middle|\; x \in K \right\}$$

always exists.

(ii) If $\mu > 0$, then f is a linear combination of $f_1, f_2, \ldots, f_p$ (with complex coefficients), and μ is equal to the supremum

$$(77) \qquad \sigma = \sup \left\{ \left| \alpha - \sum_{j=1}^{p} \lambda_j \alpha_j \right| - \sum_{j=1}^{p} |\lambda_j| r_j \right\},$$

where the supremum is taken over all p-tuples $\{\lambda_j\}$ of complex numbers satisfying

$$f = \sum_{j=1}^{p} \lambda_j f_j .$$

(iii) Conversely, if f is a linear combination of $f_1, f_2, \ldots, f_p$ and if the supremum $\sigma > 0$, then $\mu > 0$.

(iv) If $\mu > 0$ and if the system (75) of strict inequalities is also consistent (therefore $r_j > 0$), then the supremum σ defined by (77) is a maximum.

PROOF. (i) First let μ denote the infimum of $|f(x) - \alpha|$, when x varies in K. For any $\epsilon > 0$, the system of $p + 1$ inequalities

$$\begin{cases} |f_j(x) - \alpha_j| \leq r_j \\ |f(x) - \alpha| \leq \mu + \epsilon \end{cases} \qquad (1 \leq j \leq p),$$

is consistent. By Theorem 19, for any $p + 1$ complex numbers $\lambda, \lambda_1, \ldots, \lambda_p$, the relation

$$\lambda f + \sum_{j=1}^{p} \lambda_j f_j = 0$$

implies

$$\left| \lambda\alpha + \sum_{j=1}^{p} \lambda_j \alpha_j \right| \leq |\lambda|(\mu + \epsilon) + \sum_{j=1}^{p} |\lambda_j| r_j \quad \text{for all} \quad \epsilon > 0,$$

and therefore also implies

$$\left| \lambda\alpha + \sum_{j=1}^{p} \lambda_j \alpha_j \right| \leq |\lambda| \mu + \sum_{j=1}^{p} |\lambda_j| r_j .$$

Then again by Theorem 19, the system

$$\begin{cases} |f_j(x) - \alpha_j| \leq r_j \\ |f(x) - \alpha| \leq \mu \end{cases} \qquad (1 \leq j \leq p), \tag{78}$$

is consistent. Hence the infimum μ is actually a minimum.

(ii) Assume $\mu > 0$. For any ϵ such that $0 < \epsilon < \mu$, the system

$$\begin{cases} |f_j(x) - \alpha_j| \leq r_j & (1 \leq j \leq p), \\ |f(x) - \alpha| \leq \mu - \epsilon \end{cases}$$

is inconsistent. By Theorem 19, there exist $p + 1$ complex numbers $\lambda, \lambda_1, \ldots, \lambda_p$ (depending on ϵ) such that

$$\lambda f = \sum_{j=1}^{p} \lambda_j f_j$$

and

$$\left| \lambda\alpha - \sum_{j=1}^{p} \lambda_j \alpha_j \right| > |\lambda| (\mu - \epsilon) + \sum_{j=1}^{p} |\lambda_j| r_j.$$

As (78) is consistent, we must have

$$\left| \lambda\alpha - \sum_{j=1}^{p} \lambda_j \alpha_j \right| \leq |\lambda| \mu + \sum_{j=1}^{p} |\lambda_j| r_j.$$

A comparison of the last two inequalities yields $\lambda \neq 0$, so we may assume $\lambda = 1$. This shows that f is a linear combination of $f_1, f_2, \ldots, f_p$ and $\mu = \sigma$.

(iii) Assume now that f is a linear combination of $f_1, f_2, \ldots, f_p$ and that $\sigma > 0$. Then there exist p complex numbers λ_j such that

$$f = \sum_{j=1}^{p} \lambda_j f_j, \quad \left| \alpha - \sum_{j=1}^{p} \lambda_j \alpha_j \right| - \sum_{j=1}^{p} |\lambda_j| r_j > 0.$$

Hence the system

$$\begin{cases} |f_j(x) - \alpha_j| \leq r_j & (1 \leq j \leq p), \\ |f(x) - \alpha| \leq 0 \end{cases}$$

is inconsistent and $\mu > 0$.

(iv) From the definition of μ, the system of $p + 1$ strict inequalities

$$\begin{cases} \left| f_j(x) - \alpha_j \right| < r_j \\ \left| f(x) - \alpha \right| < \mu \end{cases} \qquad (1 \leq j \leq p),$$

is inconsistent. By Corollary 7, there exist $p + 1$ complex numbers $\lambda, \lambda_1, \ldots, \lambda_p$, not all zero, such that

$$\lambda f = \sum_{j=1}^{p} \lambda_j f_j, \qquad \left| \lambda\alpha - \sum_{j=1}^{p} \lambda_j \alpha_j \right| \geq |\lambda| \mu + \sum_{j=1}^{p} \left| \lambda_j \right| r_j.$$

As the system (75) is by hypothesis consistent, we have $\lambda \neq 0$ and therefore we may assume $\lambda = 1$. Then

$$f = \sum_{j=1}^{p} \lambda_j f_j, \qquad \mu \leq \left| \alpha - \sum_{j=1}^{p} \lambda_j \alpha_j \right| - \sum_{j=1}^{p} \left| \lambda_j \right| r_j.$$

Combining this with the fact $\mu = \sigma$ (see (ii)), we infer that the supremum σ is actually a maximum. This completes the proof.

In part (iv) of Theorem 20, the hypothesis that the system (75) of strict inequalities is consistent is essential. This can be seen from the following simple example. Let X be the complex plane. Let f_1, f_2, f be defined by $f_1(z) = f_2(z) = z$, $f(z) = 2z$. Let $\alpha_1 = 1$, $\alpha_2 = -1$ and let α be any complex number which is not real. Let $r_1 = r_2 = 1$. In this case, $\mu = |\alpha| > 0$, but the supremum $\sigma = |\alpha|$ is not a maximum.

§14. THE CASE OF UNITARY n-SPACE OR COMPLEX HILBERT SPACE

We apply now Theorem 20 to the special case when X is either a unitary n-space or a complex Hilbert space. As usual, the inner product of two vectors x, y in such a space will be denoted by (x, y). The following theorem concerning system (80) is analogous to Theorem 14 concerning system (59).

THEOREM 21. Let X be either a unitary n-space U^n or a complex Hilbert space. Let $a_j \in X$, complex numbers α_j and real positive numbers $r_j > 0$ $(1 \leq j \leq p)$ be such that the system of strict inequalities

(79) $$\left|(x,\ a_j) - \alpha_j\right| < r_j \qquad (1 \leq j \leq p)$$

is consistent. Let K denote the set of all solutions $x \in X$ of the system

(80) $$\left|(x,\ a_j) - \alpha_j\right| \leq r_j \qquad (1 \leq j \leq p)$$

and assume

(81) $$\mu = \operatorname{Min}\left\{ \|x\| \;\middle|\; x \in K \right\} > 0.$$

Let x_0 be the unique solution of (80) with minimum norm $\|x_0\| = \mu$. Then an element $x \in X$ can be expressed in the form

(82) $$x = \mu \sum_{j=1}^{p} \lambda_j a_j$$

with complex coefficients λ_j satisfying

(83) $$\left\| \sum_{j=1}^{p} \lambda_j a_j \right\| = 1, \qquad \left| \sum_{j=1}^{p} \lambda_j \bar{\alpha}_j \right| - \sum_{j=1}^{p} |\lambda_j|\, r_j = \mu,$$

if and only if $x = \lambda x_0$ for some complex number λ with $|\lambda| = 1$.

PROOF. We shall need the fact that

(84) $$\operatorname{Min}\left\{ \left|(x,\ x_0)\right| \;\middle|\; x \in K \right\} = \mu^2,$$

which is analogous to (63) in the proof of Theorem 14 and can be established by a similar argument. According to parts (ii) and (iv) of Theorem 20, it follows from (84), (81) and the consistency of (79) that x_0 can be expressed in the form (82) with coefficients λ_j satisfying (83). This property of x_0 is clearly common to all elements x of the form $x = \lambda x_0$ with $|\lambda| = 1$.

Next, assume that an element $x \in X$ can be expressed in the form (82) with coefficients λ_j satisfying (83). We shall prove that $x = \lambda x_0$ for some λ with $|\lambda| = 1$. As $x_0 \in K$, we can write

$$(x_0,\ a_j) = \alpha_j + \rho_j e^{i\theta_j}, \quad \text{where} \quad 0 \leq \rho_j \leq r_j.$$

Multiplying this equation by $\mu\bar{\lambda}_j$ and then summing over $j = 1, 2, \ldots, p$, we get

$$(x_0, x) = \mu \sum_{j=1}^{p} \bar{\lambda}_j \alpha_j + \mu \sum_{j=1}^{p} \bar{\lambda}_j \rho_j e^{i\theta_j}$$

and therefore, in view of the second relation in (83),

$$|(x_0, x)| \geq \mu \left| \sum_{j=1}^{p} \lambda_j \bar{\alpha}_j \right| - \mu \sum_{j=1}^{p} |\lambda_j| r_j = \mu^2.$$

But the first relation in (83) implies $\|x\| = \mu$, so

$$\mu^2 \leq |(x_0, x)| \leq \|x_0\| \cdot \|x\| = \mu^2.$$

Hence $x = \lambda x_0$ for some λ. Since $\|x_0\| = \|x\| = \mu$, we must have $|\lambda| = 1$.

In the theorem just proved, if we only assume the consistency of (80) instead of that of (79), then x_0 need not be expressible in the form (82) with coefficients λ_j satisfying (83), although x_0 is still a linear combination of the a_j's.[8] Let X be the one-dimensional unitary space, i.e., the complex plane. Let $a_1 = a_2 = 1$, $\alpha_1 = i$, $\alpha_2 = 2 + i$ and $r_1 = r_2 = 1$. In this case, $x_0 = 1 + i$, $\mu = \sqrt{2}$. No pair of complex numbers λ_1, λ_2 can satisfy both relations

$$1 + i = \sqrt{2}(\lambda_1 + \lambda_2), \qquad |-\lambda_1 i + \lambda_2(2 - i)| - |\lambda_1| - |\lambda_2| = \sqrt{2}.$$

§15. INFINITE SYSTEMS ON A COMPLEX NORMED LINEAR SPACE

In this paragraph, the system of inequalities considered may be finite or infinite. Results concerning system (85) in this paragraph are analogous to Theorems 12, 13 concerning system (52) in §8.

THEOREM 22. Let X be a complex normed linear space. Let I be an arbitrary set of indices, finite or infinite. For each $\nu \in I$, let $x_\nu \in X$, α_ν be a complex number and $r_\nu \geq 0$. Let $\rho \geq 0$. Then the system of inequalities

---

[8] According to part (ii) of Theorem 20, (84) and $\mu > 0$ imply that x_0 is a linear combination of the a_j's.

(85) $$\left| f(x_\nu) - \alpha_\nu \right| \le r_\nu \qquad (\nu \in I)$$

has a solution $f \in X^*$ with $\|f\| \le \rho$, if and only if

(86) $$\left| \sum_{j=1}^{n} \lambda_j \alpha_{\nu_j} \right| - \sum_{j=1}^{n} |\lambda_j| r_{\nu_j} \le \rho \left\| \sum_{j=1}^{n} \lambda_j x_{\nu_j} \right\|$$

holds for any finite number n of indices $\nu_1, \nu_2, \ldots, \nu_n$ of I and for any n complex numbers $\lambda_1, \lambda_2, \ldots, \lambda_n$.

PROOF. To prove the "only if" part, let $f_0 \in X^*$ be a solution of (85) with $\|f_0\| \le \rho$. Consider any finite number n of indices $\nu_1, \nu_2, \ldots, \nu_n$ of I and any n complex numbers $\lambda_1, \lambda_2, \ldots, \lambda_n$. For each $j = 1, 2, \ldots, n$, write

$$f_0\left(x_{\nu_j}\right) = \alpha_{\nu_j} + \rho_j e^{i\theta_j}, \quad \text{where} \quad 0 \le \rho_j \le r_{\nu_j} .$$

Then

$$\rho \left\| \sum_{j=1}^{n} \lambda_j x_{\nu_j} \right\| \ge \left| \sum_{j=1}^{n} \lambda_j f_0\left(x_{\nu_j}\right) \right| = \left| \sum_{j=1}^{n} \lambda_j \alpha_{\nu_j} + \sum_{j=1}^{n} \lambda_j \rho_j e^{i\theta_j} \right|$$

$$\ge \left| \sum_{j=1}^{n} \lambda_j \alpha_{\nu_j} \right| - \sum_{j=1}^{n} |\lambda_j| \, r_{\nu_j} .$$

Next, assume that the condition stated in the theorem is fulfilled. We shall first prove that, for any finite number n of indices $\nu_1, \nu_2, \ldots, \nu_n$ of I, the finite system

(87) $$\left| f\left(x_{\nu_j}\right) - \alpha_{\nu_j} \right| \le r_{\nu_j} \qquad (1 \le j \le n)$$

has a solution $f \in X^*$ with $\|f\| \le \rho$. Let $S^*_\rho = \{f \in X^* \mid \|f\| \le \rho\}$. Let Q denote the set in the unitary n-space U^n formed by all points of the form

$$\left(\alpha_{\nu_1} - f\left(x_{\nu_1}\right), \alpha_{\nu_2} - f\left(x_{\nu_2}\right), \ldots, \alpha_{\nu_n} - f\left(x_{\nu_n}\right)\right),$$

when f varies in S^*_ρ. Let R denote the set of all points $(z_1, z_2, \ldots, z_n) \in U^n$ for which $|z_j| \le r_{\nu_j}$ $(1 \le j \le n)$. R is obviously compact.

With respect to the w^*-topology of X^* (i.e., the weak topology of X^* induced from X) and the usual topology of U^n, the mapping

$$f \longrightarrow \left(\alpha_{\nu_1} - f\left(x_{\nu_1}\right), \alpha_{\nu_2} - f\left(x_{\nu_2}\right), \ldots, \alpha_{\nu_n} - f\left(x_{\nu_n}\right)\right)$$

from S_ρ^* onto Q is continuous. Since S_ρ^* is compact with respect to the w^*-topology of X^*, the continuous image Q of S_ρ^* is also compact. We regard the unitary n-space U^n as a Euclidean (2n)-space E^{2n}, in which Q and R are two compact convex sets. Now suppose that no $f \in S_\rho^*$ satisfies (87). This means that Q and R are disjoint. Then they can be strictly separated by a hyperplane in the real linear space E^{2n}. Hence there exist n complex numbers λ_j $(1 \leq j \leq n)$ and a real number c such that

$$\operatorname{Re} \sum_{j=1}^{n} \lambda_j \left[\alpha_{\nu_j} - f\left(x_{\nu_j}\right)\right] > c \quad \text{for all} \quad f \in S_\rho^* ,$$

$$\operatorname{Re} \sum_{j=1}^{n} \lambda_j z_j < c \quad \text{whenever each} \quad \left|z_j\right| \leq r_{\nu_j} .$$

The second inequality implies

$$\sum_{j=1}^{n} \left|\lambda_j\right| r_{\nu_j} < c .$$

The first inequality implies

$$\left|\sum_{j=1}^{n} \lambda_j \alpha_{\nu_j}\right| - \operatorname*{Max}_{f \in S_\rho^*} \operatorname{Re} f\left(\sum_{j=1}^{n} \lambda_j x_{\nu_j}\right) \geq c .$$

But[9]

$$\operatorname*{Max}_{f \in S_\rho^*} \operatorname{Re} f\left(\sum_{j=1}^{n} \lambda_j x_{\nu_j}\right) = \rho \left\|\sum_{j=1}^{n} \lambda_j x_{\nu_j}\right\| ,$$

so we have

$$\left|\sum_{j=1}^{n} \lambda_j \alpha_{\nu_j}\right| - \rho \left\|\sum_{j=1}^{n} \lambda_j x_{\nu_j}\right\| > \sum_{j=1}^{n} \left|\lambda_j\right| r_{\nu_j} ,$$

---

9 See [1], p. 55, Theorème 3; [31], p. 146, Theorem 5.

against our hypothesis (86). We have thus proved that every finite subsystem of (85) has a solution $f \in S^*_\rho$. Finally, to derive the existence of a solution f of the entire system (85) with $\|f\| \leq \rho$, we can use the same argument given in the proof of Theorem 12 and based on the compactness (with respect to the w^*-topology) of S^*_ρ.

COROLLARY 8. Let $\{x_\nu\}_{\nu \in I}$ be a family of elements, not all 0, in a complex normed linear space X, and let $\{\alpha_\nu\}_{\nu \in I}$ be a corresponding family of complex numbers, and $\{r_\nu\}_{\nu \in I}$ a family of non-negative real numbers. Let

$$\sigma = \sup \left\{ \left| \sum_{j=1}^{n} \lambda_j \alpha_{\nu_j} \right| - \sum_{j=1}^{n} |\lambda_j| \, r_{\nu_j} \right\}, \tag{88}$$

when $n = 1, 2, 3, \ldots$; $\nu_j \in I$ and complex numbers λ_j vary under the condition

$$\left\| \sum_{j=1}^{n} \lambda_j x_{\nu_j} \right\| = 1. \tag{89}$$

Then the system of inequalities (85) has a solution $f \in X^*$, if and only if σ is finite.

COROLLARY 9. Under the hypothesis of Corollary 8, if the system (85) has a solution $f \in X^*$ and if the zero-functional is not a solution, then the supremum σ defined by (88) is equal to the minimum of the norms of all solutions f of (85).

Corollaries 8 and 9 are derived from Theorem 22 similarly as Theorem 13 is from Theorem 12.

§16. FORMULATION IN TERMS OF LINEAR TRANSFORMATIONS

THEOREM 23. Let X, Y be two complex normed linear spaces of which Y is reflexive.[10] Let A be a continuous linear transformation from X into Y with the property that $A(S_1)$ is closed set in Y, where

[10] A normed linear space X is called <u>reflexive</u>, if the natural imbedding $x \longrightarrow \xi$ from X into its second conjugate space X^{**} defined by $\xi(f) = f(x)$ (for every $f \in X^*$) is onto X^{**}.

$S_1 = \{x \in X \mid \|x\| \leq 1\}$. Let $y_0 \in Y$ and $\delta \geq 0$, $\rho \geq 0$. Then there exists an $x \in X$ satisfying $\|Ax - y_0\| \leq \delta$ and $\|x\| \leq \rho$, if and only if the relation

$$|g(y_0)| \leq \rho\|A^*g\| + \delta\|g\| \tag{90}$$

holds for every $g \in Y^*$.

PROOF. The "only if" part is trivial. In fact, let $x_0 \in X$ be such that $\|Ax_0 - y_0\| \leq \delta$ and $\|x_0\| \leq \rho$. Let $z_0 = Ax_0 - y_0$. Then $\|z_0\| \leq \delta$. For any $g \in Y^*$, we have

$$|g(y_0)| = |g(Ax_0 - z_0)| = |(A^*g)(x_0) - g(z_0)|$$

$$\leq |(A^*g)(x_0)| + |g(z_0)| \leq \rho \|A^*g\| + \delta\|g\|.$$

To prove the "if" part, we shall use the weak topology of the complex normed linear space Y. With respect to its weak topology, Y becomes a locally convex[11] complex topological linear space, which will be denoted by Y_w. By restricting the scalars to the real field, this complex topological linear space Y_w may be regarded as a real topological linear space, which will be denoted by Y_{wr}. (See [3], p. 106.) Let

$$S_\rho = \left\{x \in X \;\middle|\; \|x\| \leq \rho\right\}$$

and

$$T_\delta = \left\{y \in Y \;\middle|\; \|y\| \leq \delta\right\}.$$

According to a classical theorem of S. Mazur [21], every closed convex set in a normed linear space is also weakly closed. Now by hypothesis, the convex set $A(S_\rho)$ is closed in Y, so it is weakly closed in Y. In other words, $A(S_\rho)$ is a closed set in Y_w or Y_{wr}. According to a well-known theorem of Banach-Bourbaki (see [8], p. 130, Théorème 24), the reflexivity of Y means that T_δ (and therefore also $y_0 + T_\delta$) is weakly compact in Y. In other words, $y_0 + T_\delta$ is a compact set in Y_w or Y_{wr}. Now assume that no element $x \in X$ satisfies both $\|Ax - y_0\| \leq \delta$ and $\|x\| \leq \rho$. Then in the locally convex real topological linear space Y_{wr}, the closed convex set $A(S_\rho)$ is disjoint from the compact convex set $y_0 + T_\delta$. It follows ([3], p. 73, Proposition 4) that there exists a (real) continuous linear functional f on Y_{wr} and a real number c such that

[11] A topological linear space is <u>locally convex</u> if the null-element of the linear space has a fundamental system of neighborhoods formed exclusively by convex sets.

$$(91) \qquad f(Ax) < c \quad \text{for} \quad x \in S_\rho ,$$

$$(92) \qquad f(y) > c - f(y_0) \quad \text{for} \quad y \in T_\delta .$$

Define a (complex) linear functional g on Y by

$$g(y) = f(y) - i\, f(iy) \qquad (y \in Y),$$

then clearly g is continuous on Y_w and therefore also continuous on Y, so $g \in Y^*$. (91) may be written

$$\operatorname{Re} g(Ax) < c \quad \text{for} \quad x \in S_\rho .$$

But $x \in S_\rho$ implies $e^{i\theta}x \in S_\rho$ for any real θ, so we must have

$$|(A^*g)(x)| = |g(Ax)| < c \quad \text{for} \quad x \in S_\rho ,$$

whence

$$(93) \qquad \rho \|A^*g\| \leq c .$$

On the other hand, T_δ being compact in Y_{wr}, (92) implies

$$\operatorname{Min}\left\{ f(y) \;\middle|\; y \in T_\delta \right\} > c - f(y_0)$$

or

$$\operatorname{Min}\left\{ \operatorname{Re} g(y) \;\middle|\; y \in T_\delta \right\} > c - \operatorname{Re} g(y_0) \geq c - |g(y_0)| .$$

Again, since $y \in T_\delta$ implies $e^{i\theta}y \in T_\delta$ for any real θ, we have

$$\operatorname{Min}\left\{ \operatorname{Re} g(y) \;\middle|\; y \in T_\delta \right\} = - \operatorname{Max}\left\{ |g(y)| \;\middle|\; y \in T_\delta \right\} = - \delta \|g\| .$$

Therefore

$$- \delta \|g\| > c - |g(y_0)| ,$$

which combined with (93) gives the strict reversed inequality of (90). This completes the proof.

As an illustration, we mention a special case of Theorem 23:

COROLLARY 10. Let $x_j (1 \leq j \leq p)$ be elements in a complex normed linear space X, and $\alpha_j (1 \leq j \leq p)$

complex numbers. Let $\delta \geq 0$, $\rho \geq 0$. Then there exists an $f \in X^*$ satisfying $\|f\| \leq \rho$ and

(94) $$\sum_{j=1}^{p} \left| f(x_j) - \alpha_j \right| \leq \delta,$$

if and only if the inequality

(95) $$\left| \sum_{j=1}^{p} \lambda_j \alpha_j \right| \leq \rho \left\| \sum_{j=1}^{p} \lambda_j x_j \right\| + \delta \operatorname{Max}_{1 \leq j \leq p} |\lambda_j|$$

holds for any p complex numbers λ_j.

PROOF. Let C^p denote the complex p-space in which the norm is defined as the sum of the absolute values of the coordinates. Then in the conjugate space of C^p, the norm is the maximum absolute value of the coordinates. C^p is obviously reflexive. Let α denote the point in C^p with coordinates $\alpha = (\alpha_1, \alpha_2, \ldots, \alpha_p)$. Let A denote the linear transformation from X^* into C^p defined by $Af = (f(x_1), f(x_2), \ldots, f(x_p)) \in C^p$ (for every $f \in X^*$). Then inequality (94) becomes $\|Af - \alpha\| \leq \delta$. With respect to the w^*-topology of X^*, $S_1^* = \{f \in X^* \mid \|f\| \leq 1\}$ is compact and A is continuous. Hence $A(S_1^*)$ is compact and therefore closed. Thus Corollary 10 is merely a special case of Theorem 23.

If X is the complex n-space in which the norm is defined as the maximum absolute value of the coordinates, then the inequality considered in Corollary 10 takes the following form:

(96) $$\begin{cases} \displaystyle\sum_{j=1}^{p} \left| \sum_{k=1}^{n} a_{jk} z_k - \alpha_j \right| \leq \delta, \\ \displaystyle\sum_{k=1}^{n} |z_k| \leq \rho ; \end{cases}$$

where the complex numbers a_{jk}, α_j and the real numbers $\delta \geq 0$, $\rho \geq 0$ are given, and where the unknowns are the complex numbers z_k. A sufficient condition for (96) to have solutions has been given by N. G. de Bruijn and D. van Dantzig ([4], Theorem 3.1).

We shall now apply Theorem 23 to completely continuous linear transformations. A linear transformation A from a normed linear space X into a normed linear space Y is said to be <u>completely continuous</u>, if the closure $\overline{A(S_1)}$ of the image $A(S_1)$ is a compact set in Y, where $S_1 = \{x \in X \mid \|x\| \leq 1\}$. According to a classical result due to F. Riesz ([1], p. 151), if A is a completely continuous linear transformation from a normed linear space X into itself, and if $\lambda \neq 0$ is a complex number, then the linear transformation A_λ defined by $A_\lambda x = Ax - \lambda x$ transforms every bounded closed subset of X into a closed set. By virtue of this fact, the following result follows directly from Theorem 23.

THEOREM 24. Let X be a reflexive complex normed linear space, and let A be a completely continuous linear transformation from X into itself. Let $y_0 \in X$, $\delta \geq 0$, $\rho \geq 0$ and let $\lambda \neq 0$ be a complex number. Then there exists an element $x \in X$ satisfying

$$\|Ax - \lambda x - y_0\| \leq \delta \quad \text{and} \quad \|x\| \leq \rho, \tag{97}$$

if and only if

$$|g(y_0)| - \delta\|g\| \leq \rho\|A^*g - \lambda g\| \tag{98}$$

holds for every $g \in X^*$.

The following two results are variants of Theorems 23 and 24 respectively. In the special case $\delta = 0$, Theorem 24' becomes the well-known Riesz-Schauder's generalization of Fredholm's "alternative theorem" (See [1], p. 160, Théorème 21; [31], p. 340, Theorem 16), except that the reflexivity of the normed linear space is required here.

THEOREM 23'. Let X, Y be two complex normed linear spaces of which Y is reflexive. Let A be a continuous linear transformation from X into Y with the property that the image $A(X)$ is a closed set in Y. Let $y_0 \in Y$ and $\delta \geq 0$. Then there exists an $x \in X$ satisfying $\|Ax - y_0\| \leq \delta$, if and only if every solution $g \in Y^*$ of the equation $A^*g = 0$ satisfies the relation $|g(y_0)| \leq \delta\|g\|$.

THEOREM 24'. Let X be a reflexive complex normed linear space, and let A be a completely continuous linear transformation from X into itself. Let $y_0 \in X$, $\delta \geq 0$ and let $\lambda \neq 0$ be a complex number. Then there exists an $x \in X$ satisfying

$\|Ax - \lambda x - y_0\| \leq \delta$, if and only if every solution $g \in X^*$ of the equation $A^*g = \lambda g$[12] satisfies the relation $|g(y_0)| \leq \delta\|g\|$.

Theorem 23' can be established by a slight modification of the proof of Theorem 23, namely: the closed convex subset $A(S_\rho)$ of Y is now replaced by the closed linear subspace $A(X)$.

Theorem 24' is a special case of Theorem 23'. In fact, according to a theorem of F. Riesz ([1], p. 151), the complete continuity of A implies that $A_\lambda(X)$ is closed.

BIBLIOGRAPHY

[1] BANACH, S., Théorie des Opérations Linéaires, Warszawa, 1932.

[2] BLUMENTHAL, L. M., "Two existence theorems for systems of linear inequalities," Pacific Journ. Math. 2(1952), pp. 523-530.

[3] BOURBAKI, N., Espaces Vectoriels Topologiques (Chap. I, II), Hermann, Paris, 1953.

[4] de BRUIJN, N. G. and van DANTZIG, D., "Inequalities concerning determinants and systems of linear equations," Proc. Kon. Nederl. Akad. Wetensch. Amsterdam, Ser. A, 55(1952), pp. 315-321.

[5] CARVER, W. B., "Systems of linear inequalities," Annals of Math. 23(1921-22), pp. 212-220.

[6] ČERNIKOV, S. N., "A generalization of Kronecker-Capelli's theorem on systems of linear equations," Matem. Sbornik, N.S. 15(57), (1944), pp. 437-448. (Russian, English summary).

[7] ČERNIKOV, S. N., "Systems of linear inequalities," Uspehi Matem. Nauk, N.S. 8, No. 2(54), (1953), pp. 7-73. (Russian).

[8] DIEUDONNÉ, J., "La dualité dans les espaces vectoriels topologiques," Ann. Ecole Normale Sup. 59(1942), pp. 107-139.

[9] FAN, K., "Fixed-point and minimax theorems in locally convex topological linear spaces," Proc. Nat. Acad. Sci. 38(1952), pp. 121-126.

[10] FAN, K., "Minimax theorems," Proc. Nat. Acad. Sci. 39(1953), pp. 42-47.

[11] FARKAS, J., "Über die Theorie der einfachen Ungleichungen," Journ. für die reine u. angewandte Math. 124(1902), pp. 1-27.

[12] FAVARD, J., "Sur les zéros réels des polynômes," Bull. Soc. Math. France 59(1931), pp. 229-255.

[13] FAVARD, J., Les Théorèmes de la Moyenne pour les Polynômes, (Actualités Scient. et Industr., No. 302), Hermann, Paris, 1936.

---

[12] It is a well-known theorem in Riesz's theory of completely continuous linear transformations that the equation $A^*g = \lambda g$ has only a finite number of linearly independent solutions (See [1], p. 152, Théorème 12).

[14] FINSLER, P., "Über das Vorkommen definiter und semidefiniter Formen in Scharen quadratischer Formen," Commentarii Math. Helvetici 9(1937), pp. 188-192.

[15] GADDUM, J. W., "A theorem on convex cones with applications to linear inequalities," Proc. Amer. Math. Soc. 3(1952), pp. 957-960.

[16] GALE, D., KUHN, H. W., and TUCKER, A. W., "Linear programming and the theory of games," Activity Analysis of Production and Allocation, Edited by T. C. Koopmans, John Wiley, New York, 1951; pp. 317-329.

[17] GLICKSBERG, I. L., "A further generalization of the Kakutani fixed point theorem, with application to Nash equilibrium points," Proc. Amer. Math. Soc. 3(1952), pp. 170-174.

[18] HALMOS, P. R., Measure Theory, Van Nostrand, New York, 1950.

[19] HESTENES, M. R., and McSHANE, E. J., "A theorem on quadratic forms and its application in the calculus of variations," Trans. Amer. Math. Soc. 47(1940), pp. 501-512.

[20] HOFFMAN, A. J., "On approximate solutions of systems of linear inequalities," Journ. of Research of Nat. Bureau of Standards 49(1952), pp. 263-265.

[21] MAZUR, S., "Über konvexe Mengen in linearen normierten Räumen," Studia Math. 4(1933), pp. 70-84.

[22] MOTZKIN, T., Beiträge zur Theorie der linearen Ungleichungen, Azriel, Jerusalem, 1936.

[23] von NEUMANN, J., "Zur Theorie der Gesellschaftsspiele," Math. Annalen, 100(1928), pp. 295-320.

[24] von NEUMANN, J., and MORGENSTERN, O., Theory of Games and Economic Behavior, Princeton Univ. Press, Princeton, 1944.

[25] NIKAIDÔ, H., "On von Neumann's minimax theorem," Pacific Journ. Math. 4(1954), pp. 65-72.

[26] ROSENBLOOM, P. C., "Quelques classes de problèmes extremaux," Bull. Soc. Math. France 79(1951), pp. 1-58.

[27] SCHOENBERG, I. J., "Convex domains and linear combinations of continuous functions," Bull. Amer. Math. Soc. 39(1933), pp. 273-280.

[28] STOKES, R. W., "A geometric theory of solution of linear inequalities," Trans. Amer. Math. Soc. 33(1931), pp. 782-805.

[29] VILLE, J., "Sur la théorie générale des jeux où intervient l'habileté des joueurs," Traité du Calcul des Probabilités et de ses Applications, IV, 2, edited by E. Borel and collaborators, Gauthier-Villars, Paris, 1938, pp. 105-113.

[30] WEYL, H., "The elementary theory of convex polyhedra," Contributions to the Theory of Games (Annals of Math. Studies, No. 24), edited by H. W. Kuhn and A. W. Tucker, Princeton Univ. Press, Princeton, 1950; pp. 3-18.

[31] ZAANEN, A. C., Linear Analysis, North-Holland Publishing Co., Amsterdam, 1953.

Ky Fan

University of Notre Dame
and
The American University

INFINITE PROGRAMS*

R. J. Duffin

§1. INTRODUCTION

Linear programming concerns the minimization of a linear function subject to constraints on the variables. These constraints are expressed as inequalities on linear functions [1]. With every such minimization problem it is possible to associate a similar maximization problem termed the dual. There are interesting relationships between the two problems. For example the minimum of the given problem is, in general, equal to the maximum of the dual problem. An analysis of such relationships has been given by Gale, Kuhn, and Tucker [2] for finite linear programs. A program is termed finite if there are a finite number of variables and a finite number of constraints; otherwise, a program is termed infinite.

The present paper is concerned with the duality relationships for infinite linear programs. To illustrate the nature of this problem, an example of an infinite program is now to be described.

Let A_{ij} be an anti-symmetric matrix; that is, $A_{ij} = - A_{ji}$. Suppose it is possible to satisfy the relations

$$\sum_{j=1}^{n} A_{ij}x_j + a_i \geq 0; \quad i = 1, \ldots, n$$

by non-negative x_j. Then if these relations are multiplied by x_i and summed, it is obvious that $\Sigma_1^n a_i x_i \geq 0$. This inequality is best possible; that is, under the conditions specified $\Sigma_1^n a_i x_i = 0$ for some set of x_i. This last statement is not obvious; it is a consequence of the duality theory for finite programs.

An example of an infinite program can be obtained by replacing the

* The preparation of this paper was sponsored by the Office of Ordnance Research, U. S. Army, Contract DA-36-061-ORD-378.

summation signs in the above relations by integral signs. Thus let $A(s, t)$ be a continuous function of the real variables s and t such that $A(s, t) = - A(t, s)$. Suppose it is possible to satisfy the relation

$$\int_0^1 A(s, t)x(t)dt + a(s) \geq 0; \quad 0 \leq s \leq 1$$

by a non-negative function $x(t)$. The functions a and x are assumed to be continuous. It is easy to derive the inequality $\int_0^1 a(s)x(s)ds \geq 0$. The question is whether or not this inequality is best possible. The considerations to follow will show that the above question can be answered in this way: Given an $\epsilon > 0$ there is a non-negative function x such that $\int_0^1 a(s)x(s)ds = 0$ and

$$\int_0^1 A(s, t)x(t)dt + a(s) \geq - \epsilon; \quad 0 \leq s \leq 1.$$

Other examples of this type will be treated at the end of this paper.

It is desirable to formulate such linear programming problems in an abstract fashion so that both the finite dimensional and the infinite dimensional cases are included. The first step in such a formulation is to replace the matrix A_{ij} by a linear transformation of one vector space into another. The notion of inequalities between points in such vector spaces can be introduced by arbitrarily defining a convex cone of "positive" points. In terms of such concepts an abstract formulation proves possible. It is found necessary, however, to modify some of the definitions which were adequate in the finite dimensional case. In particular three different definitions are introduced and employed for the notion of "a consistent system of inequalities." It seems necessary to make such distinctions in the definitions in order to carry over the duality theory to the infinite case.

An abstract formulation of linear programming has been given by L. Hurwicz [3] and D. Bratton [4]. The formulation given here is somewhat similar, but the development is different. References [5] and [6] also contain points of contact with this paper. According to the referee, an independent proof of Example 2, which follows, is given in a report by O. Gross and H. Scarf [9]. The referee also pointed out that the ideas in references [10] and [11] bear a relation to the general problem treated here.

In the proofs to follow, "sequences" are to be replaced by "directed systems" if the space is not metric.

§2. CONSISTENT AND SUB-CONSISTENT PROGRAMS

Let U be a real linear vector space with a locally convex topology. Let U^* be the real linear vector space of continuous linear functionals defined on U. Let (u, u^*) denote the value of the functional $u^* \in U^*$ evaluated at the point $u \in U$. The expression (u, u^*) is a real valued bilinear form relating the spaces U and U^*. (It is not necessary to assign a topology to U^*.)

A cone is a set C with the property that if $c \in C$ then $\rho c \in C$ for all $\rho \geq 0$. A cone is said to be convex if $c_1 \in C$ and $c_2 \in C$ imply $c_1 + c_2 \in C$. (Only cones with vertex at the origin are considered.)

LEMMA 1. Let C be a convex cone of U and let e be an element of U. Then e is in the closure of C if and only if $(e, x) \geq 0$ for each $x \in U^*$ such that $(C, x) \geq 0$.

PROOF. Here $(C, x) \geq 0$ is a notation meaning $(c, x) \geq 0$ for each $c \in C$. If e is in the closure of C there is a sequence $c_n \in C$ such that $e = \lim c_n$; $n = 1, 2, \ldots$. Then $(e, x) = \lim (c_n, x) \geq 0$. If e is not in the closure of C there is an $x_0 \in U^*$ such that $(C, x_0) \geq 0$ and $(e, x_0) < 0$. This is merely a statement of the separation theorem to the effect that a closed convex set and a point not in it can be strictly separated by a closed hyperplane [7].

An arbitrary closed convex cone P is selected in U and is termed the <u>positive cone</u> of U. Let X denote the set of those elements x of U^* such that $(P, x) \geq 0$. Clearly X is a convex cone; it is termed the <u>positive cone</u> of U^*. It is a corollary of Lemma 1 that $e \in P$ if and only if $(e, X) \geq 0$. As a convenient notation the statement $p \in P$ is written $p \geq 0$. Likewise the statement $x \in X$ is written $x \geq 0$.

Let V be another real linear vector space with a locally convex topology. Let V^* be the conjugate space to V. Let Q denote the arbitrary positive cone selected in V and let Y denote the corresponding positive cone of V^*. By $q \geq 0$ is meant $q \in Q$. Likewise $y \geq 0$ means $y \in Y$. The bilinear relationship between the spaces V and V^* is denoted by (v, v^*).

As far as the above definitions go the spaces U and V have similar properties. The same notation is employed for the bilinear form in both cases. This leads to some ambiguity in the considerations to follow; however, this ambiguity can be resolved by noting the context.

A program is a set (A, b, a) where A is a linear transformation of U^* into V, $b \in V$, and $a \in U$. The program is said to be <u>consistent</u> if the following relations can be satisfied

(1) $$x \geq 0, \quad Ax \geq b.$$

In other words there exists an $x \in X$ such that $Ax - b \in Q$. Such an x is said to be <u>feasible</u>. If a program is consistent its <u>value</u> is defined as

(2) $$M = \inf (a, x) \text{ for feasible } x.$$

The program is said to be <u>sub-consistent</u> if there are sequences $x_n \geq 0$ and $q_n \geq 0$ such that

(3) $$\lim (Ax_n - q_n) = b.$$

Such a sequence x_n is said to be a <u>feasible sequence</u>. If a program is sub-consistent its <u>sub-value</u> is defined as

(4) $$m = \inf \underline{\lim}_{n} (a, x_n) \text{ for feasible sequences } x_n.$$

It follows from these definitions that if a program is consistent, it is also sub-consistent, and $M \geq m$. If a program is sub-consistent it is seen that there is a feasible sequence x_n such that $m = \lim (a, x_n)$. It is understood here that m can be plus infinity or minus infinity.

Because of the symmetrical definitions relative to the spaces U and V it follows that (A', b', a') is a program if A' is a transformation of V^* into U, $b' \in U$ and $a' \in V$. The analogs of (1) and (2) are

(5) $$y \geq 0, \quad A'y \geq b'$$

and

(6) $$M' = \inf (a', y) \text{ for } y \text{ satisfying (5).}$$

The sub-value of the program is denoted by m'.

Two programs (A, b, a) and (A', b', a') are said to be <u>dual</u> if $a' = - b$, $b' = - a$, and $A' = - B$. Here A and B are <u>adjoint</u> transformations; that is, the following identity is satisfied

(7) $$(Au^*, v^*) = (Bv^*, u^*).$$

The transformations considered in this paper are all assumed to have adjoints in this sense. It is convenient to rewrite the definitions pertaining to the dual program $(- B, - a, - b)$. Thus the dual program is consistent if

y exists such that

(8) $$y \geq 0, \quad By \leq a.$$

The value of the program is

(9) $$M' = - \sup (b, y) \text{ for feasible } y.$$

The dual program is sub-consistent if there are sequences $y_n \geq 0$ and $p_n \geq 0$ such that

(10) $$\lim (By_n + p_n) = a.$$

The sub-value of the program is

(11) $$m' = - \sup \overline{\lim_n} (b, y_n) \text{ for feasible sequences } y_n.$$

Let the space U_1 be the product space of U and the real line. The points of U_1 are of the form $[u; s]$ where $u \in U$ and s is a real number. The linear continuous functionals on U_1 are of the form $(u, u^*) + ss^*$ where s^* is a real number. Likewise let V_1 denote the space whose points are of the form $[v; t]$ where $v \in V$ and t is real. It is seen that Lemma 1 applies to U_1 and V_1.

THEOREM 1. A program is consistent and has a finite value M if and only if the dual program is sub-consistent and has a finite sub-value m'. Moreover, $M + m' = 0$.

PROOF. Suppose the program (A, b, a) has the finite value M. Then

(12) $$Ax \geq b \text{ and } x \geq 0 \text{ imply } (a, x) \geq M.$$

In addition the following statement is valid:

(13) $$Ax_0 \geq 0 \text{ and } x_0 \geq 0 \text{ imply } (a, x_0) \geq 0.$$

To prove this let x_1 satisfy $Ax_1 \geq b$ and $x_1 \geq 0$. Then let $x_n = x_1 + nx_0$ for $n > 0$. Clearly $Ax_n \geq b$ and $x_n \geq 0$. Then by (12), $n(a, x_0) \geq M - (a, x_1)$ and since n is arbitrary this proves (13).

It is clearly possible to combine (12) and (13) in the following single statement:

(14) $Ax \geq bs, \quad x \geq 0, \quad \text{and} \quad s \geq 0 \quad \text{imply} \quad (a, x) \geq Ms.$

If $s > 0$ this is equivalent to (12) and if $s = 0$ this is equivalent to (13). By use of positive cones (14) can be expressed as a relation between functionals. Thus $Ax \geq bs$ is equivalent to $(Ax - bs, y) \geq 0$ for all $y \geq 0$; $x \geq 0$ is equivalent to $(p, x) \geq 0$ for all $p \geq 0$; and $s \geq 0$ is equivalent to $st \geq 0$ for all $t \geq 0$. Thus (14) is equivalent to

(15)
$$(By + p, x) + \Big[t - (b, y)\Big] s \geq 0 \text{ for all } p \geq 0,$$
$$y \geq 0, \ t \geq 0 \text{ implies } (a, x) - Ms \geq 0.$$

This is seen by taking p and t zero, then y and t zero, and then y and p zero.

Relation (15) is in a form which permits application of Lemma 1. Thus the point $[a; - M]$ in the space U_1 is in the closure of the convex cone $[By + p; t - (b, y)]$ defined by the parameters $p \geq 0$, $y \geq 0$, and $t \geq 0$. Thus there is a sequence of points of this cone given by parameter values (p_n, y_n, t_n) for $n = 1, 2, \ldots$ such that

(16) $$a = \lim By_n + p_n$$

and

(17) $$- M = \lim t_n - (b, y_n).$$

Relation (16) states that the dual program is sub-consistent. Relation (17) shows that $m' + M \leq 0$.

Now let y_n be any feasible sequence and let x satisfy $Ax \geq b$, $x \geq 0$, and $(a, x) = M + \epsilon$ for $\epsilon \geq 0$. Then $(a, x) = \lim (By_n + p_n, x)$ and

(18) $$(By_n + p_n, x) \geq (By_n, x) = (Ax, y_n) \geq (b, y_n).$$

Thus $\overline{\lim} (b, y_n) \leq M + \epsilon$. Since ϵ is arbitrary, this shows that $m' + M \geq 0$. It follows from (17) that $M + m' = 0$, and the proof of the "only if" statement is complete.

Now suppose the dual program has the finite sub-value m'. If the program is not consistent, then clearly

(19) $$Ax \geq bs \text{ and } x \geq 0 \text{ imply } s \leq 0.$$

This relation may be expressed as a relation between functionals by the same procedure employed above. Thus (19) is equivalent to

$$(20)\qquad \begin{aligned} &(By + p, x) - (b, y)s \geq 0 \quad \text{for all} \quad p \geq 0, \\ &y \geq 0 \quad \text{implies} \quad - s \geq 0. \end{aligned}$$

By Lemma 1 it follows that the point $[0; - 1]$ in the space U_1 is in the closure of the convex cone $[By + p; - (b, y)]$ defined by the parameters $p \geq 0$ and $y \geq 0$. Thus there is a sequence of points of this cone given by the parameter values (p_n', y_n') such that

$$(21)\qquad 0 = \lim By_n' + p_n'$$

and

$$(22)\qquad 1 = \lim (b, y_n').$$

By hypothesis if m' denotes the sub-value of the dual program there is a feasible y_n such that $m' = - \lim (b, y_n)$. Let $y_n'' = y_n + y_n'$, then clearly y_n'' is a feasible sequence. It follows from (22) that $- \lim (b, y_n'') = m' - 1$. This is a contradiction because m' is the minimum $- \lim (b, y_n)$ for feasible sequences y_n. The contradiction shows that the program is consistent.

Let y_n be a feasible sequence for the dual program such that $\lim (b, y_n)$ exists. If x is feasible, then

$$(a, x) = \lim (By_n + p_n, x) \geq \lim (By_n, x) \geq \lim (b, y_n).$$

It follows that (a, x) has a lower bound, so the program has a finite value. It is then seen from the first part of the proof that $M + m' = 0$, and the proof is completed.

Given a program (A, b, a) the program $(A, 0, a)$ is termed the <u>homogenized program</u>. Such a homogeneous program is consistent and sub-consistent. The value of a homogeneous program is either 0 or $- \infty$. Likewise, the sub-value is either 0 or $- \infty$. The dual of the program $(A, 0, a)$ is $(- B, - a, 0)$. If the dual is consistent (sub-consistent), its value (sub-value) is obviously zero. The following statements are thereby a consequence of Theorem 1.

COROLLARY 1. The dual of a program is consistent if and only if the homogenized program has the sub-value zero.

COROLLARY 2. The dual of a program is sub-consistent if and only if the homogenized program has the value zero.

To derive the first statement from Theorem 1 it must be noted that the second dual of a program is the program itself.

§3. SUPER-CONSISTENT PROGRAMS

The program (A, b, a) is said to be super-consistent if there is an x such that

$$x \geq 0 \quad \text{and} \quad Ax > b. \tag{23}$$

Here the notation $q > 0$ means that q is an interior point of the cone Q. Of course if Q does not have interior points the definition does not apply. An analogous definition holds for the dual program if P has interior points.

The program (A, b, a) is said to be convergent if it is consistent and has a finite value M and if there is a feasible x such that

$$(a, x) = M. \tag{24}$$

THEOREM 2. A program is convergent if the dual program is super-consistent and has a finite value. The values satisfy $m = M = -M' = -m'$.

PROOF. Let $(-B, -a, -b)$ be a super-consistent program and let M' be its value. There is an x such that

$$Ax \geq b, \quad x \geq 0, \quad \text{and} \quad (a, x) \leq -M'. \tag{25}$$

Otherwise

$$Ax \geq bs, \quad x \geq 0, \quad \text{and} \quad (a, x) \leq -M's \quad \text{imply} \quad s \leq 0. \tag{26}$$

Expressing this relation in terms of functionals as in the proof of the previous theorem gives

$$\begin{gathered} (By + p - at, x) + \left[-M't - (b, y) \right] s \geq 0 \\ \text{for all } p \geq 0,\ y \geq 0,\ t \geq 0 \text{ implies } -s \geq 0. \end{gathered} \tag{27}$$

By Lemma 1 it follows that the point $[0; -1]$ in the space U_1 is in the closure of the convex cone $[By + p - at; - M't - (b, y)]$ defined by the parameters $p \geq 0$, $y \geq 0$, and $t \geq 0$. Thus there is a sequence of points in this cone given by parameter values (p_n, y_n, t_n) such that

$$\lim By_n + p_n - at_n = 0 \tag{28}$$

and

$$1 = \lim (b, y_n) + M't_n. \tag{29}$$

By hypothesis, given an $\epsilon > 0$, there is a $y_1 \geq 0$ such that $By_1 \leq a$ and $-(b, y_1) \leq M' + \epsilon$. Also by hypothesis there is a $y_2 \geq 0$ such that $By_2 < a$. Let $y' = (1 - \delta)y_1 + \delta y_2$, then if δ is a sufficiently small positive number it results that $By' < a$ and $(b, y') \geq - M' - 2\epsilon$. Let $y_n' = y_n + y'$, then $\lim [By_n' + p_n - a(1 + t_n)] < 0$ and $\lim [(b, y_n') + M'(t_n + 1)] \geq 1 - 2\epsilon$. Thus for a sufficiently large n it follows that $By_n' < a(1 + t_n)$ and $(b, y_n') \geq - M'(t_n + 1) + 1 - 3\epsilon$. Choose $\epsilon = 1/4$ and let $y'' = y_n'/(1 + t_n)$. Then $By'' < a$, $y'' \geq 0$, and $(b, y'') \geq - M' + 1/4(1 + t_n) > - M'$. This is impossible by the definition of M'. The contradiction proves (25).

Thus the program (A, b, a) is consistent and $M \leq - M'$. From Theorem 1 we know that (A, b, a) is sub-consistent and $- M' = m$. Since $m \leq M$ it follows that $m = M = - M'$. Also (25) shows that the program is convergent. A further application of Theorem 1 gives $m' = - M$.

THEOREM 3. *The dual program is super-consistent if and only if the homogenized program has the value zero and this value is attained only by the zero vector. (The cone P is assumed to have interior points.)*

PROOF. If p is an interior point of P and x is in X but $x \neq 0$, then $(p, x) > 0$. To prove this, suppose that $(p, x) = 0$. There is a u such that $(u, x) < 0$. Then $p' = p + \epsilon u$ is in P if $\epsilon > 0$ is sufficiently small. Then $(p', x) < 0$, which is a contradiction.

If the dual program is super-consistent, there is a feasible y such that $(a - By, x) > 0$ if $x \geq 0$ and $x \neq 0$. Hence if $Ax \geq 0$ then $(a, x) > 0$. This proves one part.

Now suppose that $Ax \geq 0$ and $x \geq 0$ imply $(a, x) > 0$ or $x = 0$. Since P has an interior, it follows *a fortiori* that the cone $(By + p)$ for $y \geq 0$ and $p \geq 0$ has an interior. If the point a is not in the interior of this cone there is an $x_0 \neq 0$ such that $(By + p, x_0) \geq 0$ and $(a, x_0) \leq 0$. This is by the separation theorem for convex cones with interior points. In particular $(p, x_0) \geq 0$ so $x_0 \geq 0$. Also $(By, x_0) \geq 0$ implies $Ax_0 \geq 0$, hence $(a, x_0) > 0$, a contradiction.

Thus a is in the interior of $(By + p)$. It follows $a - \epsilon p_0$ is in the interior of $(By + p)$ if ϵ is sufficiently small. Take $p_0 > 0$ and $\epsilon > 0$, then $p' = \epsilon p_0 > 0$. There are sequences y_n and p_n such that $a - p' = \lim (By_n + p_n)$. Thus if $u_n = a - p' - By_n - p_n$, then $u_n \longrightarrow 0$. Thus if n is sufficiently large it follows that $p'' = p' + u_n > 0$. Hence $a - By_n = p'' + p_n > 0$ and it follows that the dual program is super-consistent.

A program is said to be <u>self-dual</u> if it is identical with its dual. Thus if (A, b, a) is a self-dual program, $b = - a$, $B = - A$, and U and V are identical.

COROLLARY 3. If a self-dual program $(A, - a, a)$ is consistent, it has a finite value. There is a feasible sequence x_n such that $(a, x_n) = 0$.

PROOF. If $Ax + a \geq 0$, then $(Ax, x) + (a, x) \geq 0$. But $(Ax, x) = (Bx, x) = - (Ax, x)$, so $(Ax, x) = 0$. Thus $\inf (a, x) \geq 0$ and the program is seen to have a finite value $M \geq 0$.

According to Theorem 1 the sub-value is $- M$. Thus there is a feasible sequence x_n' such that $(a, x_n') \longrightarrow - M$. If $M = 0$ there is nothing more to prove. If $M > 0$ there is an n_0 such that $(a, x_n') < 0$ for $n > n_0$. Also there is a feasible x such that $(a, x) > 0$. Let $x_n = \delta_n x_n' + (1 - \delta_n)x$ where δ_n is defined by $\delta_n(a, x_n') + (1 - \delta_n)(a, x) = 0$. Thus $0 < \delta_n < 1$ for $n > n_0$. It is seen that the sequence x_n so defined is feasible and $(a, x_n) = 0$ for $n > n_0$.

COROLLARY 4. If a self-dual program is super-consistent, it is convergent and the value is zero.

PROOF. From Corollary 3 it follows that the value is finite. The proof is then given by Theorem 2.

§4. EXAMPLES OF SELF-DUAL PROGRAMS

In the introductory paragraphs an example of an infinite linear program was described. Two other examples are now to be given.

EXAMPLE 2. Let $A(s, t)$ be a continuous function of the real variables s and t such that

(30) $$A(s, t) = - A(t, s).$$

Suppose there is a continuous function $a(s)$ and a non-decreasing function $x_0(t)$ such that

(31) $$\int_0^1 A(s, t)dx_0(t) + a(s) > 0; \quad 0 \leq s \leq 1.$$

Then there exists a non-decreasing function $x(t)$ such that

(32) $$\int_0^1 A(s, t)dx(t) + a(s) \geq 0; \quad 0 \leq s \leq 1$$

and

(33) $$\int_0^1 a(t)dx(t) = 0.$$

PROOF. The space U is taken to be the space of continuous functions on the interval $(0, 1)$. The norm is the maximum of the absolute value of the function. According to the theorem of F. Riesz, the continuous linear functionals on U are of the form

(34) $$(u, z) = \int_0^1 u(t)dz(t)$$

where $z(t)$ denotes a function of bounded variation. Without loss of generality it may be supposed that $z(0) = 0$ and $2z(t) = z(t + 0) + z(t - 0)$. This normalization makes the space of such functions isomorphic to U^*.

The positive cone P is taken to be the class of non-negative functions of U. If z is a non-decreasing function, it follows from the definition of the Stieltjes integral that $(P, z) \geq 0$. On the other hand, suppose $(P, z) \geq 0$. Let u be a trapezoidal function of unit altitude and such that $u = 1/2$ for $t = a$ and $t = b$ with $a < b$. As the sides of the trapezoid become steeper it is seen that $\int_0^1 u(t)dz(t) \longrightarrow \int_a^b dz(t) = z(b) - z(a)$. Thus $z(b) - z(a) \geq 0$, so z is non-decreasing. It follows that the positive cone X consists of the non-decreasing functions.

Relation (31) can be written $Ax_0 + a > 0$ for $x_0 \geq 0$. It results from (30) and a fundamental property of the Stieltjes integral that $(Ax, y) = - (Ay, x)$. Then (32) and (33) are a consequence of Corollary 4, and the proof is complete.

EXAMPLE 3. Let s and t denote points of the plane. Let $A(s, t)$ and $a(s)$ be continuous functions and

(35) $$A(s, t) = - A(t, s).$$

Let R be a finite region of the plane. Suppose there are continuous non-negative functions $x(t)$ such that

(36) $$\int_R A(s, t)x(t)dt + a(s) > 0 \quad \text{for all} \quad s \in R.$$

Then for this class of functions

(37) $$\inf \int_R a(t)x(t)dt = 0.$$

PROOF. Here dt symbolizes the element of area in the plane. The region R is assumed sufficiently regular so $\int_R\int_R A(s, t)x(t)y(s)dsdt$ can be evaluated in either order. The space U is taken to be the space of continuous functions defined on R. The norm is the maximum of the absolute value of the function. The positive cone P is taken to be the class of non-negative functions.

LEMMA 2. Let (u, z) be a continuous linear functional defined on the space U of continuous functions. Then there is a sequence of continuous functions $z_n(t)$ such that

(38) $$(u, z) = \lim \int_R u(t)z_n(t)dt$$

and

(39) $$\overline{\lim} \int_R |z_n(t)|dt < \infty.$$

If (u, z) is in the positive cone of functionals, the functions $z_n(t)$ can be taken to be non-negative.

PROOF. This lemma is due essentially to Hadamard [8]; only an outline of the proof will be given here. There exists a sequence of continuous positive functions $\delta_n(s, t)$ such that

(40) $$u(s) = \lim \int_R \delta_n(s, t)u(t)dt.$$

(Such a sequence δ_n can be selected in many ways.) Thus if $z \in U^*$

(41) $$(u, z) = \lim \int_R (\delta_n, z)u(t)dt.$$

Writing $z_n(t) = (\delta_n, z)$ yields (38). If $z \in X$, the positive cone, then $(\delta_n, z) \geq 0$ because δ_n is a positive function.

A transformation A of U^* into U may be defined by

(42) $$Az = \lim \int_R A(s, t)z_n(t)dt$$

where z_n is the sequence of Lemma 2. The convergence in (42) is uniform with respect to s. It then follows from (35) that $(Ax, y) = -(Ay, x)$. Relation (36) may now be written in the form $Ax + a > 0$ for $x \in X$. Corollary 4 applies, so there is a $y \in X$ such that $Ay + a \geq 0$ and $(a, y) = 0$. If x and y satisfy these last relations, let $z = (1 - \delta)y + \delta x$; $0 < \delta < 1$. Then $Az + a > 0$ and (a, z) can be made small by choosing δ small. It follows from Lemma 2 that $\int_R A(s, t)z_n(t)dt + a(s) > 0$ for n sufficiently large. Likewise $\int_R a(t)z_n(t)dt$ is "small". This completes the proof of Example 3.

Example 3 is stated for a plane region; however, the same argument applies to any number of dimensions. In particular it is valid for a one-dimensional region. In the latter case it can be used to prove the first example, given in the introduction. Thus let x be a non-negative function which satisfies $\int_0^1 A(s, t)x(t)dt + a \geq 0$. Then $\int_0^1 a(s)x(s)ds \geq 0$. If $\epsilon > 0$ is given, let $a' = a + \epsilon$. By Example 3 there is a sequence x_n such that $\int_0^1 Ax_n dt + a' > 0$ and $\int_0^1 a'x_n ds \longrightarrow 0$. If $\int_0^1 x_n ds \longrightarrow 0$, the problem is seen to be trivial; otherwise $\int_0^1 ax_n ds < 0$ for sufficiently large n. For such a value of n let $y = \delta x + (1 - \delta)x_n$ then $\int_0^1 ayds = 0$ for some value of δ in the range $0 < \delta \leq 1$. Moreover, $\int_0^1 Aydt + a \geq -\epsilon$, so this proves the statement made in the introduction.

Similar examples, but not of the self-dual type, can be devised by omitting the assumption that $A(s, t) = -A(t, s)$. These more general examples can be treated by essentially the same methods employed for the self-dual examples considered above.

BIBLIOGRAPHY

[1] CHARNES, A., COOPER, W. W., and HENDERSON, A., "An Introduction to Linear Programming," John Wiley, New York, 1953.

[2] GALE, D., KUHN, H. W., and TUCKER, A. W., "Linear programming and the theory of games" in "Activity Analysis of Production and Allocation," edited by T. C. Koopmans, John Wiley, New York, 1951, pp. 317-329.

[3] HURWICZ, L., "The Minkowski-Farkas lemma for bounded linear transformations in Banach Spaces," Cowles Commission Discussion Papers, Mathematics No. 415, July 16, 1952; Mathematics No. 416, October 17, 1952; and Economics No. 2109.

[4] BRATTON, D., "The duality theorem in linear programming," Cowles Commission Discussion Papers, Mathematics No. 427, January 6, 1955.

[5] ROSENBLOOM, P. C., "Quelques classes de problèmes extrémaux," Bull. Soc. Math. France 79 (1951), pp. 1-58.

[6] FAN, KY, "On systems of linear inequalities," this Study.

[7] KLEE, V. L., Jr., "Convex sets in linear spaces," Duke Math. Jour. 18 (1951), pp. 443-466, 875-883.

[8] HADAMARD, J., "Sur les operations fonctionelles," C. R. Acad. Sc. Paris 136 (1903), pp. 351-354.

[9] GROSS, O., and SCARF, H., "The maximization of an integral subject to constraints," The Rand Corporation, Research Memorandum RM-1504, June 15, 1955.

[10] DANTZIG, G., and WALD, A., "On the fundamental lemma of Neyman and Pearson," Ann. of Math. Stat. 22 (1951), pp. 87-93.

[11] BOHNENBLUST, H. F., and KARLIN, S., "On a theorem of Ville," Contributions to the Theory of Games, I, Princeton University Press, 1950.

R. J. Duffin

Carnegie Institute of Technology

A PRIMAL-DUAL ALGORITHM FOR LINEAR PROGRAMS

G. B. Dantzig
L. R. Ford
D. R. Fulkerson

Kuhn, based on the work of Egerváry, has developed a special routine for solving assignment problems [10], [11], [12]. Paul Dwyer has proposed a similar type of approach for the more general transportation problem [7]. Also, along the same lines, two of the authors [8] have developed, in connection with maximal flow problems in networks, a special algorithm that has been extended to the Hitchcock-Koopmans transportation problem [3], [9].

Experiments indicate that the latter technique is very efficient. Our purpose is to generalize the process to solve the general linear programming problem. As stated here, it becomes a special variant of the simplex process [4], [2], [6], [5], [13], that promises to reduce the number of iterations by doing away with the two-phase process (in Phase I a basic feasible solution is determined which is needed to initiate Phase II in which an optimal basic feasible solution is obtained).

Any feasible solution to the dual system may be used to initiate the proposed method. Associated with the dual solution is a "restricted" primal problem that requires optimization. When accomplished, an improved solution to the dual system can be obtained. This in turn gives rise to a new restricted problem to be optimized. After a finite number of improvements of the dual, an optimal solution is obtained for both the primal and dual systems.

What distinguishes the transportation case from the more general case is that the optimization of the restricted primal problem can be accomplished without the use of the simplex process, whereas its generalization appears to require it. Thus it might seem that we are proposing a new algorithm to replace the ordinary simplex algorithm when, in fact, imbedded within it, is the simplex algorithm itself.

Actually, the entire process, as we view it, may be considered to be a way of starting with an infeasible basic solution to a linear programming problem and using a feasible solution to the dual if available (or of a pseudo-dual solution if not available) to decrease the infeasibility of the primal in such a manner that when a feasible basic solution is obtained, it will be optimal.

§1. THE PRIMAL AND DUAL PROBLEMS

We take the primal problem in the following form: determine values of $x_1, \ldots, x_n, \bar{z}$ which minimize $\bar{z}$ subject to

$$c_1x_1 + c_2x_2 + \cdots + c_nx_n = \bar{z} \tag{1}$$

$$\begin{aligned} a_{11}x_1 + a_{12}x_2 + \cdots + a_{1n}x_n &= b_1 \\ \cdots \quad \cdots \quad \cdots \quad &\cdots \\ a_{m1}x_1 + a_{m2}x_2 + \cdots + a_{mn}x_n &= b_m \end{aligned} \tag{2}$$

$$x_j \geq 0 \qquad (j = 1, \ldots, n), \tag{3}$$

where a_{ij}, c_j, and $b_i \geq 0$ are given constants. There is no loss in generality in assuming $b_i \geq 0$ since the signs of all terms in an equation can be changed if necessary.

The dual problem is to find $\pi_1, \ldots, \pi_m, \underline{z}$ which maximize $\underline{z}$ subject to

$$b_1\pi_1 + b_2\pi_2 + \cdots + b_m\pi_m = \underline{z} \tag{4}$$

$$\begin{aligned} a_{11}\pi_1 + a_{21}\pi_2 + \cdots + a_{m1}\pi_m &\leq c_1 \\ \cdots \quad \cdots \quad \cdots \quad &\cdots \\ a_{1n}\pi_1 + a_{2n}\pi_2 + \cdots + a_{mn}\pi_m &\leq c_n. \end{aligned} \tag{5}$$

It is easy to show that always $\underline{z} \leq \bar{z}$ for any solutions to (2), (3) and to (5). The fundamental duality theorem states that if feasible solutions to the primal exist and $\bar{z}$ has a finite lower bound, then optimal solutions for both primal and dual exist; moreover, any optimal solutions for the primal and dual systems have the property that $\underline{z} = \bar{z}$. Our purpose is to construct a pair of such solutions.

We shall need a feasible solution to the dual to start the algorithm. In many problems, such a solution is readily available. For example, if all $c_j \geq 0$, then obviously $\pi_i = 0$ satisfy (5). In general, however, a dual solution is not available. To get around this, we use a device due to Beale [1] and others, and append to system (2) the relations,

(6) $$x_0 + x_1 + \cdots + x_n = b_0 \quad \text{and} \quad x_0 \geq 0,$$

where b_0 is unspecified but is thought of as arbitrarily large. (More precisely, for each cycle k of the algorithm a value b_0^k can be specified such that any $b_0 \geq b_0^k$ will do. Since there will be only a finite number of cycles, we may take $b_0 \geq \max_k b_0^k$.)

The problem (1), (2), (3), (6) will be called the modified primal. The modified dual corresponding to it, is to determine $\pi_0, \pi_1, \ldots, \pi_m, \underline{y}$ which maximize $\underline{y}$ subject to

(7) $$b_0\pi_0 + b_1\pi_1 + \cdots + b_m\pi_m = \underline{y}$$

(8) $$\begin{aligned} \pi_0 \qquad\qquad\qquad\qquad &\leq 0 \\ \pi_0 + a_{11}\pi_1 + \cdots + a_{m1}\pi_m &\leq c_1 \\ \cdots \qquad \cdots \qquad \cdots & \\ \pi_0 + a_{1n}\pi_1 + \cdots + a_{mn}\pi_m &\leq c_n. \end{aligned}$$

Notice that a feasible solution is now readily available; indeed $\pi_0 = \min (0, c_j)$, $\pi_i = 0$ for $i > 0$, solves (8).

§2. THE EXTENDED PRIMAL PROBLEM

We next consider an extended primal problem with non-negative error (artificial) variables $\epsilon_0, \epsilon_1, \ldots, \epsilon_m$, where the objective (as in Phase I of the simplex process) is to minimize the sum of the errors. Thus we are to determine values of $x_0, x_1, \ldots, x_n, \epsilon_0, \epsilon_1, \ldots, \epsilon_m, \bar{w}$ which minimize $\bar{w}$ subject to

(9) $$\epsilon_0 + \epsilon_1 + \cdots + \epsilon_m = \bar{w}$$

(10) $$\begin{aligned} x_0 + x_1 + x_2 + \cdots + x_n + \epsilon_0 &= b_0 \\ a_{11}x_1 + a_{12}x_2 + \cdots + a_{1n}x_n + \epsilon_1 &= b_1 \\ \cdots \qquad \cdots \qquad \cdots \qquad \cdots & \\ a_{m1}x_1 + a_{m2}x_2 + \cdots + a_{mn}x_n + \epsilon_m &= b_m \end{aligned}$$

(11) $$x_j \geq 0, \quad \epsilon_i \geq 0 \qquad (j = 0, \ldots, n;\ i = 0, \ldots, m).$$

THEOREM 1. Any solutions to (7), (8) and to (9), (10), (11) with the properties $\bar{w} = 0$, $\pi_0 = 0$, and $x_j = 0$ if the jth relation of (8) is strict inequality, are optimal solutions to the original primal and dual problems.

PROOF. Since $\bar{w} = \epsilon_0 + \cdots + \epsilon_m = 0$ and $\epsilon_i \geq 0$, we have all $\epsilon_i = 0$. Thus, because $\pi_0 = 0$, the values of $x_1, \ldots, x_n; \pi_1, \ldots, \pi_m$ satisfy the original primal and dual constraints.

Multiplying the ith relation of (10) by π_i and summing gives

$$(12) \qquad x_1 \sum_{i=1}^{m} a_{i1}\pi_i + x_2 \sum_{i=1}^{m} a_{i2}\pi_i + \cdots + x_n \sum_{i=1}^{m} a_{im}\pi_i = \sum_{i=1}^{m} b_i\pi_i .$$

By assumption, all terms in (12) corresponding to

$$\sum_{i=1}^{m} a_{ij}\pi_i < c_j$$

have $x_j = 0$; hence, for all j, the jth term is the same as c_jx_j, i.e., (12) reduces to

$$(13) \qquad \sum_{j=1}^{n} c_jx_j = \sum_{i=1}^{m} b_i\pi_i \quad \text{or} \quad \bar{z} = \underline{z},$$

thus establishing that $x_1, \ldots, x_n$ and $\pi_1, \ldots, \pi_m$ are optimal solutions to the original primal and dual.

§3. THE ALGORITHM

Let $\pi_0, \pi_1, \ldots, \pi_m$ be any set of numbers satisfying (8). We associate with this selected solution of the modified dual a restricted primal problem, which is identical with the extended primal problem (9), (10), (11) except that certain x_j variables are "dropped" from the equations. To be more precise, the restricted primal consists in solving the extended primal under the added conditions that

$$(14) \qquad x_j = 0 \quad \text{if} \quad \delta_j < 0$$

where

(14.1)
$$\delta_0 = \pi_0$$
$$\delta_j = \left(\pi_0 + \sum a_{ij}\pi_i\right) - c_j \qquad (j = 1, 2, \ldots, n).$$

From (8) it will be noted that $\delta_j \leq 0$ for all j. Thus if we denote the set of indices where $\delta_j = 0$ by J, the restricted primal is obtained from the extended primal by dropping all variables x_j whose indices j do not belong to J.

The restricted problem is next solved using the revised simplex method [6]. (Since b_0 is unspecified, the values of the variables x_j, ϵ_i will depend linearly on b_0, with the property that for all b_0 sufficiently large, the solution is feasible.) For example, one could use $\epsilon_0, \epsilon_1, \ldots, \epsilon_m$ as an initial set of basic variables and minimize $\bar{w}$ under the assumption (14). (On succeeding restricted primal problems, the prior minimal solution may be taken as a starting solution, as we shall see.) The revised simplex algorithm provides, at the minimum of the restricted problem, a set of x_j, ϵ_i and $\sigma_0, \sigma_1, \ldots, \sigma_m$, optimal solutions to the restricted problem and its dual, such that, if quantities ρ_j are defined by

$$(15) \qquad \rho_0 = \sigma_0 \quad \text{and} \quad \rho_j = \sigma_0 + \sum_{i=1}^{m} a_{ij}\sigma_i \qquad (j = 1, 2, \ldots, n),$$

then

(16)
$$\sigma_i \leq 1 \quad (i = 0, 1, \ldots, m) \quad \text{and} \quad \sigma_i = 1 \quad \text{if} \quad \epsilon_i > 0$$
$$\rho_j \leq 0 \quad \text{for all} \quad j \in J \quad \text{and} \quad \rho_j = 0 \quad \text{if} \quad x_j > 0.$$

It follows that

$$(17) \qquad \pi_i^* = \pi_i + \theta\sigma_i \qquad (i = 0, \ldots, m)$$

satisfy the modified dual system (8) for some range of values $0 < \theta \leq \theta_0$. To see this, denote the new values of δ_j by δ_j^*, so that

$$(18) \qquad \delta_j^* = \delta_j + \theta\rho_j.$$

Now for all $j \in J$, $\delta_j = 0$ and $\rho_j \leq 0$. Thus, for $j \in J$, $\delta_j^* \leq 0$ for any $\theta \geq 0$. For $j \notin J$, $\delta_j < 0$, hence $\delta_j^* \leq 0$ for $0 < \theta \leq \theta_0$, where

$$(19) \qquad \theta_0 = \min_{\rho_j > 0} -\frac{\delta_j}{\rho_j} \quad \underline{\text{or}} \quad \theta_0 = \infty$$

according as there are or are not any $\rho_j > 0$.

Denoting the new value of $\underline{y}$ by $\underline{y}^*$, we have from (7) and (17)

$$\underline{y}^* = \sum_{i=0}^{m} b_i \pi_i^* = \sum_{i=0}^{m} b_i(\pi_i + \theta\sigma_i) = \underline{y} + \theta \sum_{i=0}^{m} b_i\sigma_i. \tag{20}$$

Now by multiplying the ith equation of (10) by σ_i, summing and noting (15) and (16),

$$\sum_{i=0}^{m} b_i\sigma_i = \sum_{j=0}^{n} \rho_j x_j + \sum_{i=0}^{m} \epsilon_i\sigma_i = \sum_{i=0}^{m} \epsilon_i$$

hence by (15) and (16), (20) becomes

$$\underline{y}^* = \underline{y} + \theta \sum_{i=0}^{m} \epsilon_i = \underline{y} + \theta\bar{w}. \tag{21}$$

We may therefore state

THEOREM 2. An optimal solution to the restricted primal with $\bar{w} > 0$ provides a new feasible solution to the modified dual with a strict increase in the maximizing form $\underline{y}$.

If $\bar{w} > 0$ and all $\rho_j \leq 0$ (so that $\theta_0 = \infty$), then $\bar{w}$ is minimal in the extended primal (9), (10), (11), because $\sigma_0, \sigma_1, \ldots, \sigma_m$ are then feasible for the extended dual and

$$\bar{w} = \sum_{i=0}^{n} b_i\sigma_i.$$

Hence in this case there is no solution to the original primal system, and the computation terminates.

Assuming that $\bar{w} > 0$ and some $\rho_j > 0$, we repeat the procedure using the new modified dual solution $\pi_i^* = \pi_i + \theta_0\sigma_i$ and its associated restricted primal. Notice, as was asserted earlier, that we may take the prior minimizing solution for $\bar{w}$ as an initial solution in the new restricted primal, since those j for which $x_j > 0$ have both $\delta_j = 0$ and $\rho_j = 0$, hence $\delta_j^* = 0$.

THEOREM 3. The algorithm terminates in a finite number of steps in one of the following situations:

(I) at some stage $\theta_0 = \infty$; hence there is no feasible solution to the original primal;

(IIa) at some stage $\bar{w} = 0$ and $\pi_0 = 0$; then $x_1, \ldots, x_n; \pi_1, \ldots, \pi_m$ are optimal solutions to the original primal and dual;

(IIb) at some stage $\bar{w} = 0$ and $\pi_0 < 0$; then the original primal form $\bar{z}$ has no lower bound.

PROOF. We suppose that degeneracy is avoided in each restricted primal by using, if necessary, a perturbation of the b_i. This means that when we minimize $\bar{w}$, the set of $x_j > 0$ and $\epsilon_i > 0$ constitute a basic feasible solution. If $\theta_0 = \infty$ at some stage, the computation ends (as we have seen) with the conclusion that no feasible solution to the primal exists. If not, then at each stage there is a $\rho_j > 0$. It follows that x_j may be introduced in place of one of the basic variables, and the non-degeneracy assumption means that $\bar{w}$ will be strictly decreased. Hence the solution of each new restricted primal results in one or more new basic solutions to the extended primal, each with a decrease in $\bar{w}$. Thus no basis can be repeated and the process must terminate in a finite number of steps with a basic solution for which $\bar{w} = 0$.

If $\pi_0 = 0$ when termination occurs, then (see Theorem 1) $x_1, \ldots, x_n; \pi_1, \ldots, \pi_m$ are optimal for the original primal and dual. If, on the other hand, $\pi_0 < 0$, then, since $\underline{y} = \bar{z}$, we see from (7) that there is no lower bound for $\bar{z}$ as $b_0 \longrightarrow +\infty$.

§4. NUMERICAL EXAMPLES

The following examples correspond to the cases of Theorem 3. All variables are non-negative.

EXAMPLE I.

$$\begin{aligned} -x_1 + x_2 - x_3 &= 1 \\ x_1 - x_2 - x_4 &= 1 \\ -x_1 &= \bar{z} \end{aligned}$$

(see Figure 1).

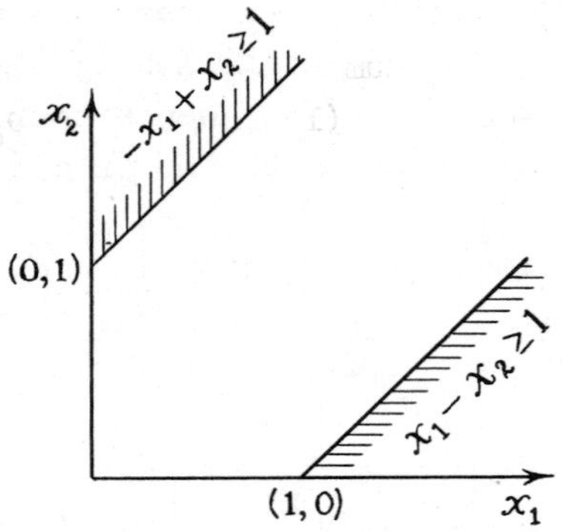

FIGURE 1

The extended primal is

$$\begin{array}{rcl}
x_o + x_1 + x_2 + x_3 + x_4 + \epsilon_o & = & b_o \\
- x_1 + x_2 - x_3 \qquad\qquad + \epsilon_1 & = & 1 \\
x_1 - x_2 \qquad - x_4 \qquad\qquad + \epsilon_2 & = & 1 \\
\epsilon_o + \epsilon_1 + \epsilon_2 & = & \bar{w} \,.
\end{array}$$

To start out, take $\pi_o = -1$, $\pi_1 = \pi_2 = 0$. Then $\delta_o = -1$, $\delta_1 = 0$, $\delta_2 = -1$, $\delta_3 = -1$, $\delta_4 = -1$. The solution of the corresponding restricted primal is $x_1 = 1$, $\epsilon_o = b_o - 1$, $\epsilon_1 = 2$ with multipliers $\sigma_o = 1$, $\sigma_1 = 1$, $\sigma_2 = 0$. Thus $\rho_o = 1$, $\rho_1 = 0$, $\rho_2 = 2$, $\rho_3 = 0$, $\rho_4 = 1$, and consequently $\theta_o = 1/2$. Hence $\pi_o^* = -1/2$, $\pi_1^* = 1/2$, $\pi_2^* = 0$, $\delta_o^* = -1/2$, $\delta_1^* = 0$, $\delta_2^* = 0$, $\delta_3^* = -1$, $\delta_4^* = -1/2$. Using the previous minimal solution $x_1 = 1$, $\epsilon_o = b_o - 1$, $\epsilon_1 = 2$ as a starting point and minimizing $\bar{w}$ for the new restricted primal gives the basic solution

$$x_1^* = \frac{b_o+1}{2}, \qquad x_2^* = \frac{b_o-1}{2} \,,$$

$\epsilon_1^* = 2$, with multipliers $\sigma_o^* = 0$, $\sigma_1^* = 1$, $\sigma_2^* = 1$. Then $\rho_o^* = 0$, $\rho_1^* = 0$, $\rho_2^* = 0$, $\rho_3^* = -1$, $\rho_4^* = -1$, and $\theta_o^* = \infty$. Since all $\rho_i^* \leq 0$, $\bar{w} = 2$ is minimal and no feasible solution exists to I.

In the next two examples, we record merely the extended primal in detached coefficient form together with a record of successive π, δ, σ, ρ and optimizing x, ϵ in the various restricted primals. The problems may be pictured geometrically as in Figure 2, where IIa and IIb denote the normals to the minimizing forms in the direction of decreasing $\bar{z}$.

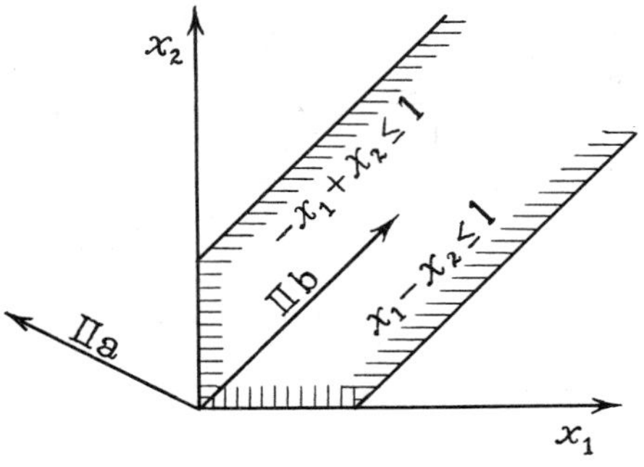

FIGURE 2

EXAMPLE IIa.

x_0	x_1	x_2	x_3	x_4	ϵ_0	ϵ_1	ϵ_2		π_i	σ_i	π_i	σ_i	π_i	σ_i
1	1	1	1	1	1	0	0	$= b_0$	-1	1	$-\frac{1}{2}$	1	0	0
0	-1	1	1	0	0	1	0	= 1	0	0	0	-2	-1	0
0	1	-1	0	1	0	0	1	= 1	0	1	$\frac{1}{2}$	-1	0	0
0	2	-1	0	0				$= \bar{z}$	(0)		(1)		(2)	
					1	1	1	$= \bar{w}$	Iteration					

	x_0	x_1	x_2	x_3	x_4	ϵ_0	ϵ_1	ϵ_2	Iteration
δ_j	-1	-3	0	-1	-1				
x_j, ϵ_i	0	0	1	0	0	b_0-1	0	2	(0)
ρ_j	1	2	0	1	2				
δ_j	$-\frac{1}{2}$	-2	0	$-\frac{1}{2}$	0				
x_j, ϵ_i	0	0	1	0	2	b_0-3	0	0	(1)
ρ_j	1	2	0	-1	0				
δ_j	0	-1	0	-1	0				
x_j, ϵ_i	b_0-3	0	1	0	2	0	0	0	(2)
ρ_j	0	0	0	0	0				

EXAMPLE IIb.

x_0	x_1	x_2	x_3	x_4	ϵ_0	ϵ_1	ϵ_2		π_i	σ_i	π_i	σ_i
1	1	1	1	1	1	0	0	$= b_0$	-1	0	-1	0
0	-1	1	1	0	0	1	0	= 1	0	1	1	0
0	1	-1	0	1	0	0	1	= 1	0	1	1	0
0	-1	-1	0	0				$= \bar{z}$	(0)		(1)	
					1	1	1	$= \bar{w}$	Iteration			

	x_0	x_1	x_2	x_3	x_4	ϵ_0	ϵ_1	ϵ_2	Iteration
δ_j	-1	0	0	-1	-1				
x_j, ϵ_i	0	$\frac{b_0-1}{2}$	$\frac{b_0+1}{2}$	0	0	0	0	2	(0)*
ρ_j	0	0	0	1	1				
δ_j	-1	0	0	0	0				
x_j, ϵ_i	0	$\frac{b_0-3}{2}$	$\frac{b_0-1}{2}$	0	2	0	0	0	(1)
ρ_j	0	0	0	0	0				

BIBLIOGRAPHY

[1] BEALE, E. M. L., "An alternative method for linear programming," Proceedings of the Cambridge Philosophical Society, Vol. 50, Part 4, pp. 513-523, 1954.

[2] CHARNES, A., COOPER, W. W., and HENDERSON, A., An Introduction to Linear Programming, John Wiley and Sons, Inc., New York, 1953.

[3] DANTZIG, GEORGE B., "Application of the simplex method to a transportation problem, "Activity Analysis of Production and Allocation, Cowles Commission for Research in Economics Monograph 13 (1951) Chapter 23, pp. 359-373.

[4] DANTZIG, GEORGE B., "Maximization of a linear function of variables subject to linear inequalities," Activity Analysis of Production and Allocation, Cowles Commission for Research in Economics Monograph 13 (1951) Chapter 21, pp. 339-347.

[5] DANTZIG, GEORGE B., "Notes on linear programming - Part XI, composite simplex dual simplex algorithm," The RAND Corporation, p-516, April 26, 1954.

[6] DANTZIG, GEORGE B., ORDEN, ALEX, and WOLFE, PHILIP, "Method for minimizing a linear form under linear inequality restraints," Pacific Journal of Mathematics, Vol. 5, No. 2, June, 1955.

* Iteration (0) of IIb requires at least two cycles of simplex algorithm since basic variables ϵ_0, ϵ_1 are replaced by x_1, x_2.

[7] DWYER, PAUL S., "The solution of the Hitchcock transportation problem with the method of reduced matrices," Engineering Research Institute Report, University of Michigan, 1955.

[8] FULKERSON, D. R., and FORD, L. R., "A simple algorithm for finding maximal network flows and an application to the Hitchcock problem," The RAND Corporation, P-743, September 26, 1955.

[9] KOOPMANS, T. C., and REITER, STANLEY, "A model of transportation," Activity Analysis of Production and Allocation, Cowles Commission for Research in Economics Monograph 13 (1951) Chapter 14, pp. 222-259.

[10] EGERVÁRY, E., "Matrixok combinatorius tulajdonságairól," Mat. és Fiz. Lapok 38 (1931) pp. 16-28 (translated as "On combinatorial properties of matrices," by H. W. Kuhn, O.N.R. Logistics Project, Department of Mathematics, Princeton University (1953) 11 pages, multilith).

[11] KUHN, H. W., "A combinatorial algorithm for the assignment problem," Issue 11 of Logistics Papers, George Washington University Logistics Research Project.

[12] KUHN, H. W., "The Hungarian Method for the assignment problem," Naval Research Logistics Quarterly, Vol. 2, Nos. 1 and 2 (1955) pp. 83-97.

[13] LEMKE, C. E., "The dual method of solving the linear programming problem," Naval Research Logistics Quarterly, Vol. 1, No. 1, March, 1954.

G. B. Dantzig

L. R. Ford

D. R. Fulkerson

The RAND Corporation

MARGINAL VALUES OF MATRIX GAMES AND LINEAR PROGRAMS*

Harlan D. Mills

We will be concerned with the rate of change of the value (i.e., the "marginal" value) of a matrix game, or the rate of change of the optimum value (the "marginal" optimum value) of the objective function of a linear program, as the entries of the game, or the parameters of the program, are varied. A determination of this rate of change (a one-sided directional derivative) is quite direct in the case of matrix games, and is treated first. This treatment is then extended to apply to dual linear programs. Ordinary matrix and set notations are used throughout.

§1. MATRIX GAMES

Let $G = \|g_{ij}\|$, $i = 1, 2, \ldots, m$, $j = 1, 2, \ldots, n$ (g_{ij} real) be a matrix game, and X, Y be the sets of strategies of players I (row-maximizing), II (column-minimizing), respectively. That is, X, Y are the sets of probability vectors in E_m, E_n,

$$X = \left\{x = (x_i) \mid x_i \geq 0, \sum_i x_i = 1\right\},$$

$$Y = \left\{y = (y_j) \mid y_j \geq 0, \sum_j y_j = 1\right\}.$$

Our interpretation of these entities is that I selects an $x \in X$, II selects a $y \in Y$, each in ignorance of the other's choice, and then, II pays I the amount $xGy = \sum_{i,j} x_i g_{ij} y_j$. The Main Theorem [4] of matrix games establishes a plausible rationale for behavior in this situation.

MAIN THEOREM. Given a matrix G, there exists a number,

$$\Delta(G) = \max_{x \in X} \min_{y \in Y} xGy = \min_{y \in Y} \max_{x \in X} xGy,$$

* This work was supported in part by the Office of Naval Research.

and non-empty sets,

$$X^o(G) = \{x \in X \mid xGy \geq \Delta(G) \quad \text{if} \quad y \in Y\},$$

$$Y^o(G) = \{y \in Y \mid xGy \leq \Delta(G) \quad \text{if} \quad x \in X\}.$$

Here, $\Delta(G)$ is called the <u>value</u> of G, and $X^o(G)$, $Y^o(G)$ are the sets of <u>optimal</u> strategies of players I, II in G. The theorem asserts that each player, from his own point of view, can guarantee himself the value of the game by playing a strategy from his optimal (non-empty) set. We consider $\Delta(G)$ as a function of the entries, g_{ij}, in mn space, and define a rate of change of $\Delta(G)$.

DEFINITION 1. Let H be a matrix the same size as G. Then,

$$\frac{\partial\Delta(G)}{\partial H} = \lim_{\alpha \to 0+} \frac{\Delta(G+\alpha H)-\Delta(G)}{\alpha}$$

is defined to be the marginal value of the matrix game G with respect to H.

For a determination of this marginal value, it will be convenient to recall certain properties of optimal strategy sets. For this purpose, we introduce some limit sets of optimal strategies.

DEFINITION 2. Let G and H be matrices of the same size; then,

$$X^o(G, H) = \left\{x \mid x \text{ is a limit point of a sequence } \{x^k\} \text{ where } x^k \in X^o(G + \alpha^k H) \text{ and } \{\alpha^k\} \longrightarrow 0+\right\},$$

$$Y^o(G, H) = \left\{y \mid y \text{ is a limit point of a sequence } \{y^k\} \text{ where } y^k \in Y^o(G + \alpha^k H) \text{ and } \{\alpha^k\} \longrightarrow 0+\right\}.$$

REMARK 1.[1] $X^o(G, H) \subset X^o(G)$, $Y^o(G, H) \subset Y^o(G)$.

THEOREM 1. The marginal value of the game G with respect to H is the value of the constrained matrix

[1] This statement is contained in the body of the proof to Lemma 6, page 56, [1].

game [2] H where the players are restricted to their sets of optimal strategies in the game G. That is,

$$\frac{\partial\Delta(G)}{\partial H} = \max_{x\in X^{o}(G)} \min_{y\in Y^{o}(G)} xHy.$$

PROOF.[2] Let

$$x \in X^{o}(G),\ x^{*} \in X^{o}(G + \alpha H),$$

$$y \in Y^{o}(G),\ y^{*} \in Y^{o}(G + \alpha H).$$

Then, for any $\alpha > 0$, we can construct the chains

$$\Delta(G + \alpha H) \geq x(G + \alpha H)y^{*} = xGy^{*} + \alpha xHy^{*} \geq \Delta(G) + \alpha xHy^{*},$$

$$\Delta(G + \alpha H) \leq x^{*}(G + \alpha H)y = x^{*}Gy + \alpha x^{*}Hy \leq \Delta(G) + \alpha x^{*}Hy,$$

which may be rearranged and combined into

$$xHy^{*} \leq \frac{\Delta(G+\alpha H)-\Delta(G)}{\alpha} \leq x^{*}Hy.$$

A particular case of these relations as $\alpha \longrightarrow 0+$ is

(1) $$\max_{x\in X^{o}(G)} \min_{y\in Y^{o}(G,H)} xHy \leq \frac{\partial\Delta(G)}{\partial H} \leq \max_{x\in X^{o}(G,H)} \min_{y\in Y^{o}(G)} xHy.$$

On the other hand, the inclusion relations of Remark 1 give,

(2) $$\max_{x\in X^{o}(G)} \min_{y\in Y^{o}(G,H)} xHy \geq \max_{x\in X^{o}(G)} \min_{y\in Y^{o}(G)} xHy \geq \max_{x\in X^{o}(G,H)} \min_{y\in Y^{o}(G)} xHy.$$

Now, a comparison of (1) and (2) gives the theorem.

COROLLARY. The marginal value of the game G with respect to a single entry is, for $i = 1, 2, \ldots, m$, $j = 1, 2, \ldots, n$:

---

[2] O. Gross furnished a proof for the corollary following this theorem which served as a model for this one; this proof also suggested the generalization from the corollary.

$$\frac{\partial\Delta(G)}{\partial g_{ij^+}} = \left(\max_{x\epsilon X^o(G)} x_i\right)\left(\min_{y\epsilon Y^o(G)} y_j\right),$$

$$\frac{\partial\Delta(G)}{\partial g_{ij^-}} = \left(\min_{x\epsilon X^o(G)} x_i\right)\left(\max_{y\epsilon Y^o(G)} y_j\right).$$

PROOF. Take $h_{ij} = \pm 1$, and all other entries of H zero. Here, $\frac{\partial\Delta(G)}{\partial g_{ij^+}}$, for instance, is the customary use of the partial derivative symbol.

§2. DUAL LINEAR PROGRAMS

Consider the dual linear programs characterized by the matrix $A = \|a_{pq}\|$, $p = 0, 1, \ldots, m$, $q = 0, 1, \ldots, n$, with a distinguished row and column (0 subscript)

Maximum Problem		Minimum Problem	
maximize	$a_{00} + \sum_i x_i a_{i0}$,	minimize	$a_{00} + \sum_j a_{0j} y_j$,
when	$a_{0j} + \sum_i x_i a_{ij} \geq 0$,	when	$a_{i0} + \sum_j a_{ij} y_j \leq 0$,
	$x_i \geq 0$,		$y_j \geq 0$,

where, free or summed, $i = 1, 2, \ldots, m$, $j = 1, 2, \ldots, n$. These programs can be recast into a saddle point problem by an "Equivalence Theorem" which follows.

REMARK 2.[3] Let
$$\phi(x, y, A) = a_{00} + \sum_i x_i a_{i0} + \sum_j a_{0j} y_j + \sum_{i,j} x_i a_{ij} y_j.$$

Then, x^o and y^o are solutions to the maximum and minimum problems, respectively, if, and only if, for all $x \geq 0$, $y \geq 0$,

$$\phi(x, y^o, A) \leq \phi(x^o, y^o, A) \leq \phi(x^o, y, A).$$

This Equivalence Theorem can be recast as a (weaker) paraphrase of the Main Theorem of Matrix Games.

REMARK 3.[4] The dual linear programs characterized by A have

---

[3] Theorem 3, et seq, p. 486, [3].

[4] Lemma 1 and Lemma 2, pp. 482, [3].

solutions (both, or neither) if, and only if, there exists a number $\Phi(A)$, and non-empty sets

$$U^{o}(A) = \{x \geq 0 \mid \phi(x, y, A) \geq \Phi(A) \quad \text{if} \quad y \geq 0\},$$

$$V^{o}(A) = \{y \geq 0 \mid \phi(x, y, A) \leq \Phi(A) \quad \text{if} \quad x \geq 0\}.$$

Furthermore, if these entities exist, $\Phi(A)$ is the (common) optimal value of the objective functions of the dual programs; $U^{o}(A)$ and $V^{o}(A)$ are the sets of solutions to the maximum and minimum problems, respectively. We will call $\Phi(A)$ the value of dual programs A.

Corresponding to the marginal value of a matrix game, we define a marginal value of the dual programs A and introduce certain ideas corresponding to those of optimal sets of strategies of matrix games which were convenient above.

DEFINITION 3. Let H be a matrix the same size as A. Then,

$$\frac{\partial \Phi(A)}{\partial H} = \lim_{\alpha \longrightarrow 0+} \frac{\Phi(A+\alpha H)-\Phi(A)}{\alpha},$$

if it exists, is defined to be the marginal value of the dual programs A with respect to H.

DEFINITION 4.

$$U^{o}(A, H) = \left\{x \mid x \text{ is a limit point of a sequence } \{x^k\} \text{ where } x^k \in U^{o}(A + \alpha^k H) \text{ and } \{\alpha^k\} \longrightarrow 0+\right\},$$

$$V^{o}(A, H) = \left\{y \mid y \text{ is a limit point of a sequence } \{y^k\} \text{ where } y^k \in V^{o}(A + \alpha^k H) \text{ and } \{\alpha^k\} \longrightarrow 0+\right\}.$$

LEMMA 1. If $\Phi(A + \alpha H)$ exists for $0 \leq \alpha <$ some α_0,

$$U^{o}(A, H) \subset U^{o}(A), \quad V^{o}(A, H) \subset V^{o}(A).$$

PROOF. If the condition of the lemma holds, we begin with two contentions. Let $|H| = \max_{i,j} |h_{ij}|$; then we claim we can pick γ, θ such that:

1. $|\Phi(A + \alpha H) - \Phi(A)| \leq |\gamma\alpha H|$,

2. If $x^* \epsilon U^o(A + \alpha H)$, then $\phi(x^*, y, H) \geq \theta$ for all $y \geq V$, where, for some α_1, γ and θ can be chosen independently of α for $0 \leq \alpha \leq \alpha_1 \leq \alpha_o$.

To see the first contention, let

$$x \in U^o(A), \quad x^* \in U^o(A + \alpha H),$$

$$y \in V^o(A), \quad y^* \in V^o(A + \alpha H).$$

Then, we can construct the chains

$$\Phi(A + \alpha H) \geq \phi(x, y^*, A + \alpha H) = \phi(x, y^*, A) + \alpha\phi(x, y^*, H)$$
$$\geq \Phi(A) + \alpha\phi(x, y^*, H),$$

$$\Phi(A + \alpha H) \leq \phi(x^*, y, A + \alpha H) = \phi(x^*, y, A) + \alpha\phi(x^*, y, H)$$
$$\leq \Phi(A) + \alpha\phi(x^*, y, H),$$

which may be rearranged and combined into

$$\alpha\phi(x, y^*, H) \leq \Phi(A + \alpha H) - \Phi(A) \leq \alpha\phi(x^*, y, H).$$

For some $\alpha_1 < \alpha_o$ and each α such that $0 \leq \alpha < \alpha_1$, we can pick vectors $x^* = x^*(\alpha)$, $y^* = y^*(\alpha)$ as above, and so that all of them lie in a bounded set. (If there are infinite rays of solutions, the choice can be made of a solution closest to the origin.) Now, choose γ such that $\gamma \geqq (m + 1)(n + 1) \max [|x||y^*(\alpha)|, |x^*(\alpha)||y|]$ for all α such that $0 \leq \alpha < \alpha_1$, and the contention follows.

The second contention holds because its falsity would deny the existence of $\Phi(A + \alpha H)$, $0 \leq \alpha < \alpha_1$, since $\Phi(A + \alpha H) = \min_{y \geq 0}[\phi(x^*, y, A) + \alpha\phi(x^*, y, H)]$.

Now, take any sequence $\{\alpha^k\} \longrightarrow 0+$, such that $0 \leq \alpha^k < \alpha_1$, and, for each k, select $x^k \in U^o(A + \alpha^k H)$. Then, for each k, and any $y \in V$,

$$\phi(x^k, y, A + \alpha^k H) \geq \Phi(A + \alpha^k H),$$

$$\phi(x^k, y, A) \geq \Phi(A) + \left[\Phi(A + \alpha^k H) - \Phi(A)\right] - \alpha^k\phi(x^k, y, H).$$

The two contentions apply to the last two terms of the right side, and we can write, then,

$$\phi(x^k, y, A) \geq \Phi(A) - \alpha^k(|\gamma H| + |\theta|).$$

Now, if x is a limit point of $\{x^k\}$, then, $x \in U^o(A)$. Thus $U^o(A, H) \subset U^o(A)$; the second statement follows similarly.

THEOREM 2. If $\Phi(A + \alpha H)$ exists for $0 \leq \alpha <$ some α_o,

$$\frac{\partial\Phi(A)}{\partial H} = \max_{x \in U^o(A)} \min_{y \in V^o(A)} \phi(x, y, H).$$

PROOF. We remark that

$$U^o(A, H) \neq \emptyset, \quad V^o(A, H) \neq \emptyset;$$

because while the positive orthant is not compact, we can define $R(\beta) = \{x \mid 0 \leq x_i \leq \beta\}$, $S(\beta) = \{y \mid 0 \leq y_j \leq \beta\}$, and pick β such that $R(\beta) \cap U^o(A + \alpha H) \neq \emptyset$ and $S(\beta) \cap V^o(A + \alpha H) \neq \emptyset$, $0 \leq \alpha < \alpha_1 < \alpha_o$, some α_1. Thus, say, sequences $\{x^k\}$, $x^k \in U^o(A + \alpha^k H)$, $x^k \in R(\beta)$, exist, and since $R(\beta)$ is compact, limit points of these sequences exist.

The proof of Theorem 1 can now be paraphrased exactly, replacing symbols Δ, X, Y by Φ, U, V, and xAy by $\phi(x, y, A)$.

COROLLARY. The marginal value of the dual programs A with respect to a single parameter is as follows, $i = 1, 2, \ldots, m$, $j = 1, 2, \ldots, n$:

$$\frac{\partial\Phi(A)}{\partial a_{io^+}} = \max_{x \in U^o(A)} x_i \qquad \frac{\partial\Phi(A)}{\partial a_{io^-}} = \min_{x \in U^o(A)} x_i$$

$$\frac{\partial\Phi(A)}{\partial a_{0j^+}} = \min_{y \in V^o(A)} y_j \qquad \frac{\partial\Phi(A)}{\partial a_{0j^-}} = \max_{y \in V^o(A)} y_j$$

$$\frac{\partial\Phi(A)}{\partial a_{ij^+}} = \frac{\partial\Phi(A)}{\partial a_{io^+}} \frac{\partial\Phi(A)}{\partial a_{0j^+}} \qquad \frac{\partial\Phi(A)}{\partial a_{ij^-}} = \frac{\partial\Phi(A)}{\partial a_{io^-}} \frac{\partial\Phi(A)}{\partial a_{0j^-}} .$$

PROOF. Set $h_{ij} = \pm 1$, and all other entries of H zero.

THEOREM 3.[5] Let A be a matrix with a distinguished row and column (0 subscripts) which characterizes a pair of dual programs and suppose that $\Phi(A + \alpha H)$

---

[5] Remarks by a referee suggested this development.

exists, $0 \leq \alpha <$ some α_0. Let $\bar{a}_{00} = a_{00} - \Phi(A)$, and $\bar{A}$ be identical to A except that $\bar{a}_{00}$ replaces a_{00}. Let

$$B = \begin{Vmatrix} H & \bar{A} \\ \bar{A} & 0 \end{Vmatrix}$$

(where the first row and column are distinguished in B) and suppose $\Phi(B)$ exists. Then, the marginal value of the dual programs A with respect to H is the value of the dual programs B. That is,

$$\frac{\partial\Phi(A)}{\partial H} = \Phi(B).$$

PROOF. B is $(2m + 2)$ by $(2n + 2)$ and calls for vectors with $(2m + 1)$, $(2n + 1)$ components for the maximum and minimum problem, respectively. Let the maximizing vector be partitioned into an m vector, $x = (x_1, \ldots, x_m)$ and an $(m + 1)$ vector, $u = (u_0, u_1, \ldots, u_m)$; similarly partition the minimizing vector into an n vector y and an $(n + 1)$ vector v. The dual programs defined by B are, then,

maximize $$h_{00} + \sum_i x_i h_{i0} + u_0 \bar{a}_{00} + \sum_i u_i a_{i0}$$

when $$h_{0j} + \sum_i x_i h_{ij} + u_0 a_{0j} + \sum_i u_i a_{ij} \geq 0$$

$$\bar{a}_{00} + \sum_i x_i a_{i0} \geq 0$$

$$a_{0j} + \sum_i x_i a_{ij} \geq 0$$

$$x_i \geq 0$$

$$u_0 \geq 0$$

$$u_i \geq 0,$$

minimize $$h_{00} + \sum_j h_{0j} y_j + \bar{a}_{00} v_0 + \sum_j a_{0j} v_j$$

when
$$h_{io} + \sum_j h_{ij} y_j + a_{io} v_0 + \sum_j a_{ij} v_j \leq 0$$
$$\bar{a}_{00} + \sum_j a_{0j} y_j \leq 0$$
$$a_{io} + \sum_j a_{ij} y_j \leq 0$$
$$y_j \geq 0$$
$$v_0 \geq 0$$
$$v_j \geq 0 .$$

The second, third, and fourth condition of each program simply defines $U^0(A)$, $V^0(A)$, respectively. We wish to show now that the components corresponding to x and y from solutions to B determine a saddle point as required by Theorem 2 for $\phi(x, y, H)$ over $U^0(A)$, $V^0(A)$, and that $\Phi(B)$ is the value of this saddle point.

Let (x^0, u^0), (y^0, v^0) be optimal vectors in the programs, and $x \in U^0(A)$, $y \in V^0(A)$. Then the objective function of the maximizing problem takes the form

$$h_{00} + \sum_i x_i^0 h_{io} = \Phi(B) - u_0^0 \bar{a}_{00} - \sum_i u_i^0 a_{io} . \tag{3}$$

Multiplying the first constraint of the maximizing problem by y · and comparing with the second and third constraints of the minimizing problem, multiplied by u^0, we get

$$\begin{aligned} \sum_j h_{0j} y_j + \sum_{i,j} x_i^0 h_{ij} y_j &\geq -\sum_j u_0^0 a_{0j} y_j - \sum_{i,j} u_i^0 a_{ij} y_j \\ &\geq u_0^0 \bar{a}_{00} + \sum_i u_i^0 a_{io} . \end{aligned} \tag{4}$$

Summing (3) and (4) gives

$$\phi(x^0, y, H) \geq \Phi(B).$$

The transpose of these operations leads to

$$\phi(x, y^0, H) \leq \Phi(B).$$

Hence, $\Phi(B)$ is the value of a saddle point of $\phi(x, y, H)$ over $U^o(A)$, $V^o(A)$, and $U^o(B)$, $V^o(B)$, suitably interpreted, give its sets of optimal strategies.

Whereas the dual linear programs considered here have been presented in a "pure" inequality form, it is well known that duality exists between programs with mixed equality and inequality constraints and arbitrary or non-negative variables. Precisely, in the formulation above, any inequality of one program can be changed to an equality, the restriction of non-negativeness dropped on the corresponding (same free index) variable of the other program, and the corresponding pair of programs will remain dual to each other.

It is a simple matter to verify that, given a mixed presentation (equalities and inequalities, with corresponding restrictions or not of non-negativeness on variables) that the marginal value of such dual programs is of the same form as given above, except that the obviously induced mixed presentation is used. I.e., if an equality is specified in a constraint of A, then this equality holds in the two rows or columns of B induced by identifying the indices of A in B.

§3. OPEN QUESTIONS

The form of the statement of Theorem 3 suggests several questions which, unfortunately, have not been answered. The principal of these is:

1. Is the existence of $\Phi(B)$ necessary and sufficient for the existence of

$$\frac{\partial\Phi(A)}{\partial H} \ ?$$

Other related questions are, assuming $\Phi(A)$ exists:

2. Is the existence of

$$\frac{\partial\Phi(A)}{\partial H}$$

necessary for the existence of $\Phi(A + \alpha H)$, $0 < \alpha <$ some α_0?

3. Is the existence of $\Phi(A + \alpha H)$, $0 < \alpha <$ some α_0 necessary and sufficient for the existence of $\Phi(B)$?

§4. MARGINAL VALUES AND LAGRANGE MULTIPLIERS

The connection between Lagrange multipliers and their generalization and variables of dual linear programs is made in [3]. In [5], Chapter IV, it is shown, in a certain formulation of the theory of cost and production, that a Lagrange multiplier, introduced in an extremal problem, is also a marginal cost of production.

The Corollary to Theorem 2 reinforces these connections. In particular, if a linear program has a unique dual solution, its marginal value with respect to a constant of one of its constraints is the corresponding component of this dual solution, which is also a "generalized" Lagrange multiplier for the program. This connection between marginal values of programs and Lagrange multipliers can be extended to non-linear programs under quite general conditions.

BIBLIOGRAPHY

[1] BOHNENBLUST, H. F., KARLIN, S., and SHAPLEY, L. S., "Solutions of discrete, two-person Games," Annals of Math., Study No. 24, Princeton University Press, 1950.

[2] CHARNES, A., "Constrained games and linear programming," Proceedings of National Academy of Sciences, Vol. 38, No. 7 (July, 1953), pp. 639-641.

[3] KUHN, H. W., TUCKER, A. W., "Non-linear programming," Proceedings of Second Berkeley Symposium on Mathematics, Statistics and Probability, 1951, pp. 481-492.

[4] MORGENSTERN, O., von NEUMANN, J., Theory of Games and Economic Behavior, Princeton University Press, 1947.

[5] SAMUELSON, P. A., Foundations of Economic Analysis, Harvard University Press, 1948.

Harlan D. Mills

General Electric Company
and
Princeton University

DETERMINATENESS OF POLYHEDRAL GAMES*

Philip Wolfe

The following problem, which arose in connection with marginal values of linear programs, has been posed by Harlan Mills: Let A be an n by m matrix, and X, Y be non-empty polyhedral subsets of E_m (the set of all m-component column vectors) and E_n (n-component row vectors) respectively. Let

$$v_1 = \sup_{x \in X} \inf_{y \in Y} yAx, \qquad v_2 = \inf_{y \in Y} \sup_{x \in X} yAx$$

(values $+\infty$, $-\infty$ admitted). Under what conditions does $v_1 = v_2$? (The customary inequality $v_1 \leq v_2$ can be easily shown.)

The definition of the quantities v_1 and v_2 suggests the use here of some terminology from the theory of games (a concise account of which may be found in Part 4 of [3]). We shall call the triple (A, X, Y) a <u>polyhedral game</u>; members of X, Y will be called <u>strategies for player 1, 2</u> respectively; any x_o such that

$$\inf_{y \in Y} yAx_o = v_1$$

will be called an <u>optimal</u> strategy for player 1; similarly for player 2; and (A, X, Y) will be said to have the <u>value</u> V if $V = v_1 = v_2$.

As a special case, if X and Y are chosen to be the sets of probability vectors in their respective spaces, then (A, X, Y) is just an n by m matrix game played with mixed strategies; and if X and Y are further restricted to be the sets of probability vectors lying in polyhedra in their spaces, (A, X, Y) is the 'constrained game' studied by Charnes [1]. Using methods like those of [1], we will find the conditions

---

* This paper was written for the Office of Naval Research Logistics Project in the Department of Mathematics at Princeton University.

under which a polyhedral game has a value in the proof of the

THEOREM. If a polyhedral game has a finite value, then there are optimal strategies for both players. If the game does not have a value, then $v_1 = -\infty$ and $v_2 = +\infty$. There are games having: finite value, value $+\infty$, value $-\infty$, no value.

PROOF. Let the polyhedron $X = \{x \in E_m \mid Bx \leq b\}$, where B is a k by m matrix and b is a k-component column vector. Let likewise $Y = \{y \in E_n \mid yC \geq c\}$, C being n by ℓ and c being 1 by ℓ. The vectors used below are: v, r, s, column vectors with ℓ, m, ℓ, components respectively; u, p, q, row vectors with k, n, k components.

To motivate the sequel, consider that player 1 has chosen the strategy x. Knowing this, player 2 would select a strategy y solving the linear programming problem: $\text{Min } y(Ax)$ subject to $yC \geq c$. Now the dual program to this is: $\text{Max } cv$ subject to $v \geq 0$, $Cv = Ax$ (see eg. [3], Part 3); and if the dual program is feasible, $\text{Min } y(Ax) = \text{Max } cv$. Player 1 can thus obtain at least v_1 by using a strategy x from a solution x, v of the linear program

$$(1) \qquad \text{Max } cv \quad \text{subject to} \quad Bx \leq b, \quad -Ax + Cv = 0, \quad v \geq 0,$$

if one exists. Similar considerations for player 2 lead to his use of y from the solution y, u of the program

$$(2) \qquad \text{Min } ub \quad \text{subject to} \quad yC \geq c, \quad -yA + uB = 0, \quad u \geq 0 .$$

Programs (1) and (2) are themselves dual, and can be so exhibited in the figure below, as in Part 3 of [3]. Nothing, however, is guaranteed

$$\begin{array}{c|cc|c} & x & v \geq 0 & \\ \hline y & -A & C & = 0 \\ u \geq 0 & B & 0 & \leq b \\ \hline & \shortparallel & \text{IV} & \\ & 0 & c & \end{array}$$

regarding the feasibility of these programs. Indeed, the four possible outcomes of the game arise from the four separate cases below.

CASE 1: Both programs are feasible.

The duality theorem for linear programs with mixed constraints [3, Part 3] yields vectors x, v, y, u solving both programs and such that $cv = ub$. Then for any $\bar{x}, \bar{y}$ such that $B\bar{x} \leq b$, $\bar{y}C \geq c$, we have

(3) $$\bar{y}Ax = \bar{y}Cv \geq cv = ub \geq uB\bar{x} = yA\bar{x} ,$$

from which $v_1 \geq cv = ub \geq v_2$ follows, yielding by virtue of $v_1 \leq v_2$ that x, y are optimal strategies, and the game has the value $cv = ub$.

CASE 2: Program (1) is feasible, program (2) is not.

We employ a device due to Dantzig [2, Footnote 2], constructing for the constraints of (2) a 'feasibility program', with which one determines the feasibility of the given linear program by trying to minimize to zero the slack variables (z_1, z_2 here) of the program

(4) $$\begin{gathered} \text{Min } z_1 1^c + z_2 1^c \text{ subject to } yC \geq c, \\ -yA + uB + z_1 I - z_2 I = 0, \quad u \geq 0, \quad z_1 \geq 0, \quad z_2 \geq 0. \end{gathered}$$

(1^c is a column vector having all components 1.) This expanded program is feasible -- we may choose y so that $yC \geq c$, take $u = 0$, and choose z_1, z_2 to satisfy the rest. Since (2) is not feasible, the minimum of (4) is positive, and its dual

(5) $$\begin{gathered} \text{Max } cs \text{ subject to } -Ar + Cs = 0, \quad Br \leq 0, \\ -Ir \leq 1^c, \quad Ir \leq 1^c, \quad s \geq 0 \end{gathered}$$

has a positive solution, i.e., there are r, s so that

(6) $$-Ar + Cs = 0, \quad Br \leq 0, \quad s \geq 0, \quad cs > 0.$$

Now $\bar{y}C \geq c$ implies $\bar{y}Ar = \bar{y}Cs \geq cs > 0$; so that if x, v satisfying the constraints of (1) are chosen,

$$\inf_{\bar{y} \in Y} \bar{y}A(x + \lambda r) \geq \inf_{\bar{y} \in Y} [\bar{y}Cv + \lambda cs] \geq cv + \lambda cs \longrightarrow +\infty$$

as $\lambda \longrightarrow +\infty$; and $(x + \lambda r) \in X$ for $\lambda \geq 0$, since $B(x + \lambda r) = Bx + \lambda Br \leq b$. Thus the value of the game is $+\infty$, since $v_1 = +\infty$ and in any case $v_1 \leq v_2$.

CASE 3: Program (2) is feasible, program (1) is not.

Proceeding as in Case 2, we can obtain p, q such that

(7) $$-pA + qB = 0, \quad pC \geq 0, \quad q \geq 0, \quad qb < 0,$$

and have that if y, u satisfy the constraints of (2), then

$$\sup_{\bar{x} \in X} (y + \mu p)A\bar{x} \leq ub + \mu qb \longrightarrow -\infty$$

as $\mu \longrightarrow +\infty$, with $(y + \mu p) \in Y$, so that the value of the game is $-\infty$.

CASE 4. Both programs are infeasible.

Using r, s and p, q from (6) and (7), we have

$$0 \leq (pC)s = p(Cs) = pAr = (qB)r = q(Br) \leq 0,$$

so that $pAr = 0$. Let $Bx \leq b$, $yC \geq c$. Then for $\lambda, \mu \geq 0$: $(x + \lambda r) \in X$, $(y + \mu p) \in Y$, and $(y + \mu p)A(x + \lambda r) = yAx + \lambda yAr + \mu pAx$. But $yAr = yCs \geq cs > 0$ and $pAx = qBx \leq qb < 0$, so that $(y + \mu p)A(x + \lambda r) \longrightarrow +\infty$ if $\lambda \longrightarrow +\infty$, and $\longrightarrow -\infty$ if $\mu \longrightarrow +\infty$. Thus $v_1 = -\infty$, and $v_2 = +\infty$.

The smallest example that will serve to illustrate Case 4 is:

$$A = \begin{bmatrix} 0 & -1 \\ +1 & 0 \end{bmatrix},$$

with sole constraints $x_2 = 1$, $y_2 = 1$. The other cases can be obtained from this by letting either non-zero entry of A, or both, be zero.

BIBLIOGRAPHY

[1] CHARNES, A., "Constrained games and linear programming," Proc. Nat. Acad. Sci. U.S.A. 38 (1953), pp. 639-641.

[2] DANTZIG, G. B., "Maximization of a linear function of variables subject to linear constraints," Activity Analysis of Production and Allocation, Cowles Commission Monograph No. 13, John Wiley and Sons, New York (1951), pp. 339-347.

[3] GOLDMAN, A. J., and TUCKER, A. W., "Theory of linear programming," this Study.

Philip Wolfe

Princeton University

ON SYSTEMS OF DISTINCT REPRESENTATIVES*

A. J. Hoffman and H. W. Kuhn

Let $\mathcal{S} = \{S_1, \ldots, S_n\}$ be a finite collection of subsets of a given set S. A set $R = \{a_1, \ldots, a_n\}$ of n distinct elements of S, such that $a_j \in S_j$ for $j = 1, \ldots, n$, is called a <u>system of distinct representatives</u> for $\mathcal{S}$ (henceforth abbreviated SDR). A well known theorem of König [1] and P. Hall [2] asserts that an SDR exists if and only if every s of the sets S_j contain at least s distinct elements among them. This theorem has been generalized in several directions. Recent results and a brief guide to the literature are given by Mann and Ryser in [4].

In this paper we shall consider the problem of finding an SDR whose intersection with each set in a given finite partition of S has a cardinality within prescribed lower and upper bounds. If the partition contains the single set S and the prescribed bounds are 0 and n, respectively, our theorem reduces to that of [2]. If the partition contains one element sets, for which the upper and lower bounds are both one, our theorem replaces the sufficient conditions of Theorem 2.4 of [4] by a necessary and sufficient condition. Both of these cases are accessible by a simple inductive argument (see [3]) developed for the first case by Halmos and Vaughan. We have not been able to prove the general result described below other than via the duality theorem of linear programming.

Let $\bar{A}$ denote the cardinality of a set A. By a (finite) partition of a set S, we shall mean a finite collection $\mathcal{T} = \{T_1, \ldots, T_p\}$ of subsets of S such that

$$\bigcup_{k=1}^{p} T_k = S$$

and $T_k \cap T_{k'} = \emptyset$, the void set, for $k \neq k'$. Our result may then be stated:

* The preparation of this paper was supported in part by the Office of Naval Research, and in part by the Office of Scientific Research of the Air Research and Development Command, U. S. A. F.

Let $\mathcal{S} = \{S_1, \ldots, S_n\}$ be a finite collection of subsets of a given set S. Let $0 \leqq c_k \leqq d_k$ be a set of integers associated with a (finite) partition $\mathcal{T} = \{T_k\}$ of S, for $k = 1, \ldots, p$. Then, in order that there exist a subset R of S such that:

(1) R is an SDR for $\mathcal{S}$.

(2) $c_k \leqq \overline{R \cap T_k} \leqq d_k$ for $k = 1, \ldots, p$, it is necessary and sufficient that

(3) $\overline{\left(\bigcup_{j \in A} S_j\right) \cap \left(\bigcup_{k \in B} T_k\right)} \geqq \bar{A} - n + \sum_{k \in B} c_k$

(4) $\overline{\left(\bigcup_{j \in A} S_j\right) \cap \left(\bigcup_{k \notin B} T_k\right)} \geqq \bar{A} - \sum_{k \in B} d_k$

hold for all subsets $A \subset \{1, \ldots, n\}$ and $B \subset \{1, \ldots, p\}$ of the indices.

Since each T_k contains at least c_k representatives, at most $n - \sum_{k \in B} c_k$ representatives lie outside $\bigcup_{k \in B} T_k$. The union $\bigcup_{j \in A} S_j$ contains at least $\bar{A}$ representatives. These statements prove the necessity of (3). In a similar manner, at most $\sum_{k \in B} d_k$ representatives lie in $\bigcup_{k \in B} T_k$ and hence outside $\bigcup_{k \notin B} T_k$. The necessity of (4) follows.

Several obvious remarks simplify the notation for a proof of sufficiency. First, note that we need only consider finite sets S, merely by using enough elements of S to insure the validity of (3) and (4). Then $\bar{T}_k$ is finite for every k. We may also assume that $\bar{T}_k = q$ for all k. This is arranged by setting $q = \max_k \bar{T}_k$ and adding $q - \bar{T}_k$ dummy elements which do not lie in any S_j to those T_k with $0 < \bar{T}_k < q$. The additional elements neither invalidate (3) and (4) nor increase the likelihood that we can satisfy (1) and (2). With these modifications, the elements of S are partitioned into $T_k = \{a_{k1}, \ldots, a_{kq}\}$ for $k = 1, \ldots, p$. The membership of these elements in the sets of $\mathcal{S} = \{S_j\}$ will be recorded in an incidence matrix

$$C = \left(c^j_{k\ell}\right)$$

where $c^j_{k\ell} = 1$ if $a_{k\ell} \in S_j$ and $c^j_{k\ell} = 0$ otherwise, for rows (k, ℓ) with $k = 1, \ldots, p$, and $\ell = 1, \ldots, q$ and columns $j = 1, \ldots, n$. With this preparation, we propose the following linear program:

Maximize

$$(5) \quad \sum_j \sum_k \sum_\ell c^j_{k\ell} x^j_{k\ell},$$

subject to

$$(6) \quad x^j_{k\ell} \geqq 0,$$

$$(7) \quad \sum_j x^j_{k\ell} \leqq 1,$$

$$(8) \quad \sum_k \sum_\ell x^j_{k\ell} \leqq 1,$$

$$(9) \quad c_k \leqq \sum_j \sum_\ell x^j_{k\ell} \leqq d_k,$$

where the free indices $j = 1, \ldots, n$, $k = 1, \ldots, p$, and $\ell = 1, \ldots, q$.

Observe that (8) and the definition of C imply that the maximum is at most n. On the other hand, any R satisfying (1) and (2) will define an $X = (x^j_{k\ell})$ that achieves this maximum by setting $x^j_k = 1$ if $a_{k\ell}$ "represents" S_j and $x^j_{k\ell} = 0$ otherwise. Such an X satisfies (7) because no element $a_{k\ell}$ represents two sets S_j, (8) because every S_j is represented but once, and (9) because the number of representatives from T_k lies between the prescribed bounds. The converse assertion, which will prove the sufficiency of (3) and (4), states that the maximum of the program is n and is achieved by an integral $X = (x^j_{k\ell})$. By (6), (7), and (8), this implies that each $x^j_{k\ell}$ is 0 or 1. If we "represent" S_j by $a_{k\ell}$ whenever $x^j_{k\ell} = 1$, then the set R of representatives so obtained satisfies (1) and (2). Thus, the proof of sufficiency can be completed by the following two lemmas:

LEMMA 1. The extreme points of the polyhedral convex set in npq space defined by inequalities (6) - (9) have all integral coordinates.[1]

LEMMA 2. If (3) and (4) hold, then the maximum for the program is n.

To prove Lemma 2, we formulate the dual (minimum) program which asks:

Minimize

$$(10) \quad \sum_{k,\ell} u_{k\ell} + \sum_j v_j + \sum_k f_k(z_k)$$

[1] The boundedness of the polyhedral convex set insures the existence of extreme points.

subject to

(11) $u_{k\ell} \geqq 0$,

(12) $v_j \geqq 0$,

(13) $u_{k\ell} + v_j + z_k \geqq c^j_{k\ell}$,

and where

(14)
$$f_k(z) = \begin{cases} d_k z & \text{for } z \geqq 0 \\ c_k z & \text{for } z \leqq 0 \end{cases}$$

and the free indices $j = 1, \ldots, n$, $k = 1, \ldots, p$, and $\ell = 1, \ldots, q$.

By the duality theorem of linear programming, Lemma 2 is equivalent to showing:

LEMMA 3. If (3) and (4) hold, then the minimum for the dual program is n.

In proving this, we shall be assisted by the analogue of Lemma 2 for the dual program.

LEMMA 4. The extreme points of the polyhedral convex set in $pq + n + p$ space defined by inequalities (11) - (13) have all integral coordinates.[2]

PROOF of Lemma 3, assuming Lemma 4 and the solvability of the minimum program. Thus, some $u_{k\ell}$, v_j, and z_k minimizing (10) are integral. We first show that it may be assumed that all the z_k are nonnegative. If, on the contrary, some z_k is negative, let r be the positive integer such that $\min_k z_k = - r$ and set

(15)
$$B = \left\{ k \mid z_k = - r \right\}.$$

Further, let

(16)
$$C = \left\{ (k, \ell) \mid k \in B \quad \text{and} \quad u_{k\ell} = 0 \right\}$$

---

[2] The existence of extreme points is obvious. E.g., $u_{k\ell} = v_j = 0$ for all j, k, and ℓ and $z_k = 1$ if $a^j_{k\ell} = 1$ for some j, ℓ and zero otherwise.

and

(17) $$A' = \left\{ j \;\middle|\; c^j_{k\ell} = 1 \quad \text{for some} \quad (k, \ell) \in C \right\}.$$

Denote by A and B' the sets complementary to A' and B, respectively.

Inequalities (13) require $v_j \geqq r + 1$ for $j \in A'$. Further,

(18) $$u_{k\ell} + (r + 1) + z_k > c^j_{k\ell}$$

<u>unless</u> $j \in A'$ <u>and</u> $(k, \ell) \in C$. Recalling that our object is to minimize (10), it follows that

(19) $$v_j = r + 1 \quad \text{for} \quad j \in A'$$

and

(20) $$v_j \leqq r \quad \text{for} \quad j \in A.$$

The borders of the following diagram summarize this information; it represents a matrix of the same size as the incidence matrix M with entries $u_{k\ell} + v_j + z_k$. Thus, conditions (13) demand that this matrix dominate M.

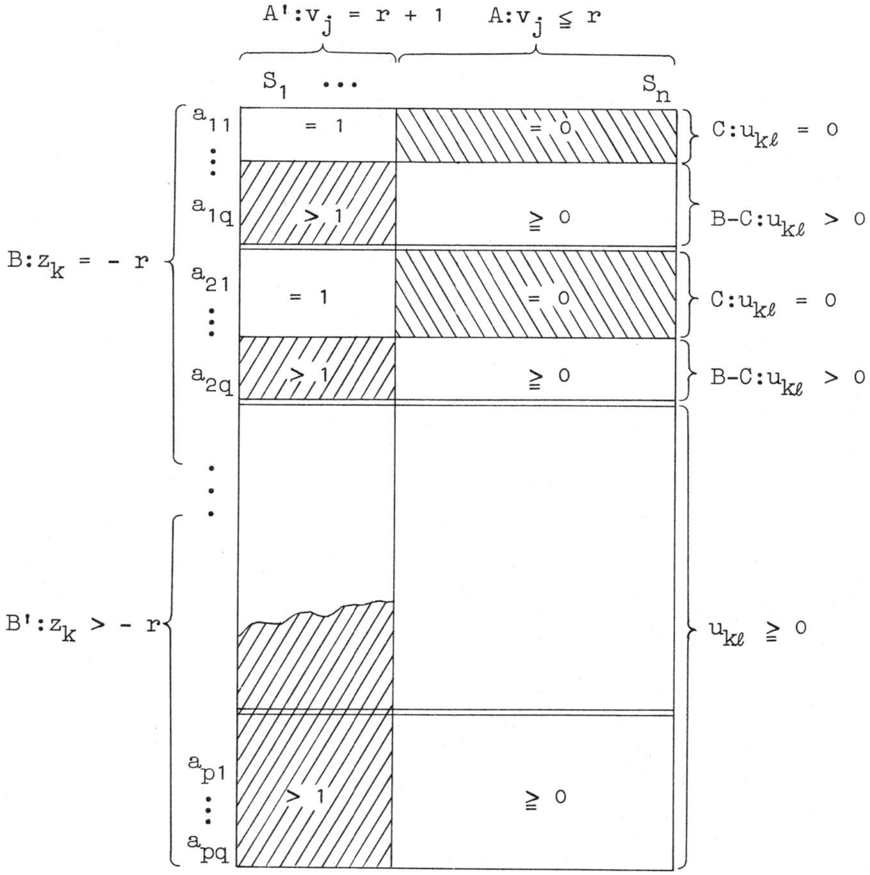

The transformation

$$\begin{aligned} z_k &\longrightarrow z_k + 1 &\quad \text{for} \quad & k \in B \\ u_{k\ell} &\longrightarrow u_{k\ell} - 1 &\quad \text{for} \quad & k \in B,\ (k, \ell) \notin C \\ v_j &\longrightarrow v_j - 1 &\quad \text{for} \quad & j \in A' \end{aligned}$$

leaves the sum $u_{k\ell} + v_j + z_k$ unchanged in the unshaded areas, increases it by one in the areas shaded \\\\\\, and decreases it by one in the areas shaded //////. The size of the sums prior to the transformation are shown in representative blocks; therefore, inequalities (11), (12), and (13) are not violated after the change. To check that (13) is still satisfied, we have only to consider those triples j, k, ℓ for which the transformed left-side of (13) is smaller than it was prior to the transformation. These occur for $j \in A'$, and either $k \notin B$, or $k \in B$ and $(k, \ell) \notin C$. In both of these cases, however, (18) held prior to the transformation, so (13) will hold after it. The total decrease in (10) is

$$(21) \qquad -\sum_{k\in B} c_k + q\bar{B} - \bar{C} + \overline{A'} .$$

To show that (21) is non-negative, remark that

$$(22) \qquad a_{k\ell} \in \left(\bigcup_{j\in A} S_j \right) \cap \left(\bigcup_{k\in B} T_k \right) \quad \text{only if} \quad k \in B \quad \text{and} \quad (k, \ell) \notin C.$$

Therefore

$$(23) \qquad \overline{\left(\bigcup_{j\in A} S_j \right) \cap \left(\bigcup_{k\in B} T_k \right)} \leqq q\bar{B} - \bar{C}$$

and hence, by (3),

$$(24) \qquad \bar{A} - n + \sum_{k\in B} c_k \leqq q\bar{B} - \bar{C} .$$

Noting that $\overline{A'} = n - \bar{A}$, we have shown that the net decrease (21) of (10) is non-negative. This means that we may replace r by $r - 1$, and so on until $z_k \geqq 0$ for $k = 1, \ldots, p$.

Now it is clear by (13) that each $u_{k\ell}$, v_j, and z_k is either 0 or 1. Let

$$A = \left\{ j \mid v_j = 0 \right\} \quad \text{and} \quad B = \left\{ k \mid z_k = 1 \right\} .$$

Then

(25) $$u_{k\ell} = 1 \text{ implies } k \notin B$$

and it is clear that

(26) $$u_{k\ell} = 1 \quad \text{if and only if} \quad a_{k\ell} \in \left(\bigcup_{j\in A} S_j \right) \cap \left(\bigcup_{k\notin B} T_j \right).$$

We now propose to lower all positive u_k and z_k to zero and raise all zero v_j to one. Obviously (11), (12), (13) are still satisfied; we need only show that the net decrease in (10) is non-negative, since its new value is n. Therefore, we need only show that:

(27) $$\overline{\left(\bigcup_{j\in A} S_j \right) \cap \left(\bigcup_{k\notin B} T_j \right)} + \sum_{k\in B} d_k - \bar{A} \geqq 0$$

But this is (4) and Lemma 3 is proved (provided that the minimum program has an integral solution).

PROOF of Lemmas 1 and 4. These lemmas can be proved simultaneously by means of a remark about the extreme solutions of finite systems of linear inequalities. It asserts that such a solution, which must satisfy certain of the inequalities as equations, is the unique solution of this system of equations. (To prove this, let α be an extreme solution of a system of inequalities, and separate them into two sets: $M_1\alpha > a_1$ and $M_2\alpha = a_2$. If $\beta \neq \alpha$ satisfies $M_2\beta = a_2$ then the distinct vectors $\alpha + \epsilon(\alpha - \beta)$ and $\alpha - \epsilon(\alpha - \beta)$ satisfy the equations, do not violate the strict inequalities for small enough $\epsilon > 0$, and have the midpoint α. Therefore, α would not be an extreme solution.) Therefore, any non-zero extreme solution can be obtained by applying Cramer's rule to an appropriate subsystem of inequalities (written as equations). Therefore:

> LEMMA 5. If, in a system of linear inequalities with integral coefficients and constant terms, every non-singular square submatrix of the coefficient matrix has determinant ± 1, then every extreme solution is integral.

It follows from this remark that, to prove Lemma 1, we need only show that every non-singular square submatrix of the matrix of coefficients of (6) - (9) has determinant ± 1. Let N be such a non-singular square submatrix. Since the rows corresponding to (6) contain at most one 1, we need not consider them. If N contains a row of (7) and a row of (9) corresponding to the same k, subtract all such rows of (7) from the corresponding rows of (9), yielding a matrix N_1 such that

(28) $$\det N_1 = \det N;$$

(29) each column of N_1 consists of 0's and at most two 1's;

(30) the rows of N_1 can be partitioned into two sets, A and B such that every column with two 1's has one in A and one in B (the sets in question are the rows corresponding to (8) and the rows corresponding to (7) and (9)).

Now consider a non-singular matrix N of least order, satisfying (29) and (30), and such that $|\det N| > 1$. If every column of N contains two 1's, then (30) implies $\det N = 0$, contrary to the hypothesis. If some column contains but one 1, then expanding the determinant of N by the cofactors of this column implies, by the induction hypothesis, that $|\det N| = 1$. This completes the proof of Lemma 1. Lemma 4 follows by the mere consideration of the transpose of the same matrix. (A general method for showing the integral character of boundary points of certain convex polyhedra, including the cases just considered, is the subject of [5].)

The reader has been led by a tortuous route to the result; we will now retrace our steps, filling minor gaps. Taking $A = \{1, \ldots, n\}$ and $B = \{k\}$ in (3) shows that $c_k \leqq \bar{T}_k$ for $k = 1, \ldots, p$. Hence there is an obvious construction of a feasible vector for the maximum program. The set of feasible vectors is closed and bounded and hence the maximum is achieved at an (integral) extreme point. Therefore the (dual) minimum program has a solution which has been shown to have the value n. Returning to the maximum program, any optimal vector defines an SDR satisfying the given bounds.

BIBLIOGRAPHY

[1] KÖNIG, DÉNES, Theorie der Endlichen und Unendlichen Graphen, Chelsea, New York, 1950, pp. 170-178.

[2] HALL, P., "On representatives of subsets," Jour. Lond. Math. Soc. 10 (1935), pp. 26 30.

[3] HALMOS, PAUL R. and VAUGHAN, HERBERT E., "The marriage problem," Amer. Jour. Math. 72 (1950), pp. 214-215.

[4] MANN, H. B. and RYSER, H. J., "Systems of distinct representatives," Amer. Math. Monthly 60 (1953), pp. 397-401.

[5] HOFFMAN, A. J., and KRUSKAL, J. B., "Integral boundary points of convex polyhedra," this Study.

A. J. Hoffman
H. W. Kuhn

National Bureau of Standards
Bryn Mawr College

DILWORTH'S THEOREM ON PARTIALLY ORDERED SETS

G. B. Dantzig and A. J. Hoffman*

§1. INTRODUCTION

The purpose of this note is to describe a linear programming approach to the finite case of a theorem of Dilworth [2] on the decomposition of a partially ordered set as a union of chains. Dilworth has shown that the smallest number of disjoint chains contained in a partially ordered set such that every element of the set belongs to one of the chains is the largest number of mutually unrelated elements in the partially ordered set. For example, in the partially ordered set represented (in the usual way) by the following diagram, the three circled elements are unrelated, and the double lines indicate the three chains.

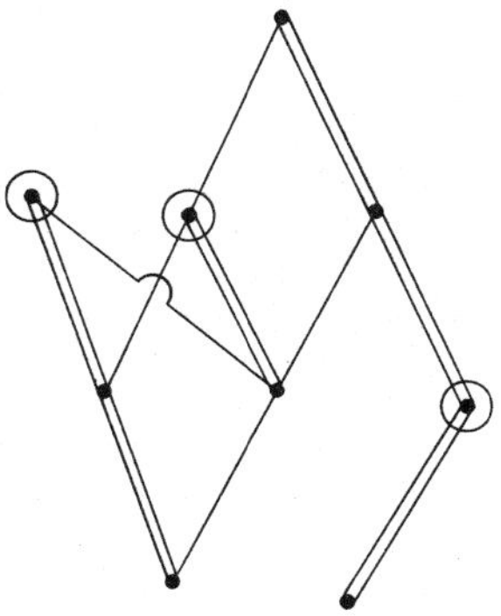

We shall reduce the problem of finding the desired chains to a linear programming problem [1, 4], and show that the problem of finding the mutually unrelated elements is equivalent to the dual of that problem. Our proof does not, however, appear to have any merit of brevity.

---

* The work of this author was supported (in part) by the Office of Scientific Research of the Air Research and Development Command, USAF.

§2. THE PROBLEM

Let P be a finite partially ordered set with elements $1, 2, \ldots, n$ with ordering relation denoted by "$\leqq$". We write $i < j$ ("i precedes j") if $i \leqq j$ and $i \neq j$. A chain is a non-empty subset $i_1, i_2, \ldots, i_k$ of P such that $i_1 < i_2 < \ldots < i_k$. Two elements i, j are unrelated if $i \neq j$, $i \nless j$ and $j \nless i$. A set of disjoint chains is a decomposition of P if each element of P is contained in a chain of the set. Our problem is to find a decomposition with the fewest chains.

We now describe an equivalent linear programming problem. Let X be an $(n+1)$ by $(n+1)$ array $X = (x_{ij})$ satisfying

(1) $$x_{ij} \geqq 0; \qquad i, j = 0, 1, \ldots, n$$

(2) $$\sum_{j=0}^{n} x_{0j} = \sum_{i=0}^{n} x_{i0} = n;$$

(3) $$\sum_{j=0}^{n} x_{ij} = 1; \qquad i = 1, 2, \ldots, n$$

(3') $$\sum_{i=0}^{n} x_{ij} = 1; \qquad j = 1, 2, \ldots, n.$$

It is clear that X may be interpreted as a vector with $(n+1)^2$ components $(x_{00}, x_{01}, \ldots, x_{nn})$. The set $\mathcal{X}$ of all X satisfying (1), (2), (3), (3'), then becomes a closed convex polyhedron in $(n+1)^2$ space.

Let $C = (c_{ij})$ be the $(n+1)$ by $(n+1)$ array:

(4) $$c_{00} = 1;$$

(5) $$c_{0j} = 0; \qquad j = 1, \ldots, n$$

(5') $$c_{i0} = 0; \qquad i = 1, \ldots, n$$

(6) $$c_{ij} = \left\{ \begin{array}{ll} 0 & \text{if } i < j \\ -\infty & \text{if } i \nless j \end{array} \right\} \text{if } i > 0 \text{ and } j > 0.$$

In particular, $c_{ii} = -\infty$, $i = 1, 2, \ldots, n$.

Our linear programming problem is:

(7) $$\text{maximize} \sum_{i,j=0}^{n} c_{ij}x_{ij} \quad \text{for} \quad X = (x_{ij}) \in \mathcal{X} .$$

Since

$$x_{oj} = 1 \qquad j = 1, 2, \ldots, n$$

$$x_{io} = 1 \qquad i = 1, 2, \ldots, n$$

all other $x_{ij} = 0$, satisfy (1), (2), (3), (3') with $\Sigma c_{ij}x_{ij} = 0$ the set $\mathcal{X}$ is non-void. Since it is clearly bounded the maximum is finite. Note further that $c_{ij} = -\infty$ is equivalent to the statement that, for a solution to (7), the corresponding $x_{ij} = 0$. Our use of $-\infty$ is simply an alternative method of stating that we require certain x_{ij} to be 0.

In order to demonstrate that solving (7) finds the smallest number of chains in a decomposition of P, we first exhibit a correspondence between the decompositions of P and matrices $X \in \mathcal{X}$ with integer entries such that $c_{ij} = -\infty$ implies $x_{ij} = 0$. First, let $C_1, C_2, \ldots, C_k$ be chains forming a decomposition of P, and let $C_\alpha (\alpha = 1, \ldots, k)$ be the chain (with β_α elements)

(8) $$i_{\alpha 1} < i_{\alpha 2} < \ldots < i_{\alpha \beta_\alpha} .$$

Set

(9) $$x_{oo} = n - k,$$

(10) $$x_{oj} = \begin{cases} 1 & \text{if } j = i_{\alpha 1}, \qquad \alpha = 1, \ldots, k \\ 0 & \text{otherwise} \end{cases}$$

(11) $$x_{io} = \begin{cases} 1 & \text{if } i = i_{\alpha \beta_\alpha}, \qquad \alpha = 1, \ldots, k \\ 0 & \text{otherwise .} \end{cases}$$

For $i > 0$, $j > 0$,

(12)
$x_{ij} = 1$ if there exists a chain in the decomposition in which i immediately precedes j,
$x_{ij} = 0$ otherwise.

Except for the variable x_{oo}, (1) follows trivially from (10)-(12). As k is clearly not larger than n, (1) holds also for x_{oo} by (9). Condition (2) is a consequence of (9)-(11). Since every element of P is in exactly one chain, and is either the terminal element of the chain or not, (12) implies (3). Similarly, since every element of P is in exactly one chain, and is either the starting element or not, (12) implies (3').

On the other hand, let $X \in \mathcal{X}$ have integer entries with $x_{ij} = 0$ if $c_{ij} = -\infty$. Then (3) and (3') imply that $x_{ij} = 0$ or 1 for all i, j with the possible exception of x_{oo}. Clearly, guided by (10)-(12), one can interpret the units in X as describing a decomposition of P into chains (8), which begin with the elements j such that $x_{oj} = 1$ and end with the elements i such that $x_{io} = 1$. The important thing to note is that there cannot exist a set of distinct positive integers $i_1, i_2, \ldots, i_\gamma$ such that

$$x_{i_1 i_2} = 1, \quad x_{i_2 i_3} = 1, \ldots, x_{i_\gamma i_1} = 1,$$

$$c_{i_1 i_2} = 0, \quad c_{i_2 i_3} = 0, \ldots, c_{i_\gamma i_1} = 0.$$

For, if this were to occur, it would imply

$$i_1 < i_2 < \ldots < i_\gamma < i_1,$$

which violates the fact that P is a partially ordered set.

Now, our linear programming problem (7) is in the form of a "transportation problem", for which it is known ([1], [5], [6], [8]) that there exist solutions X with integer entries. Indeed, the integral solutions, (which include the extreme points of $\mathcal{X}$ in $(n + 1)^2$ space) are the solutions obtained by most practical methods of computation. (Of course, if there is only one solution, it is integral, and <u>any</u> computing scheme will produce it.) Maximizing $\Sigma c_{ij} x_{ij}$, which is simply maximizing x_{oo}, minimizes

$$\sum_{j=1}^{n} x_{oj}$$

(in view of (2)); and minimizing

$$\sum_{j=1}^{n} x_{oj} ,$$

as we have seen, will minimize the number of chains in a decomposition of P.

Thus we conclude that the solution to (7) is

(13) $$n - p,$$

where p is the smallest number of chains in a decomposition of P.

§3. THE DUAL PROBLEM

The well-known duality theorem [3], applied to (7), asserts that (13) is also the minimum of

(14) $$n(u_0 + v_0) + \sum_{i=1}^{n} u_i + \sum_{j=1}^{n} v_j ,$$

where $u_0, u_1, \ldots, u_n, v_0, v_1, \ldots, v_n$ satisfy

(15) $$u_0 + v_0 \geqq 1,$$

(16) $$u_i + v_o \geqq 0 \qquad i = 1, 2, \ldots, n$$

(17) $$u_0 + v_j \geqq 0 \qquad j = 1, 2, \ldots, n .$$

For $i > 0$, $j > 0$

(18) $$u_i + v_j \geqq 0 \qquad \text{if} \qquad i < j.$$

We first show that we may assume that the u's and v's solving (14) are integers. This is an immediate consequence of the simplex method [1] of solving (7), but it is easy to outline an ad hoc proof. Assume, in order to obtain a contradiction, that among all solutions of (14), we have one with the fewest number of non-integers among the u's and v's and the number of these non-integers is greater than zero. Since the right-hand sides of (15)-(18) are integers, it is easy to see that there will be at least one non-integral u_i and at least one non-integral v_j. Let

(19) $$\epsilon = \min\left\{u_i - [u_i]\right\}, \quad \text{for } u_i \text{ not an integer,}$$

where $[u_i]$ = largest integer in u_i.

Define

(20) $$\begin{cases} u_i' = u_i - \epsilon, & \text{if } u_i \text{ is not an integer,} \\ u_i' = u_i, & \text{if } u_i \text{ is an integer;} \end{cases}$$

$$(21)\qquad \begin{cases} v_j' = v_j + \epsilon, \text{ if } v_j \text{ is not an integer,} \\ v_j' = v_j, \text{ if } v_j \text{ is an integer.} \end{cases}$$

Now, the u_i' and v_j' satisfy (15)-(18). For the only case that requires checking is for i, j such that

$$(22)\qquad u_i' = u_i - \epsilon, \qquad v_j' = v_j.$$

But it is clear that since the c_{ij} are integers, $u_i + v_j \geqq c_{ij}$, u_i is not an integer, v_j an integer imply

$$u_i' + v_j' = u_i - \epsilon + v_j \geqq u_i + v_j - \left\{u_i - [u_i]\right\} \geqq c_{ij}.$$

To complete the proof that the u's and v's can be assumed to be integers observe that

$$n(u_0' + v_0') + \sum_{i=1}^{n} u_i' + \sum_{j=1}^{n} v_j'$$

is either the same as the corresponding linear form in the u_i and v_j, or is greater. If it is the same, we have found a solution to (14) with at least one more integral u_i, which is a contradiction. If it is greater, interchange the roles of the u's and v's in the preceding discussion starting with (19). The same computation which showed previously an increase in the linear form will now exhibit a decrease. This contradicts the assumption that the u's and v's solved (14). Hence, we may assume all u's and v's integral.

Since we may add a constant to all u's and subtract the same constant from all v's without violating (15)-(18) or changing the value of our linear form, we may assume $v_0 = 0$. Further, if $u_0 > 1$, we may reduce u_0 to 1 and raise $v_j (j = 1, 2, \ldots, n)$ by the same amount, preserving (15)-(18) and not changing the value of our linear form. In summary, we may assume

$$(23)\qquad v_0 = 0$$

$$(24)\qquad u_0 = 1,$$

and our problem is

$$(25)\qquad \text{to minimize } n + \left(\sum_{i=1}^{n} u_i + \sum_{j=1}^{n} v_j\right)$$

where u_i and v_j satisfy (16)-(18).

By (23) and (16), we have

(26) $$u_i \geqq 0 \qquad i = 1, 2, \ldots, n.$$

By (24) and (17),

(27) $$v_j \geqq - 1.$$

By (26), (18), and the fact that (25) is a minimizing problem,

(28) $$v_j \leqq 0 \qquad j = 1, 2, \ldots, n.$$

Similarly, (27), (18) and the desire to minimize imply

(29) $$u_i \leqq 1 \qquad i = 1, \ldots, n.$$

Hence, (26) and (29) imply that some u_i $(i = 1, \ldots, n)$ are 0, all others are 1; and (27) and (28) imply that some v_j $(j = 1, \ldots, n)$ are 0, all others are -1.

We now introduce some notation. If $A \subset P$, we define (the predecessors of A) the set $A^* = \{i \in P \mid \exists\, i' \in A, i \prec i'\}$. In other words, every element of A^* is the predecessor of at least one element of A. Let $\bar{A}$ denote the number of elements in A.

Now, let $A \subset P$ be the set of all elements j such that $v_j = -1$. Clearly, since (25) is a minimizing problem, A^* is identical with the set of all i such that $u_i = 1$. The conclusion of our discussion, in view of (13) and (25), is

(30) $$p = \max_{A \subset P} \left\{ \bar{A} - \bar{A}^* \right\}.$$

§4. DEDUCTION OF DILWORTH'S THEOREM

Before proceeding further, let us first note that all we have used of the partial ordering of P is the impossibility of an ordered cycle, which holds for the more general "acyclic" sets [7]. It follows that (30) holds for acyclic sets. Moreover, if q denotes the largest number of mutually unrelated elements in an acyclic set, then (30) implies $p \leqq q$.

For

$$\bar{A} - \bar{A}^* \leqq \bar{A} - \overline{A \cap A^*} = \overline{A - A \cap A^*} \leqq q$$

since $A - A \cap A^*$ is a set of mutually unrelated elements.

On the other hand, the full strength of the partial ordering trivially implies $p \geqq q$.

Thus $p = q$.

BIBLIOGRAPHY

[1] DANTZIG, G. B., "Application of the simplex method to a transportation problem," Chapter XXII of Acticity Analysis of Production and Allocation, edited by T. C. Koopmans, New York, 1951.

[2] DILWORTH, R. P., "A decomposition theorem for partially ordered sets," Annals of Mathematics 51, 1950, pp. 161-166.

[3] GALE, D., KUHN, H. W., and TUCKER, A. W., "Linear programming and the theory of games," Chapter XIX of Activity Analysis of Production and Allocation, edited by T. C. Koopmans, New York, 1951.

[4] HOFFMAN, A. J., "How to solve a linear programming problem," Proceedings of the Second Symposium in Linear Programming, Washington, D. C., 1955, pp. 397-424.

[5] HOFFMAN, A. J., and WIELANDT, H. W., "The variation of the spectrum of a normal matrix," Duke Mathematical Journal 20, 1953, pp. 37-39.

[6] von NEUMANN, J., "A certain zero-sum two-person game equivalent to the optimal assignment problem," Contributions to the Theory of Games II, edited by H. W. Kuhn and A. W. Tucker, Annals of Mathematics Studies 28, Princeton, 1953, pp. 5-12.

[7] von NEUMANN, J., and MORGENSTERN, O., Theory of Games and Economic Behavior, (3rd edition), Princeton, 1953, p. 591.

[8] HOFFMAN, A. J. and KRUSKAL, J. B., "Integral boundary points of convex polyhedra," this Study.

G. B. Dantzig
A. J. Hoffman

The RAND Corporation
National Bureau of Standards

ON THE MAX-FLOW MIN-CUT THEOREM OF NETWORKS

G. B. Dantzig and D. R. Fulkerson

INTRODUCTION

The problem discussed in this paper arises naturally in the study of transportation networks. Roughly stated, it is as follows. Consider a network connecting two nodes by way of a number of intermediate nodes, and suppose the arcs and nodes can handle certain designated amounts of traffic per unit time. Assuming a steady state condition, find a maximal flow of traffic from one given node (the source) to the other (the sink).

For example, let the network be that of Figure 1

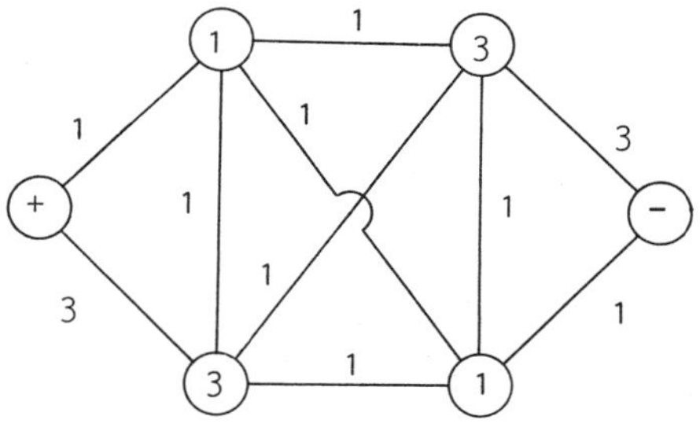

Figure 1

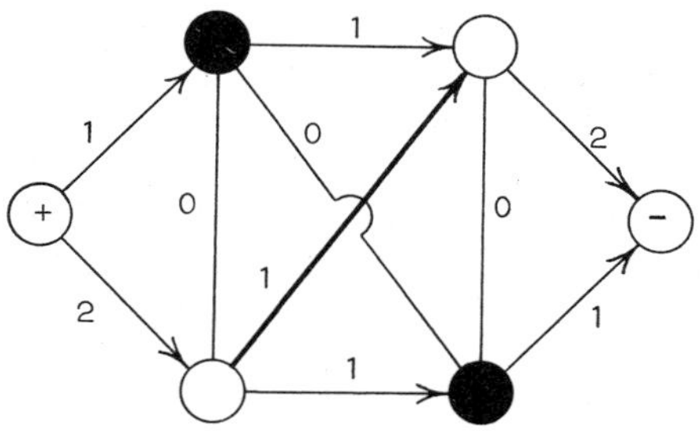

Figure 2

where source and sink are denoted by + and - respectively, with flow capacities of the arcs and nodes as indicated. A maximal flow from source to sink is shown in Figure 2. Notice that the quantity of flow leaving the source (or entering the sink) is equal to the sum of the capacities of the two nodes and one arc which are emphasized in the figure, and that this collection of nodes and arcs forms a "cut" in the network; i.e., meets every chain from source to sink.

A nonconstructive proof based on convexity arguments has been given in an unpublished manuscript by L. R. Ford, Jr. and one of the present writers (D. R. Fulkerson) that the maximal flow value, relative to a given source and sink, attainable in any network is equal to the minimal sum of capacities on arcs and nodes constituting a cut. Our aim is to formulate the problem of finding a maximal flow as a linear programming problem (§1) and to deduce the max flow min cut theorem from the dual problem (§3). In §4 we observe that a combinatorial form of this theorem yields Menger's theorem [5, p. 244] concerning linear graphs.

§1. THE PROGRAMMING PROBLEM

There are various ways of formulating the flow problem as a linear programming problem. One way[1], convenient from both a computational and theoretical viewpoint, is as follows. Set up the pseudo transportation array

$$\begin{array}{r} \\ \\ \\ \\ \\ \\ \text{Totals} \end{array} \begin{array}{c} \\ \left[\begin{array}{ccccc} -x_{00} & x_{01} & x_{02} & \cdots & x_{0n} \\ x_{10} & -x_{11} & x_{12} & \cdots & x_{1n} \\ x_{20} & x_{21} & -x_{22} & \cdots & x_{2n} \\ \vdots & \vdots & \vdots & \ddots & \\ x_{n0} & x_{n1} & x_{n2} & & -x_{nn} \end{array}\right] \\ \begin{array}{ccccc} 0 & 0 & 0 & \cdots & 0 \end{array} \end{array} \begin{array}{c} \text{Totals} \\ 0 \\ 0 \\ 0 \\ \vdots \\ 0 \\ \\ \end{array}$$

schematizing the equations

$$(1a) \qquad -x_{ii} + \sum_{j,\, j \neq i} x_{ij} = 0 \qquad (i = 0, 1, \ldots, n)$$

$$(1b) \qquad -x_{jj} + \sum_{i,\, i \neq j} x_{ij} = 0 \qquad (j = 0, 1, \ldots, n),$$

where $x_{ij} \geq 0$ $(i, j = 1, \ldots, n;\ i \neq j)$ denotes the flow from node i to node j, $x_{ii} \geq 0$ $(i = 1, \ldots, n)$ represents the total flow through node i, $x_{0j} \geq 0$ $(j = 1, \ldots, n)$ is the flow from the source to node j, and $x_{i0} \geq 0$ $(i = 1, \ldots, n)$ the flow from node i to the sink. Thus x_{00} is the total flow through the network and the problem is to maximize x_{00} subject to (1a), (1b), and

$$(2) \qquad x_{ij} + x_{ji} \leq c_{ij} \qquad (c_{ij} = c_{ji})$$

---

[1] A. Hoffman has given a different formulation of the problem which also yields the max flow min cut theorem. While the techniques employed in his approach are similar to those of this paper, he uses an entirely different set of variables which are of interest in themselves.

$$
(3)\qquad \begin{aligned} x_{ii} &\leq c_{ii} \\ x_{io} &\leq c_{io} \qquad (i,\ j = 1,\ \ldots,\ n)\ , \\ x_{oj} &\leq c_{jo} \end{aligned}
$$

$$
(4)\qquad x_{ij} \geq 0 \qquad (i,\ j = 0,\ \ldots,\ n),
$$

where the c's are given non-negative constants. We have formally included all variables x_{ij} in the problem; arcs not present in the network have $c_{ij} = 0$.

Because of (2), we refer to this as the undirected problem; that is, except for source and sink arcs, the direction of flow is not specified in the arcs.

Given an undirected problem, it is easy to describe an equivalent directed problem. Simply replace each undirected arc by a pair of oppositely directed arcs, each with capacity equal to that of the original arc. That the two problems are equivalent follows from the fact that given any $x = (x_{ij})$ satisfying (1), (3), (4), and

$$
(2')\qquad \begin{aligned} x_{ij} &\leq c_{ij} \\ x_{ji} &\leq c_{ji} \end{aligned} \qquad (c_{ij} = c_{ji})\ ,
$$

a flow x' of equal value is obtained by setting

$$
\begin{aligned}
x'_{io} &= x_{io} && (i = 0,\ \ldots,\ n) \\
x'_{oj} &= x_{oj} && (j = 0,\ \ldots,\ n) \\
x'_{ij} &= \max\ (x_{ij} - x_{ji},\ 0) && (i,\ j = 1,\ \ldots,\ n;\ i \neq j) \\
x'_{ii} &= x_{ii} - \sum_{\substack{j=1 \\ j\neq i}}^{n} \min\ (x_{ij},\ x_{ji}) && (i = 1,\ \ldots,\ n).
\end{aligned}
$$

Thus (2) may be replaced by (2') without changing the value of a maximal flow.

A cut in an undirected network has been defined as a collection of arcs and nodes meeting every chain joining source and sink; a cut in a directed network is similarly defined as a collection of directed arcs and nodes meeting every directed chain from source to sink. The value of a cut in either case is the sum of the capacities of all its member nodes and arcs.

One proves easily that the minimal cut value is the same for an undirected network and its equivalent directed network. Thus, to prove the max flow min cut theorem, it suffices to consider directed networks only. Accordingly, we shall make no further use of the condition $c_{ij} = c_{ji}$ in (2').

Let us now rewrite the inequalities (2'), (3), as

$$(5) \qquad x_{ij} + y_{ij} = c_{ij}, \quad y_{ij} \geq 0 \qquad (i, j = 0, 1, \ldots, n)$$

where, to avoid special cases, we have included a sufficiently large upper bound of c_{oo} on the variable x_{oo}; for example, choose

$$c_{oo} > \sum_{i=1}^{n} c_{io}.$$

Then the problem is to maximize x_{oo} subject to (1a), (1b), (4), and (5).

§2. BASES

We turn momentarily to the question of what constitutes a basis,[2] in order to note that the Hitchcock-Koopmans transportation theory carries over to the flow problem.

There are $(n + 1)^2 + 2(n + 1) - 1$ linearly independent equations in the set (1a), (1b), (5), since one of the set (1a), (1b), is redundant. Drop the first equation of (1a) as the redundant one, and denote by X_{ij}, Y_{ij} the column vectors of the coefficient matrix of the remaining equations corresponding to the variables x_{ij}, y_{ij}, respectively.

It is clear that at least one of X_{ij}, Y_{ij} must belong to any basis B. Thus the pairs ij fall into one of three classes:

α: those ij for which $X_{ij} \in B$, $Y_{ij} \in B$;

β: those ij for which $X_{ij} \in B$, $Y_{ij} \notin B$;

γ: those ij for which $X_{ij} \notin B$, $Y_{ij} \in B$.

---

[2] Let $\sum_{j=1}^{n} a_{ij}x_j = b_i$, $x_j \geq 0$ $(i = 1, \ldots, m)$ be the constraints of a linear programming problem, and suppose $A = (a_{ij})$ has rank m. A set of m linearly independent columns of A is a "basis", the corresponding x_j are "basic variables". The vector $\hat{x} = (\hat{x}_1, \ldots, \hat{x}_n)$ obtained by assigning non-basic variables zero values and solving the resulting equations for the basic variables is called a "basic solution". If $\hat{x}$ has non-negative components, it is termed a "basic feasible solution". Geometrically, basic feasible solutions correspond to extreme points of the convex set defined by the constraints.

The number of pairs ij of type α is always $2n + 1$. For if there are k of type α, hence $(n + 1)^2 - k$ of types β and γ, then $2k + (n + 1)^2 - k = (n + 1)^2 + 2(n + 1) - 1$, $k = 2n + 1$. Moreover, it is impossible to find among the pairs of type α a subset of the form

$$i_1j_1,\ i_1j_2,\ i_2j_2,\ i_2j_3,\ \ldots,\ i_kj_k,\ i_kj_1$$

where the i's and j's are distinct among themselves, as otherwise the column vectors X_{ij}, Y_{ij} corresponding to these pairs can easily be shown to be dependent.

These two statements together imply that B can be arranged in triangular form, just as in the Hitchcock-Koopmans case. To see this, it is convenient to associate a linear graph G with B, and to look at the problem of finding the basic solution corresponding to B in terms of this graph.[3]

Let $a_0, \ldots, a_n, b_0, \ldots, b_n$ be the nodes of G; the arcs of G are those a_ib_j for which ij is of type α. As we have seen, G has $2n + 1$ arcs and contains no cycles. It is therefore a tree. Call a node of G which has only one arc on it an "end-node". There are at least two such.

We associate with node $a_i(b_j)$ of G the equation

$$-x_{ii} + \sum_{j,\, j \neq i} x_{ij} = 0 \left(-x_{jj} + \sum_{i,\, i \neq j} x_{ij} = 0 \right).$$

Now locate an end-node, say a_k, and let its arc be a_kb_ℓ. Since for pairs ij of type β, $y_{ij} = 0$, $x_{ij} = c_{ij}$, and similarly $x_{ij} = 0$, $y_{ij} = c_{ij}$ for pairs of type γ, all the variables of the equation

$$-x_{kk} + \sum_{j,\, j \neq k} x_{kj} = 0$$

are determined but one, $x_{k\ell}$, and thus its value may be found immediately. Then use (5) to get $y_{k\ell} = c_{k\ell} - x_{k\ell}$. Delete a_k and a_kb_ℓ from G, leaving a tree, and repeat the procedure. After $2n + 1$ steps, the values of all variables are determined.

Notice that only addition and subtraction are required. Thus, if

---

[3] There are several alternative ways one can view the equation solving process in terms of a linear graph. Since the equations came from such a graph, one way would be to use the original network. This appears to be most efficient for hand-computation. Another way, in terms of the array (1), can be developed as in [3]. A third way, the one we adopt, is suggested in [2]. In all of these, the notion of "basis" in the programming sense is closely related to the notion of "tree" in the graph sense.

the c_{ij} are integral, so are the values of all variables in a basic solution, hence in a basic feasible solution. We will make use of this fact in the concluding section.

§3. SIMPLEX CRITERION AND THE DUAL PROBLEM

Let u_i, v_j, w_{ij} be the multipliers (dual variables) corresponding to the equations (1a), (1b), (5), respectively, in applying the simplex algorithm. Then the conditions for an optimal basis B^* are:

$$(6a) \qquad -u_i - v_i + w_{ii} \geq \delta_{io} \qquad (\delta_{oo} = 1,\ \delta_{io} = 0 \text{ for } i > 0)$$

$$(6b) \qquad u_i + v_j + w_{ij} \geq 0 \qquad (i \neq j)$$

$$(6c) \qquad w_{ij} \geq 0$$

with equality holding in (6a), (6b), if the corresponding $X_{ij} \in B^*$, in (6c) if $Y_{ij} \in B^*$. Ignoring the redundant equation amounts to taking $u_o = 0$. Then, since X_{oo}, $Y_{oo} \in B^*$,[4] $w_{oo} = 0$, $v_o = -1$. For all other pairs ij of type α, $w_{ij} = 0$, and the equations $u_i + v_j = 0$ hold. It follows that all $u_i = 0$ or 1, all $v_j = 0$ or -1. (A convenient way to see this is to associate the variable $u_i(v_j)$ with node $a_i(b_j)$ of the graph G^* corresponding to B^* and the equations $u_i + v_j = 0$ with the appropriate arcs of G^*.) Substituting these values into (6a), (6b), to determine the w_{ij} corresponding to $Y_{ij} \notin B^*$ and noting (6c) shows that all $w_{ij} = 0$ or 1.

The dual programming problem is to minimize $\Sigma c_{ij} w_{ij}$ subject to (6a) - (6c), and the multipliers corresponding to an optimal primal solution solve the dual problem. Thus

$$(7) \qquad \max x_{oo} = \min \Sigma c_{ij} w_{ij} = \Sigma_{\sigma} c_{ij}$$

where σ is that set of pairs ij corresponding to $w_{ij} = 1$; in terms of the network, σ is some subset of those (directed) arcs and nodes which are at capacity in the flow x. We claim that σ is a cut. For suppose all c_{ij}, $ij \notin \sigma$, are increased by $\epsilon > 0$. This does not change the solution to the dual, hence cannot increase the flow in the network. But if there were some directed chain from source to sink not meeting σ, the maximal flow value would be increased by at least ϵ. Thus σ is a cut,

---

[4] Our choice of c_{oo} implies that $Y_{oo} \in B$ for any B yielding a basic feasible solution; also clearly $X_{oo} \in B^*$ except possibly in the trivial case where the maximal flow over the network is zero. The assertion is valid in general, however, as otherwise all multipliers have zero values, violating (6a) with $i = 0$.

and since it is clear that no flow can exceed the value of any cut, the proof of the max flow min cut theorem is complete.

§4. MENGER'S THEOREM

Given an arbitrary linear graph G, let I_1, I_2 be two disjoint sets of nodes of G. Menger's theorem states that the maximal number of pairwise node-disjoint chains joining I_1 to I_2 is equal to the minimal number of nodes necessary to separate I_1 from I_2. To deduce this theorem from the max flow min cut theorem, join all the nodes of I_1 to a new node, the source, and all the nodes of I_2 to another new node, the sink; then assign unit capacity to each of the old nodes, infinite capacity to each arc. Menger's theorem now follows by selecting a maximal flow x with integral components.

BIBLIOGRAPHY

[1] DANTZIG, G. B., "Application of the simplex method to a transportation problem," Activity Analysis of Production and Allocation, Cowles Commission monograph No. 13, T. C. Koopmans, Ed., John Wiley and Sons, Inc., New York, (1951), pp. 359-373.

[2] KOOPMANS, T. C., and REITER, S., "A model of transportation," Activity Analysis of Production and Allocation, Cowles Commission monograph No. 13, T. C. Koopmans, Ed., John Wiley and Sons, Inc., New York, (1951), pp. 222-259.

[3] FLOOD, M. M., "On the Hitchcock distribution problem," Pac. Jour. Math. 3, No. 2 (1953), pp. 369-386.

[4] HITCHCOCK, F. L., "The distribution of a product from several sources to numerous localities," Jour. Math. Physics 20 (1941), pp. 224-230.

[5] KÖNIG, D., Theorie der Endlichen und Unendlichen Graphen, Chelsea Publishing Co., New York, 1950.

G. B. Dantzig
D. R. Fulkerson

The RAND Corporation

INTEGRAL BOUNDARY POINTS OF CONVEX POLYHEDRA

A. J. Hoffman and J. B. Kruskal

INTRODUCTION

Suppose every vertex of a (convex) polyhedron in n-space has (all) integral coordinates. Then this polyhedron has the integral property (i.p.). Sections 1, 2, and 3 of this paper are concerned with such polyhedra.

Define two polyhedra[1]:

$$P(b) = \{x \mid Ax \geqq b\} ,$$

$$Q(b, c) = \{x \mid Ax \geqq b, x \geqq c\} ,$$

where A, b, and c are integral and A is fixed. Theorem 1 states that P(b) has the i.p. for every (integral) b if and only if the minors of A satisfy certain conditions. Theorem 2 states that Q(b, c) has the i.p. for every (integral) b and c if and only if every minor of A equals 0, + 1, or - 1. Section 1 contains the exact statement of Theorems 1 and 2, and Sections 2 and 3 contain proofs.

A matrix A is said to have the unimodular property (u.p.) if it satisfies the condition of Theorem 2, namely if every minor determinant equals 0, + 1, or - 1. In Section 4 we give Theorem 3, a simple sufficient condition for a matrix to have the u.p. which is interesting in itself and necessary to the proof of Theorem 4. In Section 5 we state and prove — at length — Theorem 4, a very general sufficient condition for a matrix to have the u.p. Finally, in Section 6 we discuss how to recognize the unimodular property, and give two theorems, based on Theorem 4, for this purpose.

Our results include all situations known to the authors in which the polyhedron has the integral property independently of the "right-hand sides" of the inequalities (given that the "right-hand sides" are integral of course). In particular, the well-known "integrality" of transportation

---

[1] Unless otherwise stated, we assume throughout this paper that the inequalities defining polyhedra are consistent.

type linear programs and their duals follows immediately from Theorems 2 and 4 as a special case.

1. DEFINITIONS AND THEOREMS

A point of n-space is an <u>integral point</u> if every coordinate is an integer. A (convex) polyhedron in n-space is said to have the <u>integral property</u> (i.p.) if <u>every</u> face (of every dimension) contains an integral point. Of course, this is true if and only if every <u>minimal</u> face contains an integral point. If the minimal faces happen to be vertices[2] (that is, of dimension 0), then the integral property simply means that the vertices of P are themselves all integral points.

Let A be an m by n matrix of integers; let b and b' be m-tuples (vectors), and c and c' be n-tuples (vectors), whose components are integers or $\pm\infty$. We will let $\infty(-\infty)$ also represent a vector all of whose components are $\infty(-\infty)$; this should cause no confusion. The vector inequality $b < b'$ means that strict inequality holds at every component. Let $P(b; b')$ and $Q(b; b'; c; c')$ be the polyhedra in n-space defined by

$$P(b;\ b') = \{x \mid b \leqq Ax \leqq b'\} ,$$

$$Q(b;\ b';\ c;\ c') = \{x \mid b \leqq Ax \leqq b' \quad \text{and} \quad c \leqq x \leqq c'\} .$$

Of course $Q(b; b'; -\infty, +\infty) = P(b; b')$. If S is any set of rows of A, then define

$$\gcd(S) = \begin{cases} 0, & \text{if each minor determinant in } S \text{ which has as many rows as } S \text{ equals } 0, \\ \text{greatest common divisor (g.c.d.) of all those minor determinants in } S \text{ which have as many rows as } S, & \text{otherwise.} \end{cases}$$

THEOREM 1. The following conditions are equivalent:

(1.1) $P(b; b')$ has the i.p. for every b, b';

(1.2) $P(b; \infty)$ has the i.p. for every b;

(1.2') $P(-\infty; b')$ has the i.p. for every b';

(1.3) if r is the rank of A, then for every set S of r linearly independent rows of A, $\gcd(S) = 1$;

---

[2] It is well known (and, incidentally, is a by-product of our Lemma 1) that all minimal faces of a convex polyhedron have the same dimension.

(1.4) for every set S of rows of A, $\gcd(S) = 1$ or 0.

The main value of this theorem lies in the fact that condition (1.3) implies condition (1.1). However the converse implication is of esthetic interest. If it is believed that (1.3) does not hold, (1.4) often offers the easiest way to verify this, for it may suffice to examine small sets of rows.

A matrix (of integers) is said to have the unimodular property (u.p.) if every minor determinant equals 0, $+1$, or -1. We see immediately that the entries in a matrix with the u.p. can only be 0, $+1$, or -1.

THEOREM 2. The following conditions are equivalent:

(1.5) $Q(b; b'; c; c')$ has the i.p. for every b, b', c, c';

(1.6) for some fixed c such that $-\infty < c < +\infty$, $Q(b, \infty; c; \infty)$ has the i.p. for every b;

(1.6') for some fixed c such that $-\infty < c < \infty$, $Q(-\infty; b'; c; \infty)$ has the i.p. for every b';

(1.6'') for some fixed c' such that $-\infty < c' < \infty$, $Q(b; \infty; -\infty; c')$ has the i.p. for every b;

(1.6''') for some fixed c' such that $-\infty < c' < \infty$, $Q(-\infty; b'; -\infty; c')$ has the i.p. for every b';

(1.7) the matrix A has the unimodular property (u.p.).

The main value of this theorem for applications lies in the fact that condition (1.7) implies condition (1.5), a fact which can be proved directly (with the aid of Cramer's rule) without difficulty. However the converse implication is also of esthetic interest. The relationship between Theorems 1 and 2 is that Theorem 2 asserts the equivalence of stronger properties while Theorem 1 asserts the equivalence of weaker ones. Condition (1.5) is clearly stronger than condition (1.1), and condition (1.7) is clearly stronger than condition (1.3).

For A to have the unimodular property is the same thing as for A transpose to have the unimodular property. Therefore if a linear program has the matrix A with the u.p., both the "primal" and the dual programs lead to polyhedra with the i.p. This can be very valuable when applying the duality theorem to combinatorial problems (for examples, see several other papers in this volume).

2. PROOF OF THEOREM 1

We note that (1.1) $\Longrightarrow$ (1.2) and (1.2') trivially. Likewise (1.4) $\Longrightarrow$ (1.3) trivially. To see that (1.3) $\Longrightarrow$ (1.4), let S and S' be sets of rows of A. If $S \subset S'$, then the relevant determinants of S' are integral combinations of the relevant determinants of S. Hence $\gcd(S)$ divides $\gcd(S')$. From this we easily see that (1.3) $\Longrightarrow$ (1.4).

As (1.2) and (1.2') are completely parallel, we shall only treat the former in our proofs.

Let the rows of A be $A_1, \ldots, A_m$ and the components of b and b' be $b_1, \ldots, b_m$ and $b_1', \ldots, b_m'$. Suppose that we know that (1.3) for any matrix A_* implies (1.2) for the corresponding polyhedra $P_*(b; \infty)$. Also, suppose that (1.3) holds for the particular matrix A. Then setting

$$A_* = \begin{bmatrix} A \\ \\ -A \end{bmatrix},$$

we see immediately that (1.3) holds for A_*. Consequently

$$P_*(b_1, \ldots, b_m, -b_1', \ldots, -b_m'; \infty)$$

has the i.p. But it is easy to see that this polyhedron is identical with $P(b; b')$; hence the latter also has the i.p. Therefore if for every matrix (1.3) implies (1.2), then (1.3) implies (1.1) for every matrix.

Let $P(b) = P(b; \infty)$ for convenience.

It only remains to prove that (1.2) is equivalent to (1.3)[3]. If S is any set of rows A_i of A, we define

$F_S = F_S(b) = \{x \mid Ax \geqq b \text{ and } A_i x = b_i \text{ if } A_i \text{ in } S\}$,

G_S = the subspace of n-space spanned by the rows A_i in S.

If $F_S(b)$ is not empty, it is the face of $P(b)$ corresponding to S. (We do not consider the empty set to be a face of a polyhedron.) We easily see that $F_S(b)$, if non-empty, corresponds to the usual notion of a face. Of course $F_\emptyset(b) = P(b)$, where $\emptyset$ is the empty set. We shall use the letter A to stand for the set of <u>all</u> rows of the matrix A. In general we will use the same letter to denote a set of rows and to denote the matrix formed by these rows. (This double meaning should cause no confusion.)

---

[3] The authors are indebted to Professor David Gale for this proof, which is much simpler than the original proof.

LEMMA 1. If $S \subset S'$, and if $F_S(b)$ and $F_{S'}(b)$ are faces (that is, not empty), then $F_{S'}(b)$ is a subface of $F_S(b)$. If $F_S(b)$ is a face, then it is a minimal face if and only if $G_S = G_A$, that is, if and only if S has rank r, where r is the rank of A.

PROOF. The first sentence of the lemma follows directly from the definitions. To prove the rest of the lemma, let S' be all rows of A which are in G_S. Then $G_S = G_{S'}$, and A_j is a linear combination of the A_i in S if and only if A_j is in S'. Clearly $G_S = G_A$ if and only if $S' = A$.

If $S' \neq A$, there is at least one row A_k in $A - S'$. Then there is a vector y such that $A_i y = 0$ for A_i in S, $A_k y < 0$. Let x be in F_S. As $A_k x \geqq b_k$, there is a number $\lambda_k \geqq 0$ for which $A_k(x + \lambda_k y) = b_k$. For every A_j in $A - S'$ such that $A_j y < 0$, the equation $A_j(x + \lambda y) = b_j$ has a non-negative solution. Let λ_j be that solution. Define λ = minimum λ_j, and let j' be a value such that $\lambda = \lambda_{j'}$. As λ_k exists, there is at least one λ_j, so λ exists. By the definition of λ,

$$\begin{aligned} A(x + \lambda y) &\geqq b , \\ A_i(x + \lambda y) &= b_i \qquad \text{for } A_i \text{ in } S, \\ A_{j'}(x + \lambda y) &= b_{j'} . \end{aligned}$$

Thus $F_{S \cup A_{j'}}$ is not empty, and is therefore a subface of F_S. Furthermore as $A_{j'}$ is not a linear combination of the A_i in S, $F_{S \cup A_{j'}}$ is a proper subface of F_S. Therefore F_S is not minimal.

On the other hand, if F_S is not minimal it has some proper subface $F_{S \cup A_k}$. Then there must be x_1 and x_2 in F_S such that $A_k x_1 = b_k$ and $A_k x_2 > b_k$. Therefore $A_k x$ varies as x ranges over F_S. But for A_i in S, $A_i x = b_i$ is constant as x varies over F_S. Hence A_k cannot be a linear combination of the A_i in S, so A_k is in $A - S'$. Hence $S' \neq A$. This proves the lemma.

If b, as usual, is an m-tuple and S is a set of r rows of A, then b_S is the "sub-vector" consisting of the r components of b which correspond to the rows of S. Let $\tilde{b}$ always represent an (integral) r-tuple. The components of $\tilde{b}$ and b_S will be indexed by the indices used for the rows of S, not by the integers from 1 to r. Let

$$L_S(\tilde{b}) = \{x \mid Sx = \tilde{b}\} .$$

LEMMA 2. Suppose S is a set of r linearly independent rows of A. Then for any $\tilde{b}$ there is a b such that

(2.1) $$b_S = \tilde{b} ;$$

(2.2) $F_S(b)$ is a minimal face of $P(b)$.

PROOF. As S is a set of linearly independent rows, the equation $Sx = \tilde{b}$ has at least one solution: call it y. Define b as follows:

$$b_i = \begin{cases} \tilde{b}_i & \text{if } A_i \text{ in } S, \\ [A_i y] & \text{if } A_i \text{ not in } S . \end{cases}$$

Clearly $b_S = \tilde{b}$, so (2.1) is satisfied. Obviously b is integral. Furthermore y is seen to be in $F_S(b)$, so $F_S(b)$ is not empty, and hence is a face of $P(b)$. By Lemma 1, $F_S(b)$ is a minimal face, so (2.2) is satisfied.

LEMMA 3. Suppose S' is a set of rows of A of rank r, and $S \subset S'$ is a set of r linearly independent rows. For any b such that $F_{S'}(b)$ is a face (that is, not empty),

$$F_{S'}(b) = L_S(b_S).$$

PROOF. Let y be a fixed element in $F_{S'}(b)$, and let x be any element of $L_S(b)$. As $F_{S'}(b) \subset L_S(b_S)$ is trivial, we only need show the reverse inclusion. Thus it suffices to prove that x is in $F_{S'}(b)$.

As S has rank r, any row A_k in A can be expressed as a linear combination of the rows A_i in S:

$$A_k = \Sigma\alpha_{ki}A_i .$$

Then

$$A_i x = b_i = A_i y$$

for A_i in S, so

$$A_k x = \Sigma\alpha_{ki}A_i x = \Sigma\alpha_{ki}A_i y = A_k y .$$

Then as y is in $F_{S'}(b)$, x must be also. This completes the proof of the lemma.

LEMMA 4. Any minimal face of $P(b)$ can be expressed in the form $F_S(b)$ where S is a set of r linearly independent rows of A.

PROOF. Suppose the face is $F_{S'}(b)$. By Lemma 1, S' must have rank r. Let S be a set of r linearly independent rows of S'. Then by applying Lemma 3 to both $F_{S'}(b)$ and $F_S(b)$, we see that

$$F_{S'}(b) = L_S(b_S) = F_S(b).$$

This proves the lemma.

LEMMA 5. If S is a set of r linearly independent rows of A, then the following two conditions are equivalent:

(2.3) $L_S(\tilde{b})$ contains an integral point for every (integral) $\tilde{b}$;

(2.4) $$\gcd(S) = 1.$$

PROOF. We use a basic theorem of linear algebra, namely that any integral matrix S which is r by n can be put into the form

$$S = UDV$$

where D is a (non-negative integral) diagonal matrix, and U and V are (integral) unimodular matrices. (Of course U is r by r, V is n by n, and D is r by n.) As U and V are unimodular, they have integral inverses. Furthermore $\gcd(S) = \gcd(D)$. (For proofs of these facts, see for example [3].)

Let the diagonal elements of D be d_{ii}. Clearly $\gcd(D) = d_{11}d_{22} \cdots d_{rr}$. Therefore condition (2.4) is equivalent to the condition that every $d_{ii} = 1$. Now we show that (2.3) is also equivalent to this same condition.

Suppose that some diagonal element of D is greater than 1. For convenience we may suppose that this element is $d_{11} = k > 1$. Let $\tilde{e}$ be the r-tuple $(1, 0, \ldots, 0)$, and let $\tilde{b} = U\tilde{e}$. Then $L_S(\tilde{b})$ contains no integral point. To see this, let x be in $L_S(\tilde{b})$. Then

$$Sx = UDVx = \tilde{b} = U\tilde{e} ,$$

so $DVx = \tilde{e}$. Clearly the first component of $y = Vx$ is $1/k$, so y is not integral. Hence x cannot be integral. This shows that (2.3) cannot hold if some d_{ii} is greater than 1.

Suppose every $d_{ii} = 1$. Let x be in $L_S(\tilde{b})$ and set

$$Vx = (y_1, \ldots, y_r, y_{r+1}, \ldots, y_n).$$

Then

$$U^{-1}\tilde{b} = DVx = (y_1, \ldots, y_r),$$

and so $y_1, \ldots, y_r$ are integral. Let $y = (y_1, \ldots, y_r, 0, \ldots, 0)$. Then $V^{-1}y$ is integral, and since $Dy = DVx$,

$$S(V^{-1}y) = UDV(V^{-1}y) = UDy = UDVx = \tilde{b} .$$

Thus $V^{-1}y$ is in $L_S(\tilde{b})$. This shows that (2.3) does hold if every $d_{ii} = 1$, and completes the proof of the lemma.

Now it is easy to prove that (1.2) $\Longleftrightarrow$ (1.3). First we prove $\Longrightarrow$. Let S be any set of r linearly independent rows of A. Let $\tilde{b}$ be any (integral) r-tuple. Choose a b which satisfies (2.1) and (2.2). By (1.2), $F_S(b)$ must contain an integral point x. By Lemma 3 and (2.1),

$$F_S(b) = L_S(b_S) = L_S(\tilde{b}) .$$

Hence $L_S(\tilde{b})$ contains x. Therefore (2.3) is satisfied, so by Lemma 5, $\gcd(S) = 1$. This proves $\Longrightarrow$.

To prove $\Longleftarrow$, let $F_{S'}(b)$ be some minimal face of $P(b)$. By Lemma 4 this face can be expressed as $F_S(b)$ where S consists of r linearly independent rows of A. By Lemma 3, $F_S(b) = L_S(b_S)$. By (1.3), $\gcd(S) = 1$, and by Lemma 5 $L_S(b_S)$ must contain an integral point x. Hence $F_{S'}(b)$ contains the integral point x. Therefore every minimal face of $P(b)$ contains an integral point, and hence also every face. This proves $\Longleftarrow$, and completes the proof of Theorem 1.

3. PROOF OF THEOREM 2

The role of (1.6) and its primed analogues are exactly similar, so we treat only the former in our proofs. For convenience we let

$$Q(b; c) = Q(b; \infty; c; \infty).$$

It is not hard to see that (1.7) $\Longrightarrow$ (1.5). For suppose that A has the u.p. (that is, satisfies (1.7)). Then

$$A_* = \begin{bmatrix} A \\ -A \\ I \\ -I \end{bmatrix}$$

satisfies (1.3). By Theorem 1, the associated polyhedron

$$P_*(b_1, \ldots, b_m, -b'_1, \ldots, -b'_m, c_1, \ldots, c_n, -c'_1, \ldots, -c'_n)$$

has the i.p. But it is easy to see that this polyhedron is identical with $Q(b; b'; c; c')$. Therefore the latter has the i.p., so (1.7) $\Longrightarrow$ (1.5). (An alternate proof of this can easily be constructed using Cramer's Rule.)

Clearly (1.5) $\Longrightarrow$ (1.6). Hence it only remains to prove that (1.6) $\Longrightarrow$ (1.7). We shall prove[4] this by applying Theorem 1 to the matrix

$$A^* = \begin{bmatrix} I \\ A \end{bmatrix}.$$

Let d be any (integral) (n+m)-tuple, and let

$$c \cup b = (c_1, \ldots, c_n, b_1, \ldots, b_m) .$$

Then $P^*(c \cup b) = Q(b, c)$.

To verify condition (1.2) for A^*, we need to show that $P^*(d)$ has the i.p. for every d. Condition (1.6) yields only the fact that $P^*(d)$ has the i.p. for every d such that $d_I = c$. To fill this gap, note that A^* has rank n as it contains the n by n identity matrix, and let $F^*_{S'}(d)$ be any face of $P^*(d)$. This face contains some minimal face, which by Lemma 4 can be expressed as $F^*_S(d)$ where S consists of n linearly independent rows of A^*. By Lemma 3,

$$F^*_S(d) = L^*_S(d_S) \equiv \{x \mid Sx = d_S\} .$$

As S is an n by n matrix of rank n, $F^*_S(d)$ consists only of a single point. Call this point x. We shall show that x is integral.

Let I_1 be the rows of I in S, I_2 the rows of I not in S, A_1 the rows of A in S, and A_2 the rows of A not in S. We wish to pick an integral vector q such that

[4] The authors are indebted to Professor David Gale for this proof, which is much simpler than the original proof.

(3.1) $$x + q \geqq c,$$

(3.2) $$(x + q)_{I_1} = c_{I_1} .$$

Let $q = c - d_I$. Then q satisfies these requirements, for

$$x_i + q_i \left\{ \begin{matrix} = \\ \\ \geqq \end{matrix} \right\} d_i + (c_i - d_i) = c_i \left\{ \begin{matrix} \text{if the i-th row of} \\ I \text{ is in } I_1, \\ \text{otherwise.} \end{matrix} \right.$$

Define $d' = c \cup (d_A + Aq)$. Then d' is integral, and $d'_I = c$, so by (1.6) the polyhedron $P^*(d')$ has the i.p.

Now $F^*_S(d')$ is not empty because it contains $(x + q)$, as we may easily verify:

$$A^*(x + q) = I(x + q) \cup A(x + q) \geqq c \cup (d_A + Aq) = d' ,$$

$$S(x + q) = I_1(x + q) \cup A_1(x + q) = c_{I_1} \cup (d_{A_1} + A_{1q}) = d'_S .$$

Therefore $F^*_S(d')$ must contain an integral point. However $F^*_S(d')$ can contain only a single point for the same reasons that applied to $F^*_S(d)$. Hence $x + q$ must be that single point, so $x + q$ must itself be integral. As q is integral, x must be integral also. Thus $F^*_S(d)$, and a fortiori $F^*_{S'}(d)$, contains the integral point x. This verifies condition (1.2) for A^*.

By Theorem 1, (1.3) holds for A^*. As the rank of A^* is n, $\gcd(S) = |S| = 1$ for every set S of n linearly independent rows of A^*. From this we wish to show that A has the u.p. Suppose E is any non-singular square submatrix of A. Let the order of E be s. By choosing S to consist of the rows of A^* which contain E together with the proper set of $(n - s)$ rows of I, and by rearranging columns, we can easily insure that

$$S = \begin{bmatrix} I & 0 \\ F & E \end{bmatrix}$$

where I is the identity matrix of order $(n - s)$, F is some s by $(n - s)$ matrix, and 0 is the $(n - s)$ by s matrix of zeros. Then $|S| = |E| \neq 0$, so S is non-singular. Therefore S consists of n linearly independent rows, so

$$|E| = |S| = \gcd(S) = 1.$$

This completes the proof of Theorem 2.

4. A THEOREM BY HELLER AND TOMPKINS

In this and the remaining sections we give various sufficient conditions for a matrix to have the unimodular property.

THEOREM 3. (Heller and Tompkins). Let A be an m by n matrix whose rows can be partitioned into two disjoint sets, T_1 and T_2, such that A, T_1, and T_2 have the following properties:

(4.1) every entry in A is $0, +1,$ or -1;

(4.2) every column contains at most two non-zero entries;

(4.3) if a column of A contains two non-zero entries, and both have the same sign, then one is in T_1 and one is in T_2;

(4.4) if a column of A contains two non-zero entries, and they are of opposite sign, then both are in T_1 or both in T_2.

Then A has the unimodular property.

This theorem is closely related to the central result of the paper by Heller and Tompkins in this Study. The theorem, as stated above, is given an independent proof in an appendix to their paper.

COROLLARY.[5] If A is the incidence matrix of the vertices versus the edges of an ordinary linear graph G, then in order that A have the unimodular property it is necessary and sufficient that G have no loops with an odd number of vertices.

PROOF. To prove the sufficiency, recall the following. The condition that G have no odd loops is well-known to be equivalent to the property that the vertices of G can be partitioned into two classes so that each edge of G has one vertex in each class. If we partition the rows of A correspondingly, it is easy to verify the conditions (4.1)-(4.4). Therefore A has the u.p.

If A has an odd loop, let A' be the submatrix contained in the rows and columns corresponding to the vertices and edges of the loop. Then

---

[5] The authors are indebted to the referee for this result.

it is not hard to see that $|A'| = \pm 2$. This proves the necessity.

5. A SUFFICIENT CONDITION FOR THE UNIMODULAR PROPERTY

We shall consider oriented graphs. For our purposes an oriented graph G is a graph (a) which has no circular edges, (b) which has at most one edge between any two given vertices, and (c) in which each edge has an orientation. Let V denote the set of vertices of G, and E the set of edges. If (r, s) is in E (that is, if (r, s) is an edge of G), then we shall call (s, r) an inverse edge. (Note that by (b), and inverse edge cannot be in E; thus an inverse edge cannot be an edge. This slight ambiguity in terminology should cause no confusion.) We shall often use the phrase direct edge to denote an ordinary edge.

Diagram 1

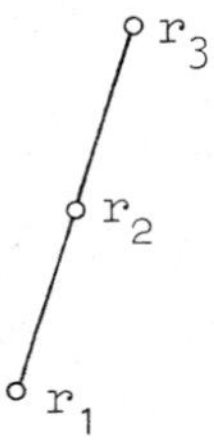

A direct path

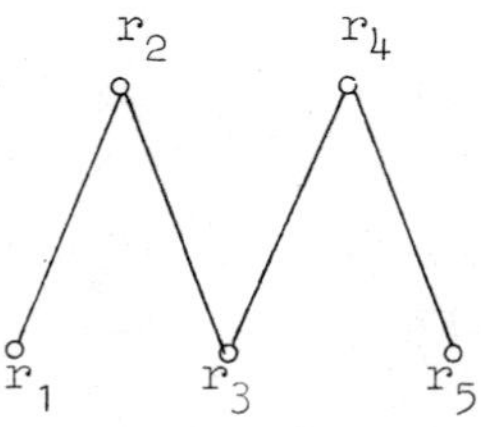

A(+ -) alternating path

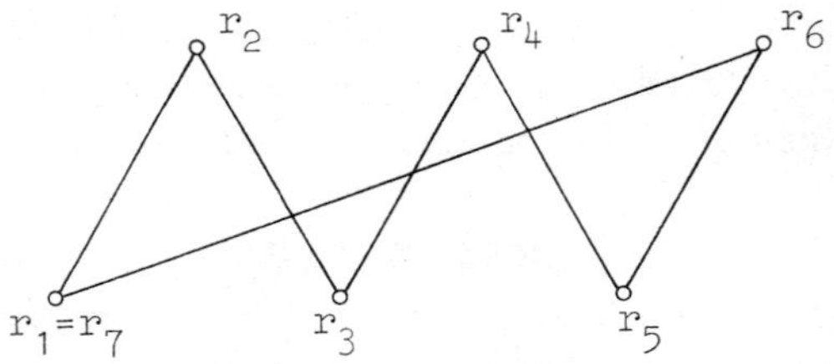

An alternating loop

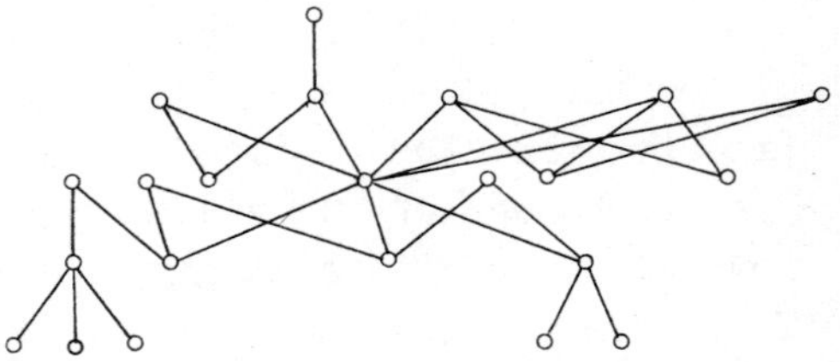
An alternating graph
(arrows omitted - all should be upward)

A path is a sequence of distinct vertices $r_1, \ldots, r_k$, such that for each i, from 1 to $k - 1$, (r_i, r_{i+1}) is either a direct or an inverse edge. A path is directed if every edge is oriented forward, that is, if every edge (r_i, r_{i+1}) in the path is a direct edge. A path is alternating if successive edges are oppositely oriented. More precisely, a path is alternating if its edges are alternately direct and inverse. An alternating path may be described as being $(++)$, $(+-)$, $(-+)$, or $(--)$. The first sign indicates the orientation of the first edge of the path, the second sign the orientation of the last edge of the path. A $+$ indicates a direct edge; a $-$ indicates an inverse edge. A loop is a path which closes back on itself. More precisely, a loop is a sequence of vertices $r_1, \ldots, r_k$ in which $r_1 = r_k$ but which are otherwise distinct, and such that for each i (r_i, r_{i+1}) is either a direct or an inverse edge. A loop is alternating if successive edges are oppositely oriented and if the first and last edges are oppositely oriented. An alternating loop must obviously contain an even number of edges.

A graph is alternating if every loop in it is alternating. Let $V = \{v_1, \ldots, v_m\}$ be the vertices of G, and let $P = \{p_1, \ldots, p_n\}$ be some set of directed paths in G. Then the incidence matrix $A = \|a_{ij}\|$ of G versus P is defined by

$$a_{ij} = \begin{cases} 1 & \text{if } v_i \text{ is in } p_j, \\ 0 & \text{if } v_i \text{ is not in } p_j. \end{cases}$$

We let A_v represent the row of A corresponding to the vertex v and A^p represent the column of A corresponding to the path p. We often write a_{vp} instead of a_{ij} for the entry common to A_v and A^p.

THEOREM 4. Suppose G is an oriented graph, P is some set of directed paths in G, and A is the incidence matrix of G versus P. Then for A to have the unimodular property it is sufficient that G be alternating. If P consists of the set of all directed paths of G, then for A to have the unimodular property it is necessary and sufficient that G be alternating.

This theorem does not state that every matrix of zeros and ones with the u.p. can be obtained as the incidence matrix of an alternating graph versus a set of directed paths. Nor does it give necessary and sufficient conditions for a matrix of zeros and ones to have the unimodular property. (Such conditions would be very interesting.) However it does provide a very general sufficient condition. For example, the coefficient matrix of the i by j transportation problem (or its transpose, depending on which way you write the matrix) is the incidence matrix of the alternating graph versus the set of all directed paths. Hence this matrix has the u.p., from which by Theorem 2 follows the well-known i.p. of transportation problems and their duals. The extent to which alternating graphs can be more general than the graph shown to the left is a measure of how general Theorem 4 is.

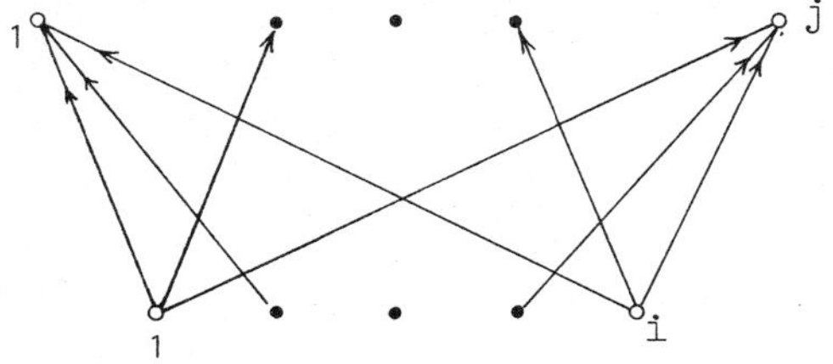

Diagram 2

So that the reader may follow our arguments more easily, we describe here what alternating graphs look like.

(As logically we do not need these facts and as the proofs are tedious, we omit them.) An integral <u>height</u> function $h(v)$ may be defined in such a way that (r, s) is a direct edge only when (but not necessarily when) $h(r) + 1 = h(s)$. If we define $r \leqq s$ to mean that there is a directed path from r to s, then $\leqq$ is a partial order. Then (r, s) is a direct edge if and only if both $r < s$ and there is no element t such that $r < t < s$.

PROOF OF NECESSITY. We consider here the case in which P is the set of <u>all</u> directed paths in G, and we prove that for A to have the u.p. it is necessary that G be alternating. It is easy to verify that the matrix (shown below) of odd order which has ones down the main diagonal and sub-diagonal and in the upper right-hand corner, and zeros elsewhere, has determinant $+ 2$.

$$\begin{bmatrix} 1 & & & & 1 \\ 1 & 1 & & & \\ & 1 & \ddots & & \\ & & \ddots & 1 & \\ & & & 1 & 1 \end{bmatrix}$$

We shall show that if G is not alternating then it contains this matrix, perhaps with rows and columns permuted, as a submatrix.

Let ℓ be a non-alternating loop in G. If ℓ has an odd number of distinct vertices, consider the rows in A which correspond to these vertices, and consider the columns in A which correspond to the one-edge directed paths which correspond to the edges in ℓ. The submatrix contained in these rows and columns is clearly the matrix shown above, up to row and column permutations. Hence in this case A does not have the u.p. If ℓ has an even number of distinct vertices, then find in it three successive vertices r, s, t such that (r, s) and (s, t) are both direct (or both inverse) edges. (To find r, s, t it may be necessary to let s be the initial-terminal vertex of ℓ, in which case r, s, t are successive only in a cyclic sense.) Consider the rows of A which correspond to all the vertices of ℓ except s. Consider the columns of A which correspond to the following directed paths: the two-edge path r, s, t (or t, s, r) and the one-edge paths using the other edges in ℓ. The submatrix contained in these rows and columns is the square matrix of odd order shown above, up to row and column permutations. Hence in this case also A does not have the u.p. This completes the proof of necessity.

The proof of the sufficiency condition, when P may be <u>any</u> set of directed paths in G, occupies the rest of this section. As this proof is long and complicated, it has been broken up into lemmas.

If $r_1, \ldots, r_k$ is a loop, then $r_i, \ldots, r_k, r_2, \ldots, r_i$ is called a <u>cyclic permutation</u> of the loop. Clearly a loop is alternating if and only if any cyclic permutation is alternating.

> LEMMA 6. Suppose A is the incidence matrix of an alternating graph G versus some set of directed paths P in G. For any submatrix A' of A, there is an alternating graph G' and a set of directed paths P' in G' such that A' is the incidence matrix of G' versus P'.

PROOF. Any submatrix can be obtained by a sequence of row and column deletions. Hence it suffices to consider the two cases in which A' is formed from A by deleting a single column or a single row. If A' is formed from A by deleting the column A^p, let $G' = G$, and $P' = P - \{p\}$. Then A' is clearly the incidence matrix of G' versus P', and G' is indeed an alternating graph.

Suppose now that A' is formed from A by deleting row A_t. Define

$$V' = V - \{t\},$$

$$E' = \{(v, w) \mid v, w \text{ in } V' \text{ and either } (v, w) \text{ in } E \text{ or } (v, t) \text{ and } (t, w) \text{ in } E\},$$

$$G' = \text{the graph with vertices } V' \text{ and edges } E',$$

$$P' = \{p - \{t\} \mid p \text{ in } P\} .$$

Clearly A' is the incidence matrix of G' versus P'. We shall prove (a) that P' is a collection of directed paths and (b) that G' is alternating.

The proof of (a) is quite simple. Suppose v, w are successive vertices of $p' = p - \{t\}$ in P'. It may or may not happen that p contains t. In either case, however, if v, w are successive vertices in p, then (v, w) is a

Diagram 3

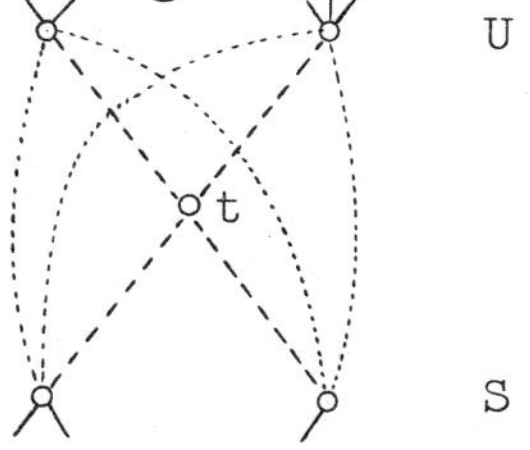

Solid edges - G and G'
Dashed edges - G only
Dotted edges - G' only

direct edge in G, so (v, w) is a direct edge in G'. If v, w are not successive vertices in p, then necessarily v, t, w are successive vertices in p. In this case (v, t) and (t, w) are direct edges in G, so (v, w) is a direct edge in G'.

The proof of (b) is more extended. Define

$$S = \{s \mid (s, t) \text{ in } E\}$$
$$U = \{u \mid (t, u) \text{ in } E\} .$$

Then each "new" edge in E', that is, each edge of E' - E, is of the form (s, u) with s in S and u in U. Let ℓ be any loop in G'. If ℓ contains no new edge, then ℓ is also a loop in G and hence alternating. If ℓ contains a new edge, it contains at least two vertices of $S \cup U$. Hence the vertices of $S \cup U$ break ℓ up into pieces which are paths of the form

$$p = v, r_1, \ldots, r_k, v'$$

where v and v' are in $S \cup U$ and the r's are not.

CASE (U, U): both v and v' belong to U. In this case

$$t, v, r_1, \ldots, r_k, v', t$$

is a loop in G, hence alternating. Therefore p is an alternating path. As (t, v) is a direct edge and (v', t) is an inverse edge in G, p must be a (- +) alternating path in G'.

CASE (S, S): both v and v' belong to S. In this case dual argument to the above proves that p must be a (+ -) alternating path in G'.

CASE (U, S): v belongs to U and v' belongs to S. In this case p must be exactly the one-edge path v, v'. For if not, p consists solely of edges in E, so the loop which we may represent symbolically v', t, p is a loop in G. But as (v', t) and (t, v) are both direct edges in G this loop is not alternating, which is impossible. As (v, v') is an inverse edge in G', p is a (- -) alternating path in G'.

CASE (S, U): v belongs to S and v' belongs to U. In this case dual argument to the above proves that p must be exactly the one-edge path v, v' and hence a (+ +) alternating path in G'.

Using these four cases, we easily see that the pieces of ℓ are alternating and fit together in such a way that ℓ itself is alternating - except for one technical difficulty, namely the requirement that the initial and terminal edges of ℓ must have opposite orientations. However, if we form a cyclic permutation of ℓ and apply the reasoning above to this new loop, we obtain the necessary information to complete our proof that ℓ is alternating. This completes the proof of (b) and Lemma 6.

In view of Lemma 6, the sufficiency condition of Theorem 4 will be proved if we prove that every square incidence matrix of an alternating graph versus a set of directed paths has determinant, 0, + 1, or - 1. We prove this by a kind of induction on two new variables, $c(G)$ and $d(G)$, which we shall now define:

$c(G)$ = the number of unordered pairs $\{st\}$ of distinct vertices of G which satisfy

(5.1) there is a vertex u such that (s, u) and (t, u) are direct edges of G;

$d(G)$ = the number of unordered pairs $\{st\}$ of distinct vertices of G which satisfy

(5.2) there is no directed path from s to t nor any directed path from t to s.

Though not logically necessary the following information may help orient the reader to the significance of these two variables. Assume G is alternating. Then using the partial-order $\leqq$ introduced informally earlier, $d(G)$ is the number of pairs of vertices which are incomparable under $\leqq$. Any pair $\{st\}$ which satisfies (5.1) also satisfies (5.2), so $c(G) \leqq d(G)$. If $c(G) = 0$, then each vertex of G has at most one "predecessor", and G consists of a set of trees, each springing from a single vertex and oriented outward from that vertex. If $d(G) = 0$, then G is even more special: it consists of a single directed path.

LEMMA 7. If G is alternating, and $\{st\}$ satisfies (5.1), then it also satisfies (5.2). Hence $c(G) \leqq d(G)$.

PROOF. Let u be a vertex such that (s, u) and (t, u) are direct edges of G. Suppose there is a directed path

$$s, r_1, \ldots, r_k, t \,.$$

If none of the r's is u, then

$$s, r_1, \ldots, r_k, t, u, s$$

is a loop, hence alternating. As (t, u) is a direct edge, (r_k, t) is an inverse edge, so the path is not directed, a contradiction. If one of the r's is u, take the piece from u to t. By renaming, we may call this directed path

$$u, r_1, \ldots, r_k, t .$$

Then

$$t, u, r_1, \ldots, r_k, t$$

is a loop, hence alternating. As (t, u) is a direct edge, (u, r_1) must be an inverse edge, so the path is not directed, a contradiction. Therefore, there can be no directed path from s to t. By symmetrical argument, there can be no directed path from t to s. Therefore {st} satisfies (5.2). It follows trivially that $c(G) \leqq d(G)$. This completes the proof of Lemma 7.

The induction proceeds in a slightly unusual manner. The "initial case" consists of all graphs G for which $c(G) = 0$. The inductive step consists of showing that the truth of the assertion for a graph G such that $c(G) > 0$ follows from the truth of the assertion for a graph G' for which $d(G') < d(G)$. It is easy to see that by using the inductive step repeatedly, we may reduce to a graph G^* for which either $c(G^*)$ or $d(G^*)$ is 0. But as $d(G^*) = 0$ implies $c(G^*) = 0$ by the inequality between c and d, we are down to the initial case either way.

We now treat the initial case.

LEMMA 8. Let A be the incidence matrix of an alternating graph G versus some set of directed paths P. Suppose that P contains as many directed paths as G contains vertices, so A is square. Suppose that $c(G) = 0$. Then $|A| = 0, +1$, or -1.

PROOF. If (r, s) is a direct edge of G, we call r a <u>predecessor</u> of s and s a <u>successor</u> of r. The fact that $c(G) = 0$ means that each vertex of G has at most one predecessor. If V' is a subset of V, and r is in V' but has no predecessor in V', then r is called an <u>initial vertex</u> of V'.

Every non-empty subset V' of V has at least one initial vertex. For if V' has none, then we can form in V' a sequence $r_1, r_2, \ldots$ of vertices such that for every i, r_{i+1} is a predecessor of r_i. Let r_j be the first term in the sequence which is the same as a vertex picked earlier, and let r_i be the earlier name for this vertex. Then r_i, r_{i+1}, ..., r_j is a loop all of whose edges are inverse. As G is alternating, this is impossible.

Let $U(r) = \{s \mid s$ is a successor of $r\}$. Let r_1 be an initial vertex in V. Recursively, let r_i be an initial vertex of $V - \{r_1, r_2, \ldots, r_{i-1}\}$. Then define matrices B(i) recursively:

$$B(0) = A,$$

$$B(i) = B(i - 1)$$

with the row $B_{r_i}(i - 1)$ replaced by

$$B_{r_i}(i - 1) - \sum_{s \text{ in } U(r_i)} B_s(i - 1) .$$

Let B be the final B(i). We see immediately that $|A| = |B(1)| = \ldots = |B|$. Thus we only need show that $|B| = 0, + 1,$ or $- 1$.

We claim that each column B^p of B consists of zeros with either one or two exceptions: if w is the final vertex of the directed path p, then $b_{wp} = 1$, and if v is the unique predecessor to the initial vertex of p, then $b_{vp} = - 1$. As the initial vertex of p may have no predecessor at all, the $- 1$ may not occur.

We shall not prove in detail the assertions of the preceding paragraph. We content ourselves with considering the column corresponding to a fixed path p during the transition from B(i - 1) to B(i). Only one entry is altered, namely $b_{r_ip}(i - 1)$. There are four possible cases.

CASE (i): neither r_i nor any of its successors is in p.

CASE (ii): r_i is not in p but one of its successors is in p.

CASE (iii): both r_i and one of its successors is in p.

CASE (iv): r_i is in p but none of its successors is in p.

At most one successor of a vertex can be in a directed path because G is alternating, so these cases cover every possibility. In case (i), the entry we are considering starts as 0 and ends as 0. In case (ii), it starts as 0 and ends as $- 1$. In case (iii), it starts as 1 and ends as 0. In case (iv), it starts as 1 and ends as 1. From these facts, it is not hard to see that B satisfies our assertions.

From our assertions about B it is trivial to check that B satisfies the hypotheses of Theorem 3. It is only necessary to partition the rows of B into two classes, one class being empty and the other class containing every row. Then by Theorem 3, B has the u.p. Therefore, $|B| = 0, +1,$ or -1. As $|A| = |B|$, this completes the proof of Lemma 8.

We now prove the inductive step.

LEMMA 9. Suppose that A is the square incidence matrix of an alternating graph G versus a set of directed paths P. Suppose that $c(G) > 0$. Then there is a square matrix A' such that $|A'| = |A|$ and such that A' is the square incidence matrix of an alternating graph G' versus a set of directed paths P', where $d(G') < d(G)$.

PROOF. As $c(G) > 0$, G contains a vertex u which has at least two distinct predecessors, s and t. Define

$$A' = A \text{ with row } A_t \text{ replaced by } A_s + A_t.$$

Clearly $|A'| = |A|$. Define

$$V' = V,$$

$$E_s = \{(s, w) \mid (s, w) \text{ in } E\},$$

$$E_t = \{(t, w) \mid (s, w) \text{ in } E\},$$

$$E' = E \cup E_t \cup \{(s, t)\} - E_s,$$

$$G' = \text{the graph with vertices } V' \text{ and edges } E',$$

$$p' = \begin{cases} p & \text{if } p \text{ does not contain } s, \\ p \text{ with } t \text{ inserted after } s & \text{if } p \text{ does contain } s, \end{cases}$$

$$P' = \{p' \mid p \text{ in } P\}.$$

We shall prove (a) that G' is alternating, (b) that P' is a set of directed paths of G', (c) that $d(G') < d(G)$, and (d) that A' is the incidence matrix of G' versus P'.

Diagram 4

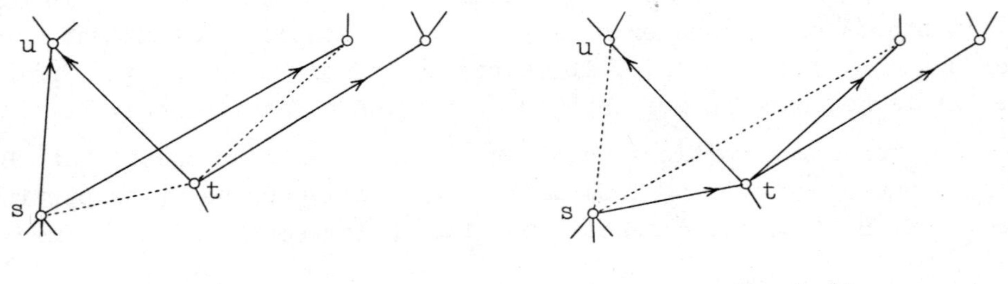

Graph G   Graph G'

The proof of (b) is simple. If p does not contain s, then every edge in $p' = p$ is in E', so p' is a directed path in G'. If p does contain s, write p thus:

$$r_1, \ldots, r_i, s, r_{i+1}, \ldots, r_j .$$

Then p' is

$$r_1, \ldots, r_i, s, t, r_{i+1}, \ldots, r_j .$$

Each edge of p except (s, r_{i+1}) is also in E'. Hence to show that p' is a directed path in G', we only need show that (s, t) and (t, r_{i+1}) are in E'. The former is in E' by definition, and the latter is in E_t because (s, r_{i+1}) must be in E. This proves (b).

To prove (c), let r_1 and r_2 be any pair of vertices such that there is a directed path p from one to the other in G. Then p' is a directed path from one to the other in G'. Hence every pair of vertices which satisfies (5.2) in G' also satisfies (5.2) in G. Furthermore, $\{st\}$ does not satisfy (5.2) in G' because (s, t) is in E', while $\{st\}$ does satisfy (5.2) in G by Lemma 7. This proves that $d(G') < d(G)$.

To prove (d), we first show that A' consists entirely of zeros and ones. The only way in which this could fail to happen is if A_s and A_t both contained ones in the same column. But if this were the case, then the directed path corresponding to this column would contain both s and t, which cannot happen by Lemma 7. To see that A' is the desired incidence matrix, consider how P' differs from P. Each directed path which did not contain s remains unchanged; each directed path which did contain s has t inserted in it. Thus the change from A to A' should be the following. Each column which has a zero in row A_s should remain unchanged; each column which has a one in row A_s should have the zero in row A_t changed to a one. But adding row A_s to A_t accomplishes exactly this. Therefore (d) is true.

The proof of (a) is more complicated.[6] Define S' to be the set of successors of s in G which are not also successors of t. Note that every edge in G' which is not in G terminates either in t, or in a vertex of S'. Let ℓ be any loop of G'. If ℓ is already a loop of G, then it is alternating. If not, it must contain either the edge (s, t) or an edge (t, s') with s' in S'. (Of course, ℓ might contain the inverse of one of these edges instead. If so, reversing the order of ℓ brings us to the situation above.) Ignoring trivial loops, that is,

---

[6] We are indebted to the referee for this proof, which replaces a considerably more complicated one.

loops of the form aba (which are alternating trivially), ℓ must have the form

$$str_1 \cdots r_k s$$

or

$$ts'r_1 \cdots r_k t, \quad \text{with} \quad s' \text{ in } S'.$$

The first form is impossible. To prove this, first suppose that no r_i is in $S' \cup \{u\}$. Then $sutr_1 \cdots r_k s$ is a loop of G, hence alternating. Thus (r_k, s) is an inverse edge and belongs to both G and G', which is impossible. Now suppose that some r_i is in $S' \cup \{u\}$, and let r_j be the last such r_i. Then $sr_j \cdots r_k s$ is a loop of G, hence alternating. Hence (r_k, s) is inverse, which is impossible as before.

We may now assume that ℓ is $ts'r_1 \cdots r_k t$. No r_i can be s. Clearly r_1 cannot be s, and if $r_j = s$, $j > 1$, then $ss'r_1 \cdots r_{j-1}s$ is a loop of G, hence alternating, so (r_{j-1}, s) is inverse and belongs to both G and G', which is impossible. Thus $r_1, \ldots, r_k$ are distinct from s. Suppose that r_k is in S'. Then $ss'r_1 \cdots r_k s$ is a loop of G, hence alternating. Consequently, so is ℓ. Suppose that r_k is not in S' and that no r_i is u. Then $ss'r_1 \cdots r_k tus$ is a loop of G, hence alternating. Thus $s'r_1 \cdots r_k t$ is a (- -) alternating path in G and also in G'. Hence ℓ is alternating. Finally, suppose that r_k is not in S' and that r_j is u. Then $ss'r_1 \cdots r_{j-1}us$ and $tur_{j+1} \cdots r_k t$ are loops of G, hence alternating. Thus $s'r_1 \cdots r_{j-1}u$ is a (- +) alternating path, and $ur_{j+1} \cdots r_k t$ is a (- -) alternating path. Fitting these paths together and adjoining t at the beginning, we see that ℓ is alternating. This completes the proof of (a), of Lemma 9, and of the sufficiency condition of Theorem 4.

6. HOW TO RECOGNIZE THE UNIMODULAR PROPERTY

To apply Theorem 3 is easy, although even there one point is important. To say that A has the unimodular property is the same thing as to say that A^T, the transpose of A, has the unimodular property. However the hypotheses of Theorem 3 or 4 may quite easily be satisfied for A^T but not for A. Consequently it is desirable to examine both A and A^T when using these theorems.

To apply Theorem 4 is not so easy: how shall we recognize whether matrix A (or matrix A^T) is the incidence matrix of an alternating graph versus some set of directed paths? We point out that in actual applications the graph G generally lies close at hand. For example, it was pointed out in Section 5 that the coefficient matrix A of the i by j transportation problem is the incidence matrix of the alternating graph shown in Diagram 2 (at the beginning of Section 5) versus all its directed paths. This graph is no strange object - it portrays the i "producing points", the j "consuming points", and the transportation routes between them.

In a given linear programming problem there will often be one (or several) graphs which are naturally associated with the coefficient matrix. Whenever the problem can be stated in terms of producers, consumers, and intermediate handlers, this is the case. It may well be possible in this situation to identify the matrix as a suitable incidence matrix.

However it is still useful to have criteria available which can be applied directly to the matrix A and which guarantee that A can be obtained as a suitable incidence matrix. The two following theorems give such conditions. Each corresponds to a very special case of Theorem 4. Theorem 5, historically, derives from the integrality of transportation-type problems, and finds application in [2]; Theorem 6 from the integrality of certain caterer-type problems (see [1]).

We shall write $A_i \geqq A_j$ to indicate that row A_i is componentwise $\geqq$ row A_j.

THEOREM 5. Suppose A is a matrix of 0's and 1's, and suppose that the rows of A can be partitioned into two disjoint classes V_1 and V_2 with this property: if A_i and A_j are both in V_1 or both in V_2, and if there is a column A^k in which both A_i and A_j have a 1, then either $A_i \leqq A_j$ or $A_i \geqq A_j$. Then A has the unimodular property.

This theorem corresponds to a generalized transportation situation, in which each upper vertex of the transportation graph has attached an outward flowing tree and each lower vertex has attached an inward flowing tree. Only directed paths which have at least one vertex in the original transportation graph can be represented as columns of the matrix A.

PROOF. Briefly the proof is this: Let vertices v_i in V correspond to the rows A_i of A. Define a partial-order $\leqq$ on the vertices:

$$\begin{aligned} v_i \leqq v_j \quad &\text{if } A_i \text{ in } V_1 \text{ and } A_j \text{ in } V_2 \\ &\text{or } A_i, A_j \text{ in } V_1 \text{ and } A_i \leqq A_j \\ &\text{or } A_i, A_j \text{ in } V_2 \text{ and } A_i \geqq A_j. \end{aligned}$$

Let G be the graph naturally associated with this partially-ordered set. We leave to the reader verification of the fact that G is alternating, and that the columns of A represent directed paths in P.

Say that two column vectors of the same size consisting of 0's and 1's are in accord if the portions of them between (in the inclusive sense) their lowest common 1 and the lower of their highest separate 1's are identical.

THEOREM 6. Suppose A is a matrix of 0's and 1's, and suppose that the rows of A can be rearranged in such a way that every pair of columns is in accord. Then A has the unimodular property.

This theorem corresponds to a situation in which $c(G) = 0$, that is, every vertex has at most one predecessor (or to the dual situation in which every vertex has at most one successor). The columns of A may represent any directed paths in the graph.

PROOF. Let vertices v_i in V correspond to the rows A_i in A. Assume that the rows are already arranged as described above. Define E as follows:

(v_i, v_j) is in E if $i > j$ and if there is a column A^k of A such that a_{ik} and a_{jk} are both 1 while all intervening entries are 0's.

Let G be the graph with vertices V and edges E. We leave to the reader verification of the fact that G is an alternating graph in which every vertex has at most one successor, and that the columns of A represent directed paths in G.

BIBLIOGRAPHY

[1] GADDUM, J. W., HOFFMAN, A. J., and SOKOLOWSKY, D., "On the solution of the caterer problem," Naval Research Logistics Quarterly, Vol. 1, 1954, pp. 223-227. See also JACOBS, W., "The caterer problem," ibid., pp. 154-165.

[2] HOFFMAN, A. J., and KUHN, H. W., "On systems of distinct representatives," this Study.

[3] JACOBSON, NATHAN, Lectures in Abstract Algebra, Vol. II, (1953), D. Van Nostrand Co., pp. 88-92.

National Bureau of Standards — A. J. Hoffman

Princeton University — J. B. Kruskal

AN EXTENSION OF A THEOREM OF DANTZIG'S[*]

I. Heller and C. B. Tompkins

By applying the Simplex Method to the Hitchcock-Koopmans Transportation Problem, G. B. Dantzig[1] showed that a particular property of the constraint matrix permits an essential reduction of the computational procedure.

Because of the obvious importance of such reduction this note will point out an extended class of matrices which have the Dantzig property.

The constraint matrix of the transportation problem has $m + n$ rows, mn columns, and is of the form (shown for $m = 2$, $n = 3$):

$$\begin{array}{cccccc|l} 1 & 1 & 1 & 0 & 0 & 0 & \multirow{2}{*}{\}\, m} \\ 0 & 0 & 0 & 1 & 1 & 1 & \\ \hline 1 & 0 & 0 & 1 & 0 & 0 & \\ 0 & 1 & 0 & 0 & 1 & 0 & \}\, n \\ 0 & 0 & 1 & 0 & 0 & 1 & \\ \multicolumn{3}{c}{\underbrace{\qquad\qquad}_{n}} & \multicolumn{3}{c}{\underbrace{\qquad\qquad}_{n}} & \end{array}$$

This matrix has the property: If a column is represented as a linear combination of a set of independent columns, then the coefficients in the combination are 0, $+1$ or -1. This is Dantzig's Theorem that will be proved for an extended class of matrices.

In a linear vector space E_p, of dimension $p = m + n$, we choose an arbitrary basis

$$u_1, u_2, \ldots, u_m; \quad v_1, v_2, \ldots, v_n,$$

---

* Research carried out under sponsorship of the Office of Naval Research and the Office of Ordnance Research.

1 George B. Dantzig, "Application of the Simplex Method to a Transportation Problem," Activity Analysis of Production and Allocation, J. Wiley and Sons, 1951.

and consider the following set S of vectors

$$\left\{u_i,\ v_j,\ u_i + v_j,\ u_i - u_i{*},\ v_j - v_j{*}\right\}$$

$$(i,\ i^* = 1, 2, \ldots, m; \quad j,\ j^* = 1, 2, \ldots, n).$$

The column vectors of the constraint matrix of the transportation problem are obtained as the subset D_0 of S defined by

$$D_0 = \left\{u_i + v_j\right\} \qquad (i = 1, 2, \ldots, m; \quad j = 1, 2, \ldots, n),$$

for the particular case that the u_i and v_j are an orthonormal system in E_p.

In S distinction will be made between original basis vectors u_i, v_j, called elementary, and all others, called composite. E_m and E_n denote the subspaces determined by the u_i and v_j, respectively.

Now let s be a vector and B a basis, both arbitrary, in S.

> THEOREM 1. The set S has the Dantzig Property; i.e., in the representation of s as linear combination of vectors of B the coefficients can only take on the values 0, $+1$ or -1.

The coefficients of elementary vectors in B admit the more specific

> THEOREM 2.
> (i) If s is elementary, then in its representation exactly one of the elementary vectors in B, say e, has a coefficient different from zero; this coefficient is $+1$ if e and s belong to the same factor space (i.e., if both belong to E_m or both belong to E_n), -1 otherwise.
> (ii) If s is composite, then, in its representation, either all elementary vectors in B have coefficient zero, or exactly two of them, say e_1 and e_2, have coefficients different from zero; these two coefficients are $+1$ or -1; they are of opposite sign if e_1 and e_2 belong to the same factor space, of equal sign otherwise.

We first prove Theorem 2 by induction on the number of composite vectors in B.

If B contains only elementary vectors, then it contains all of them, and the theorem is trivially verified. From the assumption that the theorem holds for any basis B with $k - 1$ composite vectors, it will be concluded that it holds for any basis with k composite vectors:

$$B = \left\{ e_1, e_2, \ldots, e_r; \quad c_1, c_2, \ldots, c_k \right\} \qquad (k \geq 1).$$

Distinguishing whether the represented vector is elementary or composite, we consider each case separately.

Case I. The represented vector is elementary, say e. There are two possibilities:

a) None of the composite vectors of B enter in the representation of e with non-zero weight; then e is necessarily one of the elementary vectors in B and the theorem holds trivially.

b) At least one composite vector, say c_1, has coefficient $\neq 0$. Then in replacing c_1 by e we obtain a new basis

$$B^* = \left\{ e_1, e_2, \ldots, e_r, e; \quad c_2, \ldots, c_k \right\}$$

with only $k - 1$ composite vectors. We consider the representation c_1 as linear combination of vectors of B^*. One of the elementary vectors in B^*, namely e, certainly enters with non-zero coefficient (this is equivalent to assumption b). Hence (by the induction hypothesis) this must be the case for exactly one more, say e_1, and we have

$$c_1 = \epsilon_1 e_1 + \epsilon e + L(c_2, \ldots, c_k), \tag{1}$$

where $\epsilon_1 = \pm 1$, $\epsilon = \pm 1$, $\epsilon_1 = -\epsilon$ if and only if e and e_1 are in the same factor space, and L is a linear combination of composite vectors only. Thus,

$$e = -\frac{\epsilon_1}{\epsilon} e_1 + L^*(c_1, c_2, \ldots, c_k), \tag{2}$$

where L^* is a linear combination of composite vectors. Since $-\frac{\epsilon_1}{\epsilon} = 1$ if and only if e and e_1 are in the same factor space, this completes the induction for Case I.

Case II. The represented vector is composite, say c. Then c is a sum or difference of two elementary vectors, say e^* and e^{**}. By (I) the representations of both e^* and e^{**} contain exactly one elementary vector from the basis, say e_1 and e_2 respectively, with coefficients ± 1. Hence the representation of c will be of the form

$$c = \epsilon_1 e_1 + \epsilon_e e_2 + L(c_1, c_2, \ldots, c_k) \quad (\epsilon_i = \pm 1),$$

not excluding the possibility that $e_1 = e_2$.

In order to verify the relation between ϵ_1 and ϵ_2, we first remark:

If a vector d of E_p is a linear combination of composite vectors of S, then the coordinates of d relative to the original basis

$$B_0 = \left\{ u_1, u_2, \ldots, u_m, v_1, v_2, \ldots, v_n \right\}$$

satisfy the following relation:

"Sum of the coordinates in E_m minus sum of the coordinates in E_n equals zero."

PROOF. The relation holds for each composite vector of S and is invariant under linear combinations.

Applying this remark to $c - L = \epsilon_1 e_1 + \epsilon_2 e_2$ yields

$\epsilon_1 + \epsilon_2 = 0$ if e_1 and e_2 belong to the same factor space (this in particular implies cancellation for the case $e_1 = e_2$), and

$\epsilon_1 - \epsilon_2 = 0$ otherwise.

This immediately verifies the induction for Case II, and completes the proof of Theorem 2.

In order to prove Theorem 1, let an arbitrary vector s of S be represented as linear combination of vectors of an arbitrary basis B in S. In that combination the coefficients of the elementary vectors of B are $0, +1$ or -1, by Theorem 2. There remains to be shown that this is also the case for the coefficients of the composite vectors of B (if any). Let c_1 be an arbitrary composite vector of B. We show: If the coefficient of c_1 is not zero, then it is ± 1.

There exists at least one elementary vector e, in whose representation the coefficient of c_1 is not zero (else all elementary vectors, which certainly span the entire E_p, could be represented without using c_1, and B would not be a basis). In B we replace c_1 by e, and obtain a new basis B^*. If we represent c_1 by vectors of B^*, e will enter the representation with non-zero weight, which (by Theorem 2) can only be ± 1. This being established, we now assume that, in the representation of an arbitrary vector s of S by vectors of B, the coefficient of c_1 is $\lambda \neq 0$. If in this representation of s we substitute for c_1 its representation in B^*, we obtain a representation of s by B^* with $\pm \lambda$ as coefficient of e (note that B did not contain e). By Theorem 2 we must have $\lambda = \pm 1$. This completes the proof of Theorem 1.

It should be noted that the determinants of any two bases in S have the same absolute value (it is sufficient to prove this for any two bases A and B which differ in only one column, say a is in A but not in B, and b is in B but not in A; application of Cramer's rule to compute the coefficient of a in $Ax = b$ immediately yields the result).

It may be of interest to note that the Dantzig Property admits a weaker formulation.

A linear combination of a set of vectors may be called basic if the vectors are linearly independent, and integral if the coefficients are integers.

If a matrix A has the Dantzig Property, then, trivially, any basic representation of a column through other columns is integral.

But the converse is also true.

To see this, assume that any basic representation is integral. If the Dantzig Property does not hold, then for some basic representation of some column b of A at least one coefficient, say of column c, is $\lambda \neq 0, 1, -1$:

$$b = \lambda c + L(a_1, \ldots, a_k).$$

This yields a basic representation of c:

$$c = \frac{1}{\lambda} b - L(a_1, \ldots, a_k),$$

where $\frac{1}{\lambda}$ is not integral, in contradiction to the assumption.

A relation between the Dantzig Property of A and the existence of integral solutions to a linear program, constrained by $Ax = b$, can be stated as

> THEOREM 3. If A has the Dantzig Property, then either all basic representations of b in A are integral or b has no integral representation (basic or not) in A.

For linear programs this simply says: If A has the Dantzig Property, then the existence of one solution (basic or not) with integral coordinates is sufficient (and trivially necessary) to assure that all basic solutions, hence in particular the optimal ones, have integral coordinates.

For the proof it is sufficient to observe that, given an integral representation $b = L_1(C)$ and a basic representation $b = L_2(B)$, any vector of C is an integral linear combination of B, and therefore (the unique) $L_2(B)$ is an integral linear combination of integral linear combinations, hence integral.

I. Heller
C. B. Tompkins

George Washington University
and
Numerical Analysis Research,
University of California, Los Angeles

APPENDIX*

In the terminology of Hoffman and Kruskal, the principal result of this paper (Theorem 1) can be formulated as follows:

THEOREM. Let A by an m by n matrix whose rows can be partitioned into two disjoint sets B and C, with the following properties:

(1) every column of A contains at most two non-zero entries;
(2) every entry in A is 0, + 1, or - 1;
(3) if two non-zero entries in a column of A have the same sign, then the row of one is in B, and the other in C;
(4) if two non-zero entries in a column of A have opposite signs, then the rows of both are in B, or both in C.

Then every minor determinant of A is 0, +1, or - 1.

PROOF. (A. J. Hoffman) It is a routine matter to verify that

* Since this paper treats a problem considered in Paper 13 ("Integral Boundary Points of Convex Polyhedra" by A. J. Hoffman and J. B. Kruskal) from a quite different approach, the authors have allowed the editors to add this appendix as a bridge between the papers. The results appearing here have been contributed, as indicated, by A. J. Hoffman and David Gale.

any submatrix of A also satisfies the hypotheses of the theorem. Hence, it will suffice to prove that any square matrix A satisfying the hypotheses of the theorem has determinant $|A|$ equal to $0, +1,$ or -1. The proof is by induction; the case of 1 by 1 matrices follows from (2) above. Suppose that the theorem is true for $(n-1)$ by $(n-1)$ matrices, and that A is an n by n matrix. If every column of A has two non-zero entries, then the linear relation

$$\sum_{A_i \text{ in } B} A_i = \sum_{A_i \text{ in } C} A_i$$

between the rows A_i of A follows directly from (1) - (4), and $|A| = 0$. If some column of A has all zero entries, then $|A| = 0$. Thus, we are left with the case in which some column of A has exactly one non-zero entry. In this case, expand the determinant of A on that column; then, $|A| = \pm |A'|$, where A' is the cofactor of the non-zero entry and has determinant ± 1 by the induction hypothesis. This completes the proof of the theorem.

The conditions of this theorem, which correspond to the rather special construction of S in this paper, would seem to be highly restrictive. However, the following converse demonstrates a sense in which they are the weakest possible. Note that, although this converse is valid only in the presence of (1), these matrices include the incidence matrices of graphs and thus form an important class.

THEOREM. (David Gale) If the matrix A satisfies (1) above, then (2), (3), and (4) are necessary in order that every minor determinant be $0, +1,$ or -1.

PROOF. The necessity of (2) is obvious. To prove the necessity of (3) and (4), it is sufficient to consider matrices A in which every column contains exactly two non-zero elements, since any column containing fewer non-zero elements can be deleted without affecting the validity of the theorem. For this case, associate a graph Γ with the matrix A as follows: the vertices of Γ are the rows of A and the edges of Γ are the columns of A. An edge is called special if the two non-zero elements in the corresponding column have the same sign. Suppose that there is a cycle in Γ containing an odd number of special edges. Then the rows and columns corresponding to the vertices and edges in the cycle can be arranged as follows:

$$A' = \begin{bmatrix} x & & & & x \\ x & x & & & \\ & x & \ddots & & \\ & & \ddots & x & \\ & & & x & x \end{bmatrix}$$

Each x in this diagram marks a non-zero entry; the remaining entries are zero. An odd number of columns have entries of the same sign and an elementary argument proves that $|A'| = \pm 2$. Hence, every cycle in Γ must contain an even number of special edges. Therefore, if the vertices joining non-special edges are identified and the non-special edges deleted, a well-known theorem of König (Theorie der endlichen und unendlichen Graphen, New York, 1950, p. 170) asserts that the new vertices can be partitioned into two sets so that the remaining (special) edges only join vertices in different sets. Since each row is a vertex of Γ, it is assigned (after possible identification with other rows) to one of these sets. The resulting partition of the rows satisfies (3) and (4) and this proves the theorem. It should be noted that the same partition can be derived directly from a theorem of Harary (Mich. Math. J. 2 (1953-54), 144) which asserts that, if every cycle in Γ contains an even number of special edges, then the vertices of Γ can be partitioned into two sets so that each special edge joins two vertices of different sets and each non-special edge joins two vertices of the same set.

NEIGHBORING VERTICES ON A CONVEX POLYHEDRON

David Gale

§1. INTRODUCTION

A convex polyhedron P is the convex hull of a finite set of vertices $a_1, \ldots, a_n$ in a Euclidean space. If a_i and a_j are distinct vertices of P, the segment joining them is called an edge if it is the intersection of P with a supporting hyperplane. In this case the vertices a_i and a_j are called neighbors.

We shall be concerned here with convex polyhedra every two of whose vertices are neighbors. In 3-space it is intuitively clear, and easily proved, that the only polyhedra with this property are the segment, triangle and tetrahedron, i.e., the simplexes of dimension at most 3. The analogous result is no longer true in higher dimensions. It is easy to exhibit a polyhedron in R_4 having 6 vertices every two of which are neighbors. In connection with certain computational problems other examples of this sort have been found. Kuhn has recently discovered a polyhedron in 11-space with 24 vertices every two of which are neighbors, and posed the following question: What is the largest number of vertices an m-dimensional polyhedron can have such that every two are neighbors? This is settled as a special case of our first theorem as follows: For any positive integer n there exists a polyhedron in R_4 with n vertices every two of which are neighbors.

In order to state our more general result we generalize the notion of neighboring points.

> DEFINITION. The vertices $b_1, \ldots, b_k$ of a convex polyhedron P are called neighbors if their convex hull is the intersection of P with a supporting hyperplane.

The first main result of this paper is:

THEOREM I. For any positive integer n there exists a polyhedron P in 2m-space having n vertices every m of which are neighboring.

The theorem is proved by reducing it to the second main result which we introduce in the following manner: a set of $2j + k$ points on the surface of the unit k-sphere, S_k, in (k+1)-space, R_{k+1}, is called <u>evenly distributed</u> if every open hemisphere of S_k contains at least j points.

THEOREM II. For any positive integers k and j there exists a set of $2j + k$ points on S_k which are evenly distributed.

It is sometimes more convenient to rephrase this theorem in a dual form. Let us say that a family of subsets $\{U_\alpha\}$ of a set S forms a <u>j-fold covering</u> of S if every point of S lies in at least j of the sets U_α.

THEOREM II'. For any positive integers j and k there exists a j-fold covering of S_k by $2j + k$ open hemispheres.

§2. THE THEOREMS

NOTATION. In what follows Latin letters will denote vectors, Greek letters real numbers. The scalar product of vectors a and b will be written ab and the norm of a vector a will be written $|a|$.

If $a_1, \ldots, a_n$, are a set of vectors in R_m and $a_i = (\alpha_i^1, \ldots, \alpha_i^m)$ then a^i will denote the vector in R_n, $a^i = (\alpha_1^i, \ldots, \alpha_n^i)$.

LEMMA 1. Let $a_1, \ldots, a_n$ be n vectors in R_k. A sufficient condition that every m of the vectors a_i be neighbors is that for every non-zero solution $(\lambda_1, \ldots, \lambda_n)$ of the equations

$$\sum_{i=1}^{n} \lambda_i a_i = 0, \quad \sum_{i=1}^{n} \lambda_i = 0,$$

at least $m + 1$ of the numbers λ_i are positive.

PROOF. It will be sufficient to show that the hypothesis of the lemma implies that $a_1, a_2, \ldots, a_m$, are neighbors.

Let e^i denote the vector in R_n whose ith coordinate is 1 and whose remaining coordinates are zero, and let $e = \Sigma_i e^i$. The hypothesis of the lemma can then be rephrased to read: If $x \in R_n$, $x \neq 0$ then, if $xa^i = 0$ for all i and $xe = 0$ then $xe^i > 0$ for at least $m + 1$ vectors e^i. In particular, $xe^i > 0$ for at least one index $i > m$.

Now define,

$$C = \left\{ y \;\middle|\; y = \lambda_0 e + \sum_{i=1}^{k} \lambda_i a^i - \sum_{i=m+1}^{n} \mu_i e^i, \text{ where } \mu_i \geq 0 \right\}.$$

The set C is a closed convex cone, that is, C is closed, $C + C \subset C$ and $\lambda C \subset C$ for $\lambda \geq 0$. We assert that C is, in fact, all of R_n, for if this were not so one could find a supporting hyperplane to C, thus a vector x such that $xy \geq 0$ for all $y \in C$. In particular this would mean $xa_i \geq 0$ and $x(-a_i) \geq 0$ for all i hence $xa_i = 0$ for all i, and similarly $xe = 0$ and $x(-e^i) \geq 0$ for $i > m$ or $xe^i \leq 0$ for $i > m$. Since this contradicts the hypothesis, the assertion is proved. Therefore we can write

$$e + \sum_{i=m+1}^{n} e^i = \lambda_0 e + \sum_{i=1}^{k} \lambda_i a^i - \sum_{i=m+1}^{n} \mu_i e^i$$

or

$$\sum_{i=1}^{k} \lambda_i a^i = (1 - \lambda_0)e + \sum_{i=m+1}^{n} (1 + \mu_i)e^i.$$

Let b be the vector $(\lambda_1, \ldots, \lambda_k)$ and let H be the hyperplane in R_k defined by,

$$H = \left\{ x \;\middle|\; b\,x = 1 - \lambda_0 \right\}.$$

Now, $ba_i = 1 - \lambda_0$ for $i \leq m$ and $ba_i = (1 - \lambda_0) + (1 + \mu_i)$ for $i > m$. Since $\mu_i \geq 0$ this shows that H is a supporting hyperplane for the polyhedron P spanned by the vertices a_i and intersects P in the convex hull of the vertices a_i, $i \leq m$, hence these vertices are neighbors.

We shall adopt the following notation: If a is a point of the unit k-sphere S_k then $H(a)$ will denote the open hemisphere

$$H(a) = \left\{ x \;\middle|\; x \in S_k \text{ and } xa > 0 \right\},$$

and $S(a)$ will denote the $(k-1)$-sphere

$$S(a) = \left\{ x \;\middle|\; x \in S_k \text{ and } xa = 0 \right\}.$$

The equivalence of Theorems II and II' is now immediate, for from the definitions it follows that the points $a_1, \ldots, a_{2j+k}$ are evenly distributed on S_k if and only if the hemispheres $H(a_i)$ provide a j-fold covering of S_k.

In order to show that Theorem II implies Theorem I we shall need one more preliminary result.

LEMMA 2. If $a_1, \ldots, a_n$ are vectors in R_m such that the origin is an interior point of their convex hull C then there exist positive numbers λ_i, $i = 1, \ldots, n$ such that $\Sigma_i \lambda_i a_i = 0$.

PROOF. Let $b = -\Sigma_i a_i$. Since 0 is an interior point of C there exists a sufficiently small positive number δ such that $\delta b \in C$ so

$$\delta b = \sum_{i=1}^{n} \mu_i a_i \quad \text{where} \quad \mu_i \geq 0,$$

or

$$\sum_{i=1}^{n} \mu_i a_i + \delta \sum_{i=1}^{n} a_i = \sum_{i=1}^{n} (\mu_i + \delta) a_i = 0,$$

and since $\mu_i + \delta > 0$ the lemma is proved.

We now show,

THEOREM II' implies THEOREM I.

PROOF. We must show that there exists a polyhedron P in R_{2m} having n vertices every m of which are neighbors. The result is immediate for $n \leq 2m + 1$, for if we merely take the points a_i to be in general position, they will be the vertices of an $(n-1)$-simplex which has the desired property. We shall therefore assume that $n \geq 2m + 2$.

Let $j = m + 1$ and let $k = n - (2m + 2) = n - 2j$ so that $n = 2j + k$. By Theorem II there exist points $b_1, \ldots, b_n$ which are evenly distributed on S_k. If C is the convex hull of the points b_i then 0 must be an interior point of C, as otherwise one could find a supporting hyperplane to C at 0, thus a vector h such that $hb_i \geq 0$ for all

i, hence $(-h)b_i \le 0$ for all i, so $H(-h)$ would contain none of the points b_i contrary to hypothesis. From Lemma 2 it follows that there exist positive numbers λ_i such that $\Sigma_i \lambda_i b_i = 0$.

Let $b_i' = \lambda_i b_i$. These vectors now satisfy the following two conditions.

(1) $\Sigma_i b_i' = 0$

(2) for any vector $x \in R_{k+1}$, $xb_i' > 0$ for at least j of the vectors b_i'.

If B is the matrix whose ith row is b_i' then B has rank $k + 1$ for if the b_i' were linearly dependent one could find a vector x such that $xb_i' = 0$ for all i contrary to (2). Let b^i be the ith column vector of B and let L be the linear space in R_n generated by the b^i. Then L has dimension $k + 1$ and

(1)' If $y \in L$ then the sum of the coordinates of y is zero (since this is true for each b^i by condition (1)).

(2)' If $y \in L$ then at least j of its coordinates are positive (for

$$y = \sum_{i=1}^{k+1} \lambda_i b^i$$

and letting $x = (\lambda_1, \ldots, \lambda_{k+1})$ we see that the rth coordinate of y is xb_r', and the assertion follows from (2)).

Now let L^* be the orthogonal complement of L in R_n. From (1') it follows that $e \in L^*$ (e as in Lemma 1). Also L^* has dimension $n - (k + 1)$ so we may choose a basis, $e, a^1, \ldots, a^{n-k-2} = a^{2m}$, for L^*.

We now assert that the vectors $a_1, \ldots, a_n$ satisfy the hypothesis of Lemma 1, for suppose

$$\sum_{i=1}^{n} \eta_i a_i = 0 \quad \text{and} \quad \sum_{i=1}^{n} \eta_i = 0.$$

Letting $y = (\eta_1, \ldots, \eta_n)$ we have $ya^i = 0$, for $i = 1, \ldots, 2m$, and $ye = 0$. Accordingly, $y \in L$ and hence at least $j(= m + 1)$ of its coordinates are positive. Thus, from Lemma 1 every m points from among the a_i are neighbors and Theorem I is established.

In order to prove Theorem II' we need to state a somewhat stronger result.

THEOREM III. Let Γ be a j-fold covering of S_k by $n = 2j + k$ open hemispheres $H(a_1), \ldots, H(a_n)$. Then there exist vectors a_{n+1} and a_{n+2} such that the hemispheres $H(a_i)$ form a (j+1)-fold covering of S_k, $i = 1, \ldots, n + 2$.

Note that Theorem II' follows from this result once we have established the existence of a 1-fold covering of S_k by $k + 2$ hemispheres in R_{k+1}. This is easily done by choosing $a_i = e_i$, $i \leq k + 1$ and $a_{k+2} = - e$. Then clearly if $x \in S_k$ and $xe_i \leq 0$ for all i then $x(- e) > 0$ so the hemispheres $H(e_i)$, $H(- e)$ cover S_k. Theorem II' now follows by applying Theorem III j times.

Theorem III is easily proved if $k = 0$, for S_0 consists only of the points 1 and $- 1$. If $H(a_1), \ldots, H(a_n)$ form a j-fold covering of S_0, let $a_{n+1} = 1$, $a_{n+2} = - 1$, and we have the desired (j+1)-fold covering.

The proof now proceeds by induction on k. Before continuing we derive an auxiliary inequality.

If C is a closed subset of S_k and $x \in S_k$ then the distance $|x - C|$ of x from C is defined by

$$|x - C| = \min_{y \in C} |x - y|.$$

LEMMA 3. If $a, x \in S_k$ then

$$|x - S(a)| \leq \sqrt{2}\, |xa|.$$

PROOF. Let $L(a)$ be the linear space orthogonal to a. Then $x = \alpha a + y$ where $y \in L(a)$ or if $b = y/_{|y|}$ then

$$x = \alpha a + \beta b$$

where a and b are orthonormal, $\alpha^2 + \beta^2 = 1$ and $\beta \geq 0$. Now

$$(x - b)^2 = x^2 - 2xb + b^2 = 2(1 - xb) = 2(1 - \beta)$$

$$= 2\left(1 - \sqrt{1 - \alpha^2}\right) = 2\alpha^2 \Big/ \left(1 + \sqrt{1 - \alpha^2}\right) \leq 2\alpha^2.$$

Hence

$$|x - S_a| \leq |x - b| \leq \sqrt{2}\, |\alpha| = \sqrt{2}\, |xa|.$$

PROOF OF THEOREM III. Suppose given a j-fold covering of S_k by $n = 2j + k$ hemispheres, $H(a_1), \ldots, H(a_n)$. We assert that the hemispheres $H(a_i)$, $i < n$ form a j-fold covering of $S(a_n)$, for if $x \in S(a_n)$ then $x \notin H(a_n)$, hence x lies in j of the hemispheres $H(a_i)$ for $i < n$. Since $S(a_n)$ is a $(k-1)$-sphere we have by the induction hypothesis that there exist points b and b' on $S(a_n)$ such that $H(a_i), \ldots, H(a_{n-1})$, $H(b)$, $H(b')$ form a $(j+1)$-fold covering of $S(a_n)$. Let U be the set of all points $x \in S_k$ such that x lies in at least $j + 1$ of the above collection of hemispheres. Since U is an open set and $S(a_n) \subset U$ it follows that if c is a point sufficiently close to a_n then $S(c) \subset U$. In particular if $c = a_n - \lambda b$ and λ is positive but sufficiently small then $S(c) \subset U$. We now assert that $S(c)$ is covered $(j+1)$-times by $H(a_i)$, $i \leq n$, and $H(b')$, for suppose $x \in S(c)$ and $xb > 0$. Then since

$$xa_n - \lambda xb = xc = 0$$

it follows that $xa_n > 0$, proving the assertion.

Now let U' be the open set of all $x \in S_k$ such that x lies in at least $j + 1$ of the hemispheres $H(a_i)$, $i \leq n$ and $H(b')$. Then $S(c) \subset U'$ and since $S(c)$ is compact there exists a positive number δ such that if $|x - S(c)| < \delta$ then $x \in U'$. Let $\bar{c} = c/|c|$. Then clearly $S(\bar{c}) = S(c)$. Choose μ so that $0 < \mu < \delta/\sqrt{2}$ and let

$$a_{n+1} = \mu b' + \bar{c}, \qquad a_{n+2} = \mu b' - \bar{c}.$$

We shall now show that the hemispheres $H(a_i)$, $i \leq n + 2$ provide the desired $(j+1)$-fold covering of S_k. For any $x \in S_k$, $xa_i > 0$ for at least j of the original points a_i. Hence we need only be concerned with points x such that $xa_{n+1} \leq 0$ and $xa_{n+2} \leq 0$, that is

$$\mu(xb') + x\bar{c} \leq 0 \quad \text{and} \quad \mu(xb') - x\bar{c} \leq 0,$$

or

$$\mu(xb') \leq x\bar{c} \leq -\mu(xb')$$

which implies

$$(xb') \leq 0 \quad \text{and} \quad |x\bar{c}| \leq \mu|xb'| \leq \mu|x|\ |b'| \leq \delta/\sqrt{2}.$$

From Lemma 3 then

$$|x - S(c)| \leq \delta$$

and therefore $x \in U'$. But since $xb' \leq 0$ this means that $x \in H(a_i)$ for

$j + 1$ of the points a_i, $i \leq n$, and the proof is complete.

§3. REMARKS

It is easy to show that the results of Theorem I is "best possible" in a well-defined sense as the following remarks indicate.

Let P be a polyhedron in R_k with vertices in general position such that every m vertices of P are neighbors. If $k < 2m$ then P can have at most $k + 1$ vertices.

To see this, suppose P has more than $k + 1$ vertices and let the first $k + 2$ be $a_1, \ldots, a_{k+2}$. Then the equations

$$\sum_{i=1}^{k+2} \lambda_i a_i = 0 \quad \text{and} \quad \sum_{i=1}^{k+2} \lambda_i = 0,$$

constitute a system of $k + 1$ equations in $k + 2$ unknowns and hence have a non-zero solution. Since the a_i are in general position none of the λ_i are zero. By reordering and multiplying the λ_i by a suitable constant we may write

$$\sum_{i=1}^{r} \mu_i a_i = \sum_{i=r+1}^{k+2} \nu_i a_i \tag{3}$$

where $\mu_i, \nu_i > 0$, $\Sigma\mu_i = \Sigma\nu_i = 1$ and $r \leq \frac{k+2}{2} \leq m$. If now $a_i, \ldots, a_m$ are neighbors then there exists a supporting hyperplane to P containing exactly these vertices, in other words a vector b such that $ba_i = \beta$ for $i \leq m$ and $ba_i > \beta$ for $i > m$. However, taking the inner product of both sides of equation (3) with b we would get β on the left and some number greater than β on the right, giving a contradiction.

We conclude with a speculative remark. It would seem that the likelihood of getting polyhedra every m of whose vertices are neighbors increases rapidly with the dimension of the space. Returning to the example of the polyhedron P with 24 vertices in 11-space, it can be shown that the condition that some pair of points of P not be neighbors is that a certain set of 24 points on the surface of an 11-sphere S are distributed so that 22 of these points lie in an open hemisphere of S. Intuitively speaking, if the 24 points on S_{11} were chosen in a random fashion one would not expect to find them distributed in such an uneven manner. Thus we might guess that finding every pair of points of P neighbors would be the expected rather than the exceptional case.

The probability notions hinted at here can be made precise and investigations in this direction would be of interest in further study of the problem.

David Gale

Brown University

ON A THEOREM OF WALD

H. W. Kuhn*

§1. INTRODUCTION

The object of this paper is the analysis of a pioneering result of Abraham Wald (see [2], [3], and [4] in the Bibliography). His theorem stands (with von Neumann's research on expanding linear models and games of strategy) among the first rigorous existence proofs of general equilibrium in economic models. Wald's work has been cited by Koopmans (in the Introduction to [6]) and by Samuelson [8] as one of the important sources of the discipline of linear programming. However, on the whole, the content of these papers has been neglected.

The proof that is offered below is based on two theorems that come from areas close to general equilibrium theory: the duality theorem of linear programming and the Kakutani fixed point theorem (of course, these are tools that had not been fashioned when Wald wrote). By transferring the mathematical difficulties to an appeal to these results, the roles of the various assumptions made by Wald can be isolated in considerable detail.

The requirements of a general equilibrium in a linear model are stated in Section 2. The connections between this system and linear programming that can be established without further assumptions occupy Section 3. Section 4 is devoted to a proof of Wald's theorem in its original form. A variant of the model and the corresponding existence proof are presented in Section 5. This version of the problem and its solution have been given independently by Solow [10].

§2. STATEMENT

The Walras-Cassel equations as reformulated by Schlesinger [1] provide for <u>factors</u> of production R_i in quantities r_i $(i = 1, \ldots, m)$

* The preparation of this paper was supported, in part, by the Office of Naval Research Logistics Project, Princeton University.

and for goods S_j in quantities s_j $(j = 1, \ldots, n)$. The technology of production is assumed to be such that a_{ij} units of R_i are required to produce one unit of S_j $(i = 1, \ldots, m;\ j = 1, \ldots, n)$. The matrix $A = (a_{ij})$ is called the matrix of technological coefficients. Prices are denoted by ρ_i (for one unit of R_i) and by σ_j (for one unit of S_j), respectively. The prices of the goods are related to the quantities produced by n demand functions $f_j : (s_1, \ldots, s_n) \longrightarrow \sigma_j = f_j(s_1, \ldots, s_n)$. The precise domain of definition of f_j will not be specified until it is needed in §4.

The factor endowment $r = (r_i)$[1], the technological coefficients $A = (a_{ij})$, and the demand functions $f = (f_j)$ are assumed as given; an equilibrium consists of quantities, $\bar{s} = (\bar{s}_j)$, and prices, $\bar{\sigma} = (\bar{\sigma}_j)$ and $\bar{\rho} = (\bar{\rho}_i)$, such that:

$$(1) \quad \bar{s}_j \geq 0, \quad \bar{\sigma}_j \geq 0, \quad \text{and} \quad \bar{\rho}_i \geq 0 \qquad (i = 1, \ldots, m;\ j = 1, \ldots, n)$$

(Only non-negative quantities and prices have economic meaning.)

$$(2) \qquad \sum_j a_{ij}\bar{s}_j \leq r_i \qquad (i = 1, \ldots, m)$$

(There are constant returns to scale limited by the factor endowment.)

$$(3) \qquad \text{If} \quad \sum_j a_{ij}\bar{s}_j < r_i \quad \text{for some } i, \quad \text{then} \quad \bar{\rho}_i = 0.$$

(Any factor present in excess has a zero price.)

$$(4) \qquad \sum_i \bar{\rho}_i a_{ij} = \bar{\sigma}_j \qquad (j = 1, \ldots, n)$$

(The price of each good is equal to its production cost.)

$$(5) \qquad \bar{\sigma}_j = f_j(\bar{s}_1, \ldots, \bar{s}_n) \qquad (j = 1, \ldots, n)$$

(The price of each good is determined by the quantities produced.)

§3. RELATION TO LINEAR PROGRAMMING

We can associate with the given data, r and A, and any fixed prices $\bar{\sigma}$ for the goods, the following pair of dual linear programs.

---

[1] Here, and in the following sections, conventional vector and matrix notation is used. Thus, $\sigma \cdot s = \sigma_1 s_1 + \cdots + \sigma_n s_n$, $As = (\Sigma a_{ij} s_j)$, and vector inequalities such as $s \geq 0$ are to hold in all components.

MAXIMUM PROGRAM. Maximize $\bar{\sigma} \cdot s$ subject to $s \geq 0$ and $As \leq r$.

MINIMUM PROGRAM. Minimize $r \cdot \rho$ subject to $\rho A \geq \bar{\sigma}$ and $\rho \geq 0$.

The following facts about dual linear programs will be needed (for proofs, see [7] and [9]): If either program is solvable then both are solvable and with a common value for the maximum and minimum. If $\bar{s}$ and $\bar{\rho}$ satisfy the constraints (i. e., are feasible), then they are optimal if and only if $\bar{\sigma} \cdot \bar{s} = r \cdot \bar{\rho}$. For optimal $\bar{s}$ and $\bar{\rho}$, $\Sigma_j a_{ij} \bar{s}_j < r_i$ implies $\bar{\rho}_i = 0$ and $\Sigma_i \bar{\rho}_i a_{ij} > \bar{\sigma}_j$ implies $\bar{s}_j = 0$.

LEMMA 1. If $\bar{s}$, $\bar{\sigma}$, and $\bar{\rho}$ satisfy (1), (2), (3), and (4), then $\bar{s}$ and $\bar{\rho}$ solve the maximum and minimum programs associated with r, A, and $\bar{\sigma}$.

PROOF. Conditions (1), (2), and (4) establish the feasibility of $\bar{s}$ and $\bar{\rho}$. On the other hand,

$$\begin{aligned} \bar{\sigma} \cdot \bar{s} &= (\bar{\rho} A) \cdot \bar{s} && \text{(by (4))} \\ &= \bar{\rho} \cdot (A\bar{s}) \\ &= \bar{\rho} \cdot r && \text{(by (2) and (3))}, \end{aligned}$$

and hence $\bar{s}$ and $\bar{\rho}$ are optimal.

LEMMA 2. If $\bar{s}$ and $\bar{\rho}$ solve the maximum and minimum programs associated with $\bar{\sigma} \geq 0$, then $\bar{s}$, $\bar{\sigma}$, and $\bar{\rho}$ satisfy conditions (1), (2), and (3). If $\bar{s} > 0$, then (4) is also satisfied.

PROOF. Conditions (1) and (2) follow from the feasibility of $\bar{s}$ and $\bar{\rho}$ for the programs. To see that (3) holds, suppose that $\Sigma_j a_{ij} \bar{s}_j < r_i$ for some i with $\bar{\rho}_i > 0$. Then, by the feasibility of $\bar{s}$ and $\bar{\rho}$,

$$\bar{\sigma} \cdot \bar{s} \leq (\bar{\rho} A) \cdot \bar{s} = \bar{\rho} \cdot (A\bar{s}) < \bar{\rho} \cdot r,$$

which contradicts the optimality of $\bar{s}$ and $\bar{\rho}$. If $\bar{s} > 0$, then the same inequality requires $\bar{\sigma} = \bar{\rho} A$, which is (4).

THEOREM 1. Suppose $\bar{s}$, $\bar{\sigma}$, and $\bar{\rho}$ satisfy:

(a) The dual programs associated with $\bar{\sigma}$ are solved by $\bar{s}$ and $\bar{\rho}$, respectively.

(b) The vectors $\bar{s}$ and $\bar{\sigma}$ are related by $\bar{\sigma}_j = f_j(\bar{s})$ for $j = 1, \ldots, n$.

(c) The vector $\bar{s}$ is positive.

Then $\bar{s}$, $\bar{\sigma}$, and $\bar{\rho}$ constitute an equilibrium.

PROOF. The theorem follows directly from Lemma 2 and the fact that (5) and (b) are the same condition. Since Lemma 1 establishes (a) as a necessary condition for an equilibrium, this theorem singles out (c) for further attention.

The economic interpretation of this section is clear. If $\bar{\sigma}$ are the equilibrium prices of the goods, the quantities produced maximize the "income" subject to the limitations of the factor endowment. On the other hand, the prices for the factors minimize the "outlay" on production subject to the limitation that the price of a good should not be greater than the cost of producing it. If equality of prices and costs is required (Condition (4)) then it is sufficient to assume that a positive amount of each good is produced (Condition (c)).

The main contribution of this linear programming formulation to the existence question is that now we need only solve the maximum program so that $\bar{s}$ and $\bar{\sigma}$ are related by (5). Then (1), (2), and (3) follow immediately for any solution $\bar{\rho}$ to the dual minimum program. If $\bar{s}$ is positive, then (4) follows also.

§4. THE EXISTENCE OF AN EQUILIBRIUM

In [3], Wald proved the existence of an equilibrium with unique $\bar{s}$ and $\bar{\sigma}$ under the following hypotheses:

(A) $r_i > 0$, $(i = 1, \ldots, m)$.

(B) $a_{ij} \geq 0$, $(i = 1, \ldots, m;\ j = 1, \ldots, n)$.

(C) For every j, there is at least one i with $a_{ij} > 0$.

(D) The function f_j is defined, positive, and continuous on the set of all non-negative $s = (s_1, \ldots, s_n)$ such that $s_j > 0$, $(j = 1, \ldots, n)$.

(E) If a sequence of non-negative $s^k = (s_1^k, \ldots, s_n^k)$ with $s_j^k > 0$ for every k converges to $s = (s_1, \ldots, s_n)$ with $s_j = 0$, then $\lim_{k \to \infty} f_j(s^k) = \infty$, $(j = 1, \ldots, n;\ k = 1, 2, \ldots)$.

(F) Given distinct, positive $s = (s_1, \dots, s_n)$ and $s' = (s'_1, \dots, s'_n)$, either $\Sigma_j f_j(s)(s_j - s'_j) < 0$ or $\Sigma_j f_j(s'_j)(s'_j - s_j) < 0$.

LEMMA 3. If r and A satisfy Hypotheses (A), (B), and (C), then the set

$$S = \left\{ s \;\middle|\; s \geq 0 \quad \text{and} \quad As \leq r \right\}$$

is a non-void, compact, polyhedral convex set in the non-negative orthant and contains some vector $s > 0$.

PROOF. The set S is closed, convex, polyhedral, and lies in the non-negative orthant because it is defined as the intersection of the finite collection of closed half-spaces: $s_j \geq 0$, $\Sigma_j a_{ij} s_j \leq r_i$ for $i = 1, \dots, m$ and $j = 1, \dots, n$. By (A) and (B), if we set

$$c = \min_i \left\{ r_i \Big/ \sum_j a_{ij} \right\}$$

then $c > 0$ and $s = (c, \dots, c) \in S$.

By (C), for each j there is an i with $a_{ij} > 0$, and $0 \leq s_j \leq r_i/a_{ij}$ for this i and all $s \in S$. Hence S is bounded and the proof is complete.

The main consequence of Lemma 3 for our analysis is the fact that, under Hypotheses (A), (B), and (C), the maximum program associated with r, A, and <u>any</u> $\bar{\sigma}$ is solvable, and the maximizing vectors form a non-empty, compact, convex set.

LEMMA 4. If r, A, and f satisfy Hypotheses (A), (B), (C), (D), and (E), then there exist $\bar{\sigma}$ and a positive $\bar{s}$ such that $\bar{\sigma} = f(\bar{s})$ and $\bar{s}$ solves the maximum program associated with r, A, and $\bar{\sigma}$.

PROOF. For each <u>positive</u> $\bar{s} \in S$, $\bar{\sigma} = f(\bar{s})$ is defined by (D). Hence, by Lemma 3, $F(\bar{s})$, the set of solutions to the maximum program associated with $\bar{\sigma} = f(\bar{s})$, r, and A, is non-empty, compact and convex. The correspondence $\bar{s} \longrightarrow F(\bar{s})$ is a point-set mapping of the interior of S into S. This mapping can be extended to all of S by taking the closure in $S \times S$ of the graph of F. The closure consists of all $(\bar{s}^o, s^o)$ such that

$$s^o = \lim_{k \to \infty} s^k$$

with $s^k \in F(\bar{s}^k)$ for a sequence $\bar{s}^k > 0$ and

$$\lim_{k \to \infty} \bar{s}^k = \bar{s}^0 .$$

Since every $\bar{s}^0 \in S$ is the limit of some positive sequence $\bar{s}^k$, the closure is the graph of a point-set mapping Φ that is defined on all of S. The mapping Φ is continuous since its graph is closed by definition. Furthermore, by the characterization of the closure given above, it is clear that $\Phi(\bar{s}^0)$ is compact and convex for all $\bar{s}^0 \in S$. Finally, Φ is an extension of F, that is, $\Phi(\bar{s}^0) = F(\bar{s}^0)$ for all $\bar{s}^0 > 0$. To prove this, consider any $\bar{s}^0 > 0$ and any $s^0 \in \Phi(\bar{s}^0)$. Then

$$f(\bar{s}^0) \cdot s^0 = \lim_{k \to \infty} f(\bar{s}^k) \cdot s^k = \lim_{k \to \infty} \max_S f(\bar{s}^k) \cdot s$$

$$= \max_S \lim_{k \to \infty} f(\bar{s}^k) \cdot s = \max_S f(\bar{s}^0) \cdot s$$

and hence $s^0 \in F(\bar{s}^0)$. The reverse inclusion is trivial.

Since the point-set function Φ satisfies the hypotheses of the Kakutani fixed-point theorem [5], there exists an $\bar{s} \in S$ with $\bar{s} \in \Phi(\bar{s})$. If we can verify that $\bar{s} > 0$, then $\bar{s} \in F(\bar{s})$ and the proof of the lemma will be complete. Assume the contrary, that is, let $\bar{s}_j = 0$ for $1 \le j \le p$ and $\bar{s}_j > 0$ for $j > p$, renumbering the goods if necessary. Then there are two sequences, $\bar{s}^k > 0$ and s^k, such that $s^k \in F(\bar{s}^k)$ and

$$\lim_{k \to \infty} \bar{s}^k = \lim_{k \to \infty} s^k = \bar{s}.$$

For each k, let $c^k = \max_{1 \le j \le p} s_j^k$. Noting that $(c, \ldots, c) \in S$ for some $c > 0$ by Lemma 3,

$$c \sum_{j=1}^{p} f_j(\bar{s}^k) \le \sum_{j=1}^{n} f_j(\bar{s}^k) s_j^k \le c^k \sum_{j=1}^{p} f_j(\bar{s}^k) + \sum_{j>p} f_j(\bar{s}^k) s_j^k$$

or

$$c \le c^k + \sum_{j>p} f_j(\bar{s}^k) s_j^k \Big/ \sum_{j=1}^{p} f_j(\bar{s}^k)$$

for all k. Since $\bar{s}_j > 0$ for $j > p$,

$$\lim_{k \to \infty} \sum_{j>p} f_j(\bar{s}^k) s_j^k = \sum_{j>p} f_j(\bar{s}) \bar{s}_j$$

by (D). Since $\bar{s}_j = 0$ for $1 \leq j \leq p$,

$$\lim_{k \to \infty} \sum_{j=1}^{p} f_j(\bar{s}^k) = \infty$$

by (E). Hence,

$$\lim_{k \to \infty} c^k \geq c > 0.$$

On the other hand, since

$$c^k = \max_{1 \leq j \leq p} s_j^k \quad \text{and} \quad \lim_{k \to \infty} s_j^k = 0$$

for $1 \leq j \leq p$, we have

$$\lim_{k \to \infty} c^k = 0.$$

This contradiction completes the proof.

(Since this contradiction is the only use of Hypothesis (E) and then for the sole purpose of showing that all fixed points $\bar{s}$ are positive, it may be worthwhile to explain it in less formal terms. The essence of Hypothesis (E) states that the prices of goods that are produced in very small quantities are very large. Therefore, since the income must be maximized at equilibrium and it is possible to produce positive amounts of all goods, it is impossible to produce a zero amount of any good.)

THEOREM 2. If r, A, and f satisfy the Wald hypotheses (A) - (F), then there is an equilibrium $\bar{s}$, $\bar{\sigma}$, and $\bar{\rho}$, with unique $\bar{s}$ and $\bar{\sigma}$.

PROOF. By Lemma 4, there exist $\bar{s} > 0$ and $\bar{\sigma} = f(\bar{s})$ such that $\bar{s}$ solves the maximum program associated with r, A, and $\bar{\sigma}$. By the duality theorem, there is a $\bar{\rho}$ which solves the dual minimum program, and hence Theorem 1 asserts that $\bar{s}$, $\bar{\sigma}$, and $\bar{\rho}$ constitute an equilibrium. Hypothesis (F) establishes the uniqueness since the equilibrium quantities must maximize the income $\bar{\sigma} \cdot s$. The uniqueness of $\bar{\sigma}$ follows from (5).

§5. A VARIANT OF THE WALD MODEL

The existence proof that has been given in Section 4 isolates the difficulty in Wald's theorem quite clearly. It derives almost entirely from the necessity of showing that, at equilibrium, all goods are produced in positive amounts. This fact is used to show that the equilibrium prices of the goods are equal to their production costs. For this purpose alone, Wald introduced Hypothesis (E) which is complicated mathematically and seems unreasonable on economic grounds. Rather remarkably, these difficulties disappear if we replace the equality of prices and production costs by an inequality (which seems to be sound economics) and drop Hypothesis (E) entirely. Precisely, we propose to redefine an equilibrium as quantities $\bar{s} = (\bar{s}_j)$ and prices $\bar{\sigma} = (\bar{\sigma}_j)$ and $\bar{\rho} = (\bar{\rho}_i)$, such that Conditions (1), (2), (3), and (5) hold and (4) is replaced by:

$$(4') \qquad \sum_i \bar{\rho}_i a_{ij} \geq \bar{\sigma}_j \qquad (j = 1, \ldots, n)$$

(The price of a good is not greater than its production cost.)

$$(4'') \qquad \text{If} \quad \sum_i \bar{\rho}_i a_{ij} > \bar{\sigma}_j \quad \text{for some } j, \quad \text{then } \bar{s}_j = 0.$$

(No good with greater production cost than price is produced.)

Wald's hypotheses can then be altered by dropping (E) and (F) entirely, and replacing (D) by:

(D') The function $\sigma = f(s)$ is defined, non-negative, and continuous on the set of non-negative $s = (s_1, \ldots, s_n)$.

To emphasize the simplicity that is achieved by these changes, we shall repeat the main lines of the proof of Theorem 2 in its new form.

THEOREM 3. If r, A, and f satisfy Hypotheses (A), (B), (C), and (D'), then there is an equilibrium $\bar{s}$, $\bar{\sigma}$, and $\bar{\rho}$ satisfying (1), (2), (3), (4'), (4''), and (5).

PROOF. The function Φ used in Theorem 2 can now be defined directly. Namely, for any $\bar{s} \in S$, let

$$\Phi(\bar{s}) = \{s \mid s \text{ solves the maximum program associated with } \bar{\sigma} = f(\bar{s})\}.$$

By Lemma 3, $\Phi(\bar{s})$ is non-empty, compact and convex. It is clear that Φ is a continuous point-set function and so the Kakutani fixed-point theorem applies to yield an $\bar{s} \in \Phi(\bar{s})$. The quantities $\bar{s}$, the prices $\bar{\sigma} = f(\bar{s})$, and any prices $\bar{\rho}$ solving the dual minimum program constitute the desired equilibrium.

BIBLIOGRAPHY

[1] SCHLESINGER, K., "Über die Produktionsgleichungen der ökonomischen Wertlehre," Ergebnisse eines mathematischen Kolloquiums, No. 6 (1933-34), pp. 10-11.

[2] WALD, A., "Über die eindeutige positive Lösbarkeit der neuen Produktionsgleichungen," ibid., No. 6 (1933-34), pp. 12-20.

[3] WALD, A., "Über die Produktionsgleichungen der ökonomischen Wertlehre," ibid., No. 7 (1934-35), pp. 1-6.

[4] WALD, A., "Über einige Gleichungssysteme der mathematischen Ökonomie," Zeitschrift für Nationalökonomie 7, No. 5 (1936), pp. 637-670 (translated in Econometrica 19, No. 4 (1951), pp. 368-403).

[5] KAKUTANI, S., "A generalization of Brouwer's fixed point theorem," Duke Math. J. 8 (1941), pp. 451-459.

[6] KOOPMANS, T. C., editor, Activity Analysis of Production and Allocation, Cowles Commission Monograph 13, New York, 1951.

[7] GALE, D., KUHN, H. W., and TUCKER, A. W., "Linear programming and the theory of games," Chapter XIX in [6], pp. 317-329.

[8] SAMUELSON, P. A., "Linear programming and economic theory," Proceedings of the Second Symposium in Linear Programming, Vol. 1, Washington, D. C., 1955, pp. 251-272.

[9] GOLDMAN, A. J., and TUCKER, A. W., "Theory of linear programming," this Study.

[10] DORFMAN, R., SAMUELSON, P. A., and SOLOW, ROBERT, Linear Programming and Economic Theory, in preparation.

Harold W. Kuhn

Bryn Mawr College

ON THE SOLUTION OF A GAME-THEORETIC PROBLEM

Gerald L. Thompson*

§1. INTRODUCTION

During the consideration [1] of a generalization of von Neumann's model of an expanding economy the following game-theoretic problem arose:

> PROBLEM. Given $m \times n$ matrix games A and B with real-valued non-negative entries such that $v(-A) < 0$ and $v(B) > 0$; find a convex combination of the two matrices B and $-A$ which is a fair matrix game and for which there is a pair of optimal strategies, x for the maximizing player and y for the minimizing player, such that $xBy > 0$.

In this paper we show that there is at most a finite number (the smaller of m and n) of convex combinations for which such solutions exist. Our proof, which is essentially that in [4], utilizes the minimax theorem from the theory of games in the strong form proved by A. W. Tucker in [5]. Another proof [2], by John G. Kemeny, utilizes the weak form of the minimax theorem plus some perturbation arguments.

In Section 2 we outline the economic background of the problem and in Section 3 give some examples which illustrate the mathematical problems. The existence proof, together with the proof of another theorem, occurs in Section 4. The last example in Section 3 shows that the problem is not solvable over the rational field. A characterization of the most general field over which it is solvable would be of interest.

§2. THE ECONOMIC MODEL

Consider the following model of an economy: There are m

* The preparation of this paper was supported, in part, by the National Science Foundation.

processes which operate at discrete time intervals and which produce a finite number n of different goods. Each process operates at an intensity x. These intensities are normalized so that the ith process operates at intensity x_i where

$$0 \leq x_i \leq 1 \quad \text{and} \quad \sum_{i=1}^{m} x_i = 1.$$

We shall consider the intensity vector $x = (x_1, \ldots, x_m)$ as an m-dimensional probability vector. When the ith process is operating it requires a_{ij} units of good j $(j = 1, \ldots, n)$ and produces b_{ik} units of good k $(k = 1, \ldots, n)$ per unit of good i. It is assumed that a_{ij} and b_{ij} are non-negative real numbers for all i and j. If $A = \|a_{ij}\|$ and $B = \|b_{ij}\|$ then the components of the vector xA give the amounts of inputs used up in the production and the components of the vector xB give the amounts produced.

Each good is assigned a price y. Prices are also normalized so that the jth good is assigned price y_j where

$$0 \leq y_j \leq 1 \quad \text{and} \quad \sum_{j=1}^{n} y_j = 1.$$

Thus the price vector $y = (y_1, \ldots, y_n)$ is an n-dimensional probability vector. The components of the vector Ay give the value of the inputs entering into the processes and the components of the vector By give the value of goods produced by the processes. As a whole, the economy takes, at time $t - 1$, raw materials valued at xAy dollars and transforms them by time t into goods valued at xBy dollars.

It is assumed that in the model there is an expansion rate a and an interest rate b (both in percentages) from which we derive the expansion factor $\alpha = 1 + a/100$ and the interest factor $\beta = 1 + b/100$.

We shall say that we have a solution for our economic model if we can find vectors x and y and numbers α and β which satisfy the following five conditions:

$$x(B - \alpha A) \geq 0 \tag{1}$$

$$(B - \beta A)y \leq 0 \tag{2}$$

$$x(B - \alpha A)y = 0 \tag{3}$$

$$x(B - \beta A)y = 0 \tag{4}$$

$$xBy > 0. \tag{5}$$

If we restate condition (1) as $xB \geq \alpha xA$ we see that it is a conservation condition which requires that no more goods can be used during any time period than were produced during the preceding time period. Similarly, restating (2) as $\beta Ay \geq By$ we see that it requires that the economy be "profitless", that is, a process cannot yield a return in a given time period greater than that which would have been obtained by investing the money required to buy the inputs at the going interest rate. An equivalent way of stating (3) is the following: if $x(B^j - \alpha A^j) > 0$ (where B^j and A^j are the jth columns of B and A) then $y_j = 0$; the economic interpretation is that zero price must be charged for goods that are over produced. Similarly, an equivalent way of stating (4) is: if $(B_i - \beta A_i)y < 0$ (where B_i and A_i are the ith rows of B and A) then $x_i = 0$; economically this means that inefficient processes must be used with zero intensity. The interpretation of (5) is that it requires that the total value xBy of all goods produced must be positive.

Without further assumptions there will be, in general, no solutions to (1)-(5). Therefore we make the following economically plausible assumptions:

(i) every row of A has at least one positive entry,
(ii) every column of B has at least one positive entry.

The economic meaning of (i) is that every process must use some good and the meaning of (ii) is that every good can be produced in the economy. Since $A \geq 0$ and $B \geq 0$, these assumptions can be restated in game-theoretic terms as

$$\text{(i)} \quad v(-A) < 0,$$

and

$$\text{(ii)} \quad v(B) > 0.$$

Suppose now that we had solutions x, y, α and β to equations (1)-(5). From (5) we see that $xBy > 0$; hence from (3) and (4) $xBy = \alpha xAy = \beta xAy > 0$. From the last equation $xAy > 0$ so that $\alpha = \beta = xBy/xAy$. Thus we need look only for solutions which have $\alpha = \beta$. If $\alpha = \beta$ we see that (3) and (4) become identical and are consequences of conditions (1) and (2). Thus our equations are simply

$$(1') \quad x(B - \alpha A) \geq 0,$$

$$(2') \quad (B - \alpha A)y \leq 0,$$

$$(5') \quad xBy > 0.$$

If we interpret the matrix $(B - \alpha A)$ as a matrix game then equations (1') and (2') assert that α must be chosen so that the value of the game is zero, and x and y must be chosen to be optimal strategies for the game. Condition (5') remains as an economic condition.

If we divide the expression $B - \alpha A$ by $1 + \alpha$ and set

$p = \alpha/(1+\alpha)$ (observe that $0 \leq p < 1$ and we can close the interval by associating $p = 1$ with the expansion factor $\alpha = \infty$) we obtain the matrix $(1-p)B + p(-A)$ which is a convex combination of B and $-A$. Then our equations become:

$$(1'') \quad x[(1-p)B - pA] \geq 0,$$

$$(2'') \quad [(1-p)B - pA]y \leq 0,$$

$$(5'') \quad xBy > 0.$$

Our problem now is to find solutions to (1''), (2'') and (5'') under the assumptions (i) and (ii), and this is the problem stated in the introduction.

The model here described is discussed in somewhat greater detail in reference [1].

§3. EXAMPLES

The examples below illustrate the mathematical difficulties of the problem.

EXAMPLE 1. Consider the following matrices:

$$B = \begin{pmatrix} 0 & 0 & \cdots & 0 & n \\ 0 & 0 & \cdots & n-1 & 0 \\ & & \cdots & & \\ 0 & 2 & \cdots & 0 & 0 \\ 1 & 0 & \cdots & 0 & 0 \end{pmatrix}, \quad A = \begin{pmatrix} 0 & 0 & \cdots & 0 & 1 \\ 0 & 0 & \cdots & 1 & 0 \\ & & \cdots & & \\ 0 & 1 & \cdots & 0 & 0 \\ 1 & 0 & \cdots & 0 & 0 \end{pmatrix}.$$

Consider convex combinations of the form $M_p = (1-p)B - pA$, where $0 \leq p \leq 1$. If $p > \frac{n}{n+1}$ then the value of the game M_p is negative while if $p < 1/2$ the value of M_p is positive. If

$$\frac{1}{2} \leq \frac{k}{k+1} < p < \frac{k+1}{k+2} \leq \frac{n}{n+1},$$

where k is an integer, then the value of the game is zero but there are no solutions such that $xBy > 0$. Finally, if

$$\frac{1}{2} \leq p = \frac{k}{k+1} \leq \frac{n}{n+1},$$

where k is an integer, then the game is fair and there are pure optimal strategies for each player such that $xBy > 0$. Thus there are exactly n values of p for which solutions to the stated problem exist. From an economic point of view this represents an economy with completely disconnected sub-economies.

EXAMPLE 2. Consider the following matrices:

$$B = \begin{pmatrix} 0 & 2 \\ 1 & b \end{pmatrix}, \qquad A = \begin{pmatrix} 0 & 1 \\ 1 & a \end{pmatrix},$$

where a and b are arbitrary real numbers. Again consider the game $M_p = (1 - p)B - pA$. If $p > 2/3$ then the value of M_p is negative while if $p < 1/2$ then the value is positive. If $1/2 < p < 2/3$ then the game is strictly determined and fair but the unique optimal strategies $x = (1, 0)$ and $y = (1, 0)$ give $xBy = 0$ and hence do not solve the problem. If $p = 1/2$ then the following strategies solve the problem:

If $b \geq a$ then $x = (0, 1)$ and $y = (1, 0)$ are optimal and $xBy = 1$.

If $b \leq a$ then

$$x = \left(\frac{a-b}{1+a-b}, \frac{1}{1+a-b} \right)$$

and $y = (1, 0)$ are optimal and

$$xBy = \frac{1}{1+a-b}.$$

Finally, if $p = 2/3$ then the solutions are:

If $b \leq 2a$ then $x = (1, 0)$ and $y = (0, 1)$ are optimal and $xBy = 2$.

If $b \geq 2a$ then $x = (1, 0)$ and

$$y = \left(\frac{b-2a}{1+b-2a}, \frac{1}{1+b-2a} \right)$$

are optimal and

$$xBy = \frac{2}{1+b-2a}.$$

Here there are two possible values of p for which solutions to the problem exist. This example shows that the economy need not be totally disconnected in order that it have more than one expansion factor.

EXAMPLE 3. The following example shows that the problem is not solvable over the rational field. Consider the following matrices:

$$B = \begin{pmatrix} 2 & 1 \\ 1 & 1 \end{pmatrix}, \qquad A = \begin{pmatrix} 0 & 1 \\ 1 & 0 \end{pmatrix}.$$

Since the von Neumann condition $(A + B > 0)$ is satisfied there is a unique value of p for which the game is fair. It can be found as the positive root of the equation

$$\begin{vmatrix} 2 - 2p & 1 - 2p \\ 1 - 2p & 1 - p \end{vmatrix} = 1 - 2p^2 = 0.$$

The positive root is $1/\sqrt{2}$ which is irrational. The unique optimal strategies for this value of p are

$$x = \left(\frac{1}{\sqrt{2}+1}, \frac{\sqrt{2}}{\sqrt{2}+1} \right),$$

$$y = \left(\frac{1}{\sqrt{2}+1}, \frac{\sqrt{2}}{\sqrt{2}+1} \right),$$

whose components are not rational numbers.

§4. THE EXISTENCE PROOF

Since the value of a game depends continuously upon its entries, the value of the game $M_p = (1 - p)B - pA$ is a continuous function of p. Since the entries of A and B are non-negative $v(M_p)$ is a monotone decreasing function of p. By assumption $v(M_0) = v(B) > 0$ and $v(M_1) = v(-A) < 0$. By continuity there is at least one positive p such that $v(M_p) = 0$ and by monotonicity and continuity the set of all such p is closed and connected. Thus the existence of a p such that M_p is fair is trivial. The difficult part of the proof will be to show that there are values of p for which solutions x, y exist such that $xBy > 0$.

DEFINITION. An $m \times n$ matrix M will be called <u>decomposable</u> if, by permutations (not necessarily simultaneous) of rows and columns, M can be put in the following form:

$$M = \begin{array}{|c|c|} \hline 0 & S \\ \hline P & Q \\ \hline \end{array}$$

where 0 is an $r \times t$ matrix with all zero entries, S is an $r \times s$ matrix, P is a $p \times t$ matrix and Q is a $p \times s$ matrix, and where

$r > 0$ and $t > 0$. Thus M is decomposable if and only if it has at least one zero entry. The first r rows and the first t columns of M will be called initial rows and columns, respectively; similarly, the last p rows and the last s columns will be called terminal rows and columns, respectively. When speaking of strategy vectors for M (in decomposed form) we shall refer in the same way to the initial and terminal components of such vectors.

If G is any matrix game we shall use the notations $X(G)$ and $Y(G)$ for the sets of optimal strategies for the maximizing and minimizing players respectively. We shall use the notation x' and x'' to indicate m-vectors with zero terminal and initial components, respectively. Thus, every m-vector x has a unique decomposition, $x = x' + x''$. Similar notation will be applied to n-vectors y. We shall sometimes use inexact notations such as $x' \in X(Q)$ or $y'' \in Y(P)$ to mean that the vector x consisting of the terminal components of x' belongs to $X(Q)$ and that the vector y having the initial components of y'' belongs to $Y(P)$. These usages will always be clear in context.

Let $x^{(1)}, x^{(2)}, \ldots, x^{(e)}$ be the set of all basic optimal strategies (cf. [3]) for the maximizing player in P and let $y^{(1)}, y^{(2)}, \ldots, y^{(f)}$ be the set of all basic optimal strategies for the minimizing player in S. Then by the game $\bar{Q}$ we shall mean the $e \times f$ matrix game with entries

$$q_{ij} = x^{(i)}Qy^{(j)} .$$

Obviously any optimal strategy x for $\bar{Q}$ is also an optimal strategy in P since it is a convex combination of basic optimal strategies. We shall indicate this fact as follows: $x \in X(P) \cap X(\bar{Q})$. In a similar manner we shall use the notation $y \in Y(S) \cap Y(\bar{Q})$.

THEOREM 1. If p is the largest (or the smallest) value which makes M_p a fair game then there exists a pair (x, y) of optimal strategies for M_p such that $xBy > 0$.

PROOF. Let p be the largest value which makes $v(M_p) = 0$ (a similar proof works if p is the smallest such). Assume that for p as defined there is no solution to M_p with $xBy > 0$, i.e., all such solutions have $xBy = 0$. Then if (x, y) is a pair of optimal strategies for M_p we have $x[(1 - p)B - pA]y = 0$, and since $xBy = 0$ and $p > 0$ we have $xAy = 0$ also. Thus when $x_i y_j > 0$, also $a_{ij} = b_{ij} = 0$. Now let

x and y run over all optimal strategies for the game M_p and rearrange rows and columns of M_p so that the initial rows and columns are those and only those for which some optimal strategy has a positive component. Thus we obtain M_p in decomposed form as follows:

$$M_p = M = \begin{array}{|c|c|} \hline 0 & S \\ \hline P & Q \\ \hline \end{array}$$

Then it is easy to see that $v(S) \geq 0$ and $v(P) \leq 0$. If $v(S) > 0$ then it is easy to show that p is not maximal, hence we must have $v(S) = 0$. Let $x \in X(M)$ be the x-component of a central solution to M (see [5])[1], and write $x = x' + x''$ in decomposed form, where, by assumption, $x'' = 0$. Then, since x belongs to a central solution, we have $x'S > 0$ which implies $v(S) > 0$, a contradiction.

THEOREM 2. There are at most $\min(m, n)$ values of p such that M_p is fair and for which solutions (x, y) exist with $xBy > 0$.

PROOF. For each such p there is a pair (x, y) so that $xBy > 0$; hence corresponding to each such p we can choose components (x_i, y_j) so that $x_i b_{ij} y_j > 0$. Then, if A^j and B^j are the jth columns of A and B respectively, we have from (1) and (3) that $xA^j > 0$ and $xB^j > 0$.

We shall show that the indices of the components so chosen are pairwise distinct for different such p's. Once this fact is established we are done since the number of distinct such p's is then at most equal to the length of the longest diagonal in the $m \times n$ matrix B, and the latter is clearly $\min(m, n)$.

Let p and q be two values with $p > q$ and with corresponding component pairs (x_i, y_j) and (x_h, y_k) such that

$$x_i b_{ij} y_j > 0 \quad \text{and} \quad x_h b_{hk} y_k > 0.$$

We shall show that $j \neq k$; the proof that $i \neq h$ is similar. Suppose that $j = k$. Let x be an optimal strategy in M_p; then x is clearly also optimal in M_q since $q < p$. Letting M_p^j be the jth column of M_p we have

$$xM_p^j \geq 0 \quad \text{and} \quad xM_q^j \geq 0.$$

However, since

[1] If the reader refers to [6] in the present Study, a central solution to a matrix game is one characterized as in Corollary 2A of that reference.

$$xM_q^j = xM_p^j + (p - q)x(A^j + B^j)$$

and since, as observed above, $x(A^j + B^j) > 0$, we see that

$$xM_q^j = xM_q^k > 0.$$

By condition (3), this implies that $y_k = 0$, which, in turn, implies that $x_h b_{hk} y_k = 0$, contrary to the way in which y_k was chosen.

Theorems 1 and 2 are of interest from an economic point of view because of their interpretation in the model discussed above. The next theorem, first proved in another way by John G. Kemeny, promises to have applications to certain other game theory problems.

THEOREM 3. If M is decomposable and $v(S) = v(P) = 0$ then $v(M) = 0$; moreover,

(a) A necessary and sufficient condition that the maximizing player should have an optimal strategy with a non-zero terminal component is that $v(\bar{Q}) \geq 0$.

(b) A necessary and sufficient condition that the minimizing player should have an optimal strategy with a non-zero terminal component is that $v(\bar{Q}) \leq 0$.

PROOF. Obviously any strategy x' for the maximizing player which is optimal in S and which has zero terminal components is optimal in M; similarly, any strategy y' for the minimizing player which is optimal in P and has zero terminal components is optimal in M. Hence $v(M) = 0$. We now prove (a); the proof of (b) is similar.

NECESSITY. Let $x = (x_1, \ldots, x_m) \in X(M)$ be such that $a = x_{r+1} + \cdots + x_m > 0$. Since $v(M) = 0$, $x = x' + x''$ and we have $x''P \geq 0$ and $x'S + x''Q \geq 0$. Since $v(P) = 0$, the first inequality asserts $\frac{1}{a}x'' \in X(P)$. If the second inequality is multiplied by any $y'' \in Y(S) \cap Y(\bar{Q})$, we have $x'Sy'' + x''Qy'' \geq 0$; and since $x'Sy'' \leq 0$

$$v(\bar{Q}) \geq \frac{1}{a} x''Qy'' \geq -\frac{1}{a} x'Sy'' \geq 0.$$

SUFFICIENCY. Suppose the maximizing player has no optimal strategy with a non-zero terminal component. Then let $y = (y_1, \ldots, y_n) \in Y(M)$ be the y-component of a central solution (cf. [5][1]) to M. Then write $y = y' + y''$ so that $Py' + Qy'' < 0$. Note that $y'' \neq 0$ since otherwise y' is a mixed strategy for P and $Py' < 0$, contradicting $v(P) = 0$.

Then $b = y_{s+1} + \cdots + y_n > 0$ and $\frac{1}{b}y'' \in Y(S)$. If $x'' \in X(P)$ then $x''Py' \geq 0$ so that $x''Q(\frac{1}{b}y'') < -\frac{1}{b}x''Py' \leq 0$ and $v(\bar{Q}) < 0$.

BIBLIOGRAPHY

[1] KEMENY, JOHN G., MORGENSTERN, OSKAR, and THOMPSON, GERALD L., "A generalization of the von Neumann model of an expanding economy," Econometrica, to appear.

[2] KEMENY, JOHN G., "Game-theoretic solution of an economic problem," Progress Report Number 2, (1956), The Dartmouth Mathematics Project.

[3] McKINSEY, J. C. C., An Introduction to the Theory of Games, McGraw-Hill, 1952.

[4] THOMPSON, GERALD L., "On the solution of a game-theoretic problem," abstract, Bull. A. M. S., 1956.

[5] TUCKER, A. W., Game Theory and Programming, Multilithed Notes, Department of Mathematics, The Oklahoma Agricultural and Mechanical College, 1955.

[6] TUCKER, A. W., "Dual systems of homogeneous linear relations," this Study.

Gerald L. Thompson

Dartmouth College

THE CLOSED LINEAR MODEL OF PRODUCTION

David Gale

§1. INTRODUCTION

In 1937 J. von Neumann [1] gave the first mathematical discussion of an economic model expanding at a constant rate. His model is a production system consisting of a set of technological processes, each process being capable of consuming certain amounts of various goods and converting them into specified amounts of other goods. The model is closed in the sense that there is no flow of goods to or from the model, all goods produced by the model during a given period being used, if at all, as inputs to the model at a later time. Thus, the only function of the model is to perpetuate itself in some manner.

The word linear applied to the model means that if all inputs to a process are multiplied by a non-negative constant then the outputs are multiplied by this same constant. In other terms, the production functions are homogeneous of degree one. The constant by which a given process is multiplied is called the <u>intensity</u> of that process. It is then shown that, by operating the processes simultaneously at suitable intensities, it may be possible to cause the amounts of all goods in the system to increase. This concept of expansion is the central notion of von Neumann's paper. Roughly speaking, he defines an expansion coefficient α for the model and then shows how prices can be chosen in such a way that expansion of the model at the rate α can be interpreted as a sort of dynamic economic equilibrium.

The original proofs of von Neumann were extremely involved, depending on fixed point theorems of topology. More recently several authors have given elementary proofs of von Neumann's theorem [2], [3]. However, all treatments which have appeared so far contain one serious weakness. This is the use of the hypothesis:

(H) Each process involves each good in the economy either as input or output.

This condition, which is clearly unnatural economically, was used in [1] to prove uniqueness of the expansion coefficient.*

In the present paper we develop a model which is a slight generalization of [1]. Expansion and equilibrium theorems are proved in an elementary manner without using the assumption (H). Our point of view and definitions will be somewhat different from von Neumann's, the aim being to make the economic interpretation more transparent. In the following section we give a precise description of the model to be discussed. In Section 3 the fundamental expansion theorem is proved and interpreted economically. The result is then applied to "regular" models, where the condition of regularity is an essential weakening of assumption (H). In Section 4 the main theorems are applied to give new results for the von Neumann model which are illustrated by numerical examples in Section 5. A final section treats the special case of the Leontief model where the expansion theory takes a particularly simple and elegant form.

§2. THE MODEL

NOTATION. Throughout the paper, Latin letters will denote vectors, Greek letters real numbers. The scalar product of vectors x and y will be written, xy.

If $x = (\xi_1, \dots, \xi_n)$ is a vector, we shall say
x is positive, $x > 0$, if $\xi_i > 0$ for all i,
x is non-negative, $x \geqq 0$, if $\xi_i \geqq 0$ for all i,
x is semi-positive, $x \geq 0$, if $x \geqq 0$ and $x \neq 0$.

The vector e_j will denote the jth unit vector, i.e., the vector whose jth coordinate is 1, all others zero.

We shall find it convenient to adjoin to the real numbers the symbol for infinity, ∞. We denote the real numbers by R and the real numbers with ∞ adjoined by $\bar{R}$. We then extend the ordering of R to $\bar{R}$ by the rule;

$$\text{for any} \quad \lambda \in R, \quad \lambda < \infty .$$

We shall divide the description of the model into two parts; the first, purely technological, is concerned only with the production possibilities of the model. The second is economic, relating the operation of the model to prices. The fundamental theorems of the next section will tie together these two aspects of the model.

* Since this paper was written (see [5] and [6]), Kemeny, Morgenstern, and Thompson, have carried out an independent investigation of a model without assumption (H).

A. TECHNOLOGY

The model to be considered will involve n goods, $G_1, \ldots, G_n$. The term goods may be thought of as including services, various types of labor, etc. Goods are produced by means of processes in which amounts ξ_j of goods G_j are consumed per unit time to produce amounts η_j of these same goods. A process can thus be represented by a pair of non-negative vectors (x, y), where $x = (\xi_1, \ldots, \xi_n)$ is called the input vector, $y = (\eta_1, \ldots, \eta_n)$ the output vector of the process (x, y). The good G_j is called an input (output) of (x, y) if $\xi_j > 0$, $(\eta_j > 0)$.

We require one further condition on a process (x, y) to express the fact that one cannot get something for nothing. This takes the following form:

ASSUMPTION 1. If (x, y) is a process then $x = 0$ implies $y = 0$.

The set Z of all processes is in a natural way a subset of real 2n-space, R_{2n}. It is called the production space of the model and is assumed to satisfy the following condition:

ASSUMPTION 2. The space Z is a closed convex cone, that is,

(a) Z is closed in R_{2n},
(b) if $z, z' \in Z$ then $z + z' \in Z$
(c) if $z \in Z$ and $\lambda \geqq 0$ then $\lambda z \in Z$.

Condition (b) expresses the fact that from any two processes a third can be formed by operating the two simultaneously. Condition (c) is the linearity restriction already described. The von Neumann model corresponds to the case in which the cone Z is polyhedral, i.e., generated by a finite set of vectors.

The set of goods together with the production space Z will constitute a model $\mathcal{M}$.

DEFINITION. If $(x, y) \in Z$, $x = (\xi_1, \ldots, \xi_n)$, $y = (\eta_1, \ldots, \eta_n)$ and G_j is a good, we define the expansion rate of G_j in the process (x, y) by

$$\alpha_j(x, y) = \begin{Bmatrix} \eta_j/\xi_j \\ \infty \\ \text{undefined} \end{Bmatrix} \quad \text{for} \quad \begin{cases} \xi_j > 0 \\ \xi_j = 0,\ \eta_j > 0 \\ \xi_j = \eta_j = 0 \end{cases}$$

The <u>technological expansion rate</u> of the process (x, y) is defined by

$$\alpha(x, y) = \min_j \alpha_j(x, y).$$

(Note that from Assumption 1, $\alpha(x, y)$ is always defined for $(x, y) \neq 0$ and is a real number.)

In words, the process (x, y) produces at least $\alpha(x, y)$ times as much of each good as it consumes. If we think of the process (x, y) as operating over a period of time, then $\alpha(x, y)$ represents the maximum rate at which the process can expand by "feeding back" the outputs from one period of production as inputs during the next.

The <u>technological expansion</u> rate α_M of the model $\mathcal{M}$ is defined by

$$\alpha_M = \max \alpha(x, y), \quad \text{for} \quad (x, y) \in Z \quad \text{and} \quad (x, y) \neq 0.$$

The fact that the function α attains its maximum can be verified by observing that α is continuous at all points of Z other than the origin. Let $\hat{Z}$ be the intersection of Z with the unit sphere in 2n-space. Since Z is closed $\hat{Z}$ is compact and therefore the function α attains a maximum $\alpha(\bar{x}, \bar{y})$ on $\hat{Z}$. But this must actually be the maximum on all of Z for if $(x, y) \in Z$, $(x, y) \neq 0$, then $(x, y) = \lambda(\hat{x}, \hat{y})$, where $(\hat{x}, \hat{y}) \in \hat{Z}$, $\lambda > 0$, and from the definition of α, it follows that $\alpha(x, y) = \alpha(\hat{x}, \hat{y}) \leqq \alpha(\bar{x}, \bar{y})$.

We shall call a process (x, y) <u>optimal</u> if $\alpha(x, y) = \alpha_M$. (The word optimal is used here in a purely technical sense and should not be interpreted to mean some sort of ideal functioning of the economy. For example an optimal process might consist of rabbits multiplying at a tremendous rate while all other goods in the economy are quiescent*, which one feels to be economic nonsense. However, if we accept the fiction of a closed model, i.e., no external demand, then there is no reason for this model to "want" to produce anything other than, for instance, rabbits, if rabbit producing is what it does best. (For regular models, to be defined in the next section, this particular type of misbehavior cannot occur.)

By definition the expansion rate α_M is non-negative. Models whose expansion rate is zero will not interest us here since such models

---

* This remark and illustration is due to the referee, to whom the author is indebted for several helpful suggestions.

will "run down" at once. To eliminate this case we impose one more condition.

> ASSUMPTION 3. Every good G_j is an output of at least one process of Z.

For models satisfying Assumption 3, $\alpha_M > 0$, for, let (x_j, y_j) be a process such that $\eta_j > 0$. Then, if $(x, y) = \sum_j (x_j, y_j)$, we see that $y > 0$ and hence $0 < \alpha(x, y) \leqq \alpha_M$.

Although we have used the term expansion, there is nothing in our assumptions which requires α_M to be greater than unity. Indeed, the theory to be developed in the subsequent sections will not depend on the value of α_M, and will be equally valid for contracting models.

B. ECONOMICS

A price vector, $p = (\pi_1, \ldots, \pi_n) \geq 0$, is an assignment of prices to the goods $G_1, \ldots, G_n$, π_j being the price of one unit of G_j. Given the prices p and a process (x, y) we see that the cost of the process is xp and the income from the process is yp, thus, the process is profitable or not according as yp is greater than or less than xp. This leads to the second basic

> DEFINITION. Given a price vector p and a process (x, y) the <u>economic expansion rate</u> of the process (x, y) at prices p is defined by

$$\beta(x, y; p) = \begin{Bmatrix} yp/xp \\ \infty \\ \text{undefined} \end{Bmatrix} \quad \text{for} \quad \begin{cases} xp > 0 \\ xp = 0, \; yp > 0 \\ xp = yp = 0. \end{cases}$$

The economic expansion rate measures the rate at which the value of the goods involved in a process increases. Its significance is this: we are concerned with an economy in which each process may be thought of as a business whose sole purpose is to expand, that is to increase its scale of operation. If we think of production as being carried out over discrete time periods of say, a year, then it is the desire of each process operator to do ρ times as much business this year as he did last. The thing that determines this factor ρ is precisely the profit from last years production, for we assume that the process operator can only use last years income to pay this year's costs. Thus the rate of expansion ρ of the process (x, y) is bounded above by the economic expansion rate $\beta(x, y; p)$.

By analogy with the definition of the function α we define

$$\beta(p) = \max \beta(x, y; p), \quad \text{for} \quad (x, y) \in Z.$$

Thus, $\beta(p)$ represents the maximum rate at which the value of goods in the model can expand at prices p. The function β will not in general be real valued but will assume the value ∞ for some values of p.

Finally we define

$$\beta_m = \min_p \beta(p).$$

It is easily seen that β_m is a real number since for $p > 0$, $\beta(p) < \infty$, using Assumption 1.

The relations between the functions α and β are the central objects of the next section.

§3. THE EXPANSION THEOREMS

We are now in a position to state the central results of this paper.

THEOREM 1. If $\mathcal{M}$ is a model with technological expansion rate α_M then there exists an optimal process $(\bar{x}, \bar{y})$ and a price vector p, such that

(1) $\beta(\bar{x}, \bar{y}; p) = \alpha_M$

(2) $\beta(x, y; p) \leqq \alpha_M$ for all $(x, y) \in Z$ for which $\beta(x, y; p)$ is defined.

We pause here to interpret this theorem. As noted in the last section, we are assuming that each process (x, y) "wants" to expand at the maximum rate which is <u>economically feasible</u>, namely $\beta(x, y; p)$. On the other hand, if prices p are not "properly" set, it may not be <u>technologically possible</u> for the process to expand at this rate, meaning that the rest of the economy simply cannot supply the inputs which the operator of (x, y) is anxious and able to buy. This excess of demand over supply is not present if the prices p satisfy the conditions of Theorem 1, for we see that while some optimal process $(\bar{x}, \bar{y})$ will be economically able to expand at the maximum rate α_M, no process will be tempted or even able economically to expand at a rate greater than the maximum possible. Thus the price vector p may be thought of as a sort of equilibrium price vector which assures that demand will not exceed supply.

PROOF. We define the set

$$C = \left\{c \mid c = \alpha_M x - y, \quad (x, y) \in Z\right\}.$$

From the fact that Z is a convex cone in R_{2n}, one verifies at once that C is a convex cone in R_n. Now among all optimal processes select one, $(\bar{x}, \bar{y})$, such that $\bar{\eta}_j > 0$ on a maximal set of goods, say, $G_1, \ldots, G_k$. That is, no optimal process has more than k outputs. We now assert that the cone C contains no vector $c = (\gamma_1, \ldots, \gamma_n) \leqq 0$ such that $\gamma_j < 0$ for all $j \leq k$, for if $\alpha_M x - y$ were such a vector then, since $\gamma_j = \alpha_M \xi_j - \eta_j$, we would have $\alpha_j(x, y) \geqq \alpha_M$, when defined, and $\alpha_j(x, y) > \alpha_M$ for $j \leqq k$. Thus (x, y) would be optimal. From the above maximality assumption then for $j > k$, $\eta_j = 0$ and hence $\xi_j = 0$, so that $\alpha_j(x, y)$ is undefined. This would however, mean that $\alpha(x, y) > \alpha_M$, a contradiction.

Now let

$$Q_k = \left\{q \mid q = (\theta_1, \ldots, \theta_n), \quad \theta_j \geqq 0, \quad \text{for} \quad j \leqq k\right\},$$

$$D = Q_k + C = \left\{d \mid d = q + c, \quad q \in Q_k, \quad c \in C\right\}.$$

Then D is also a convex cone and since no vector in C has its first k coordinates negative, the same is true of D. In particular D is not all of n-space and hence by the fundamental property of convex cones it is contained in a half space H. Let $p = (\pi_1, \ldots, \pi_n)$ be a normal to H then $pd \geqq 0$ for all $d \in D$. Now, for $j \leqq k$, $\pi_j = pe_j \geqq 0$ since $e_j \in Q_k \subset D$. For $j > k$, $\pi_j = 0$ since both e_j and $-e_j$ belong to Q_k. Hence p is a semi-positive vector (thus, a price vector) and at least one of its first k coordinates is positive. Also, $pc \geqq 0$ for all $c \in C$ and hence $p(\alpha_M x - y) \geqq 0$ for all $(x, y) \in Z$. Therefore, $\alpha_M xp \geqq yp$, which means $\beta(x, y; p) \leqq \alpha_M$ when defined, which is assertion (2) of the theorem.

To verify assertion (1) we simply note that $\bar{y} \geqq \alpha_M \bar{x}$ and hence $\bar{y}p \geqq \alpha_M \bar{x}p$. Since the first k coordinates of $\bar{y}$ are positive it follows that $\bar{y}p > 0$, hence $\beta(\bar{x}, \bar{y}; p)$ is defined and $\alpha_M \leqq \beta(x, y; p)$, and combining this with (2) above we obtain (1), and the proof is complete.

COROLLARY 1. For any model , $\alpha_M \geqq \beta_m$.

Let us call a price vector satisfying the conclusion of Theorem 1, <u>optimal</u>. One of the conditions imposed on the optimal price vector in von Neumann's model was that the prices of all goods which were overproduced at equilibrium should be zero. We prove this as a simple consequence of Theorem 1.

COROLLARY 2. Let p be an optimal price vector, (x, y) an optimal process. Then, if $\eta_j > \alpha_M \xi_j$ then $\pi_j = 0$.

PROOF. By the theorem, $p(y - \alpha_M x) = 0$, and since both p and $y - \alpha_M x$ are non-negative they cannot both have positive j-th coordinates.

We now turn to an important special case.

DEFINITION. The model $\mathcal{M}$ will be called <u>regular</u> if for every optimal process (x, y), $y > 0$.

For regular models every optimal process produces a positive amount of all goods, i.e., the economy cannot expand at a maximum rate without all goods being produced. In the next section we present an economically "reasonable" condition which guarantees regularity.

For regular models we get the following concise result.

THEOREM 2. If $\mathcal{M}$ is regular then $\alpha_M = \beta_m$.

In view of Corollary 1, we need only show that $\alpha_M \leqq \beta_m$. Since $\beta_m = \min \beta(p)$ we must show that $\beta(p) \geqq \alpha_M$ for all p. Let (x, y) be an optimal process. Then $y - \alpha_M x \geqq 0$ and hence, for any price vector p, $yp \geqq \alpha_M xp$. Since $y > 0$, $yp > 0$, so $\beta(x, y; p)$ is defined (possibly infinite) and $\beta(x, y; p) \geqq \alpha_M$. But $\beta(p) = \max_{(x', y')} \beta(x', y'; p)$ so $\beta(p) \geqq \beta(x, y; p) \geqq \alpha_M$.

COROLLARY 3. If (x, y) is a process and p a price vector such that $\alpha(x, y) = \beta(p)$ then (x, y) and p are optimal.

This corollary provides a simples means for testing a process (x, y) for optimality.

NOTE: The only case in which Theorem 2 can fail to hold is one in which there exists an optimal process (x, y) and a price vector p such that $\beta(x, y; p)$ is not defined, that is, all goods "involved" in the process (x, y) are free. An example of this will be given in Section 5.

§4. THE VON NEUMANN MODEL

As noted earlier von Neumann's model corresponds to the special case in which the production space Z is generated by a finite set of vectors (a_i, b_i) $i = 1, \ldots, m$, which we shall call <u>basic processes</u>. The general process (x, y) is a non-negative linear combination of the basic processes, thus

$$(x, y) = \sum_{i=1}^{m} \lambda_i (a_i, b_i),$$

where $\lambda_i \geqq 0$ is called the <u>intensity</u> of the ith basic process. Clearly the intensity vector $v = (\lambda_1, \ldots, \lambda_m)$ determines the process (x, y). This is conveniently expressed in matrix notation as follows: Let the <u>input</u> and <u>output matrices</u> A and B of $\mathcal{M}$ be the matrices whose ith rows are the vector a_i and b_i respectively. Then the process (x, y) corresponding to the intensity vector v is given by $(x, y) = (vA, vB)$. For the von Neumann model, it is convenient to work with the vector v rather than the process (x, y). If we let a^j and b^j denote the jth column vectors of A and B, then the technological expansion functions become

$$\alpha_j(v) = vb^j/va^j, \qquad \alpha(v) = \min_j \alpha_j(v).$$

The economic expansion function for the basic processes can now be written,

$$\beta_i(p) = b_i p/a_i p$$

(with the conventions of Section 2 in case $a_i p = 0$).

By definition the function $\beta(p) = \max_{(x,y)} (yp/xp) = \max_v (vBp/vAp)$. It is easily seen, however, that this maximum is attained on some basic process, for suppose $\beta(p) = vBp/vAp$. Then $0 = vBp - \beta(p)vAp = v(Bp - \beta(p)Ap)$. Since $v \geq 0$ it follows that not all coordinates $b_i p - \beta(p)a_i p$ are negative and the assertion follows, thus

$$\beta(p) = \max_i \beta_i(p).$$

(For the case in which $vAp = 0$, $\beta(p) = \infty$, an even simpler argument shows the above equation to be correct.)

We now use Theorem 1 to give a simple proof of von Neumann's result.

THEOREM 3. (von Neumann). There exist semi-positive vectors v and p and positive numbers α and β such that

(3) $\alpha vA \leq vB$, and

(3') if $\alpha va^j < vb^j$ then $\pi_j = 0$.

(4) $\beta Ap \geqq Bp$, and

(4') if $\beta a_i p > b_i p$ then $\lambda_i = 0$.

PROOF. Let $\alpha = \beta = \alpha_M$ and let v be an optimal intensity vector (i.e., (vA, vB) is an optimal process). Condition (3) is simply the statement that v is optimal. If now p is an optimal price vector then (3') is precisely the statement of Corollary 2.

Condition (4) states that $\alpha_M a_i p \geqq b_i p$ for all i, or $\beta_i(p) \leqq \alpha_M$, which is conclusion (2) of Theorem 1. Condition (4') follows from conclusion (1) of Theorem 1, that is, for the optimal vector v,

$$\alpha_M vAp = vBp \quad \text{or} \quad v(\alpha_M Ap - Bp) = 0,$$

and since $\alpha_M Ap - Bp \geqq 0$ by (4) it follows that $\alpha_M Ap - Bp$ and v cannot both have positive ith coordinates.

For von Neumann models which are regular, Theorem 2 can be written in a particularly elegant form:

THEOREM 2'. For regular von Neumann models

$$\max \alpha(v) = \min \beta(p) \text{ or alternatively, } \max_v \min_j \alpha_j(v) = \min_p \max_i \beta_i(p).$$

In the first form above this result is reminiscent of the duality theorem of linear programming, while the second form suggests the minimax theorem of game theory. However, one essential difference should be noted. The optimum of a linear program and the value of a game can always be expressed rationally in terms of the coefficients of the problem. On the other hand the expansion coefficient of a linear model may be irrational, as we shall see from examples, even though the basic processes are given by rational vectors. Thus, no rational proof can be given for the expansion theorems, as is possible in the other two cases.

We shall now give a condition which guarantees regularity of a von Neumann model and represents an essential weakening of the hypothesis (H).

DEFINITION. Let $\mathcal{M}$ be a von Neumann model and let S be a subset of the indices $1, \ldots, \mathcal{M}$. The set of processes (a_i, b_i), $i \in S$ span a submodel $\mathcal{M}'$ of $\mathcal{M}$ if the model $\mathcal{M}'$ satisfies Assumption 3. In words, every good consumed by a process of $\mathcal{M}'$ is produced by at least one process of $\mathcal{M}'$. This guarantees that the technological expansion coefficient of $\mathcal{M}'$ is positive.

A model $\mathcal{M}$ is called irreducible if it contains no proper submodels. It is called decomposable if it is the union of disjoint submodels.

A good G_j will be called an input (output) of the submodel $\mathcal{M}'$ if there exists at least one process of $\mathcal{M}'$ having G_j as input (output).

We now make the following hypothesis:

(H'). Every submodel $\mathcal{M}'$ of $\mathcal{M}$ has all goods G_j as outputs.

This hypothesis (H') has a plausible economic interpretation. It means that no process in the model can sustain production unless every good in the economy is produced. This does not, of course, mean that each good is used as an input to every process. However, if a process does not use the good G_j, it must use some other good G_k whose production in turn requires the good G_j, perhaps again indirectly, etc. The hypothesis (H) together with Assumption 3 clearly implies (H'), although (H') is much weaker. Irreducible models obviously satisfy (H').

THEOREM 4. If $\mathcal{M}$ satisfies (H') then it is regular.

PROOF. Let $v = (\lambda_1, \ldots, \lambda_m)$ be an optimal intensity vector. Then the processes (a_i, b_i) for which $\lambda_i > 0$ constitute a submodel $\mathcal{M}'$ since each input of $\mathcal{M}'$ is also an output as the expansion coefficient of $\mathcal{M}'$ is $\alpha_M > 0$. Hence every good is an output of $\mathcal{M}'$ and thus since every basic process of $\mathcal{M}'$ is used in the optimal process, it follows that $\mathcal{M}$ is regular.

We now return to the case of the general von Neumann model and prove a reduction theorem which is especially useful when the number of basic processes exceeds the number of goods.

THEOREM 5. If $\mathcal{M}$ is a von Neumann model involving n goods, then there exists an optimal process using at most n basic processes.

The proof depends on the following important geometric fact.

LEMMA. Let S be a set of vectors in n-space such

that the vector v is a positive linear combination of the vectors of S. Then

(a) if $v \neq 0$, there exists a set of at most n vectors of S such that v is a positive linear combination of these vectors, and

(b) if $v = 0$, there exists a set of at most $n + 1$ vectors of S such that v is a positive linear combination of these vectors.

For a proof the reader is referred to [4].

PROOF of THEOREM 5. Let $v = (\lambda_1, \ldots, \lambda_m)$ be optimal and suppose $\lambda_i > 0$ for $i \leqq k$, $\lambda_i = 0$ for $i > k$. Let

$$c = v(\alpha A - B) = \sum_{i=1}^{k} \lambda_i(\alpha a_i - b_i),$$

where α is the expansion coefficient and v is optimal so that $c \geqq 0$. Let p be an optimal price vector. Then by (4') $(\alpha a_i - b_i)p = 0$ for $i \leqq k$, hence the vectors $\alpha a_i - b_i$ lie in a linear subspace of dimension at most $n - 1$. From the above lemma one can therefore choose a subset S of at most n of the indices $i \leqq k$, and positive scalars μ_i such that

$$c = \sum_{i \in S} \mu_i(\alpha a_i - b_i).$$

If v_0 is the vector whose ith coordinate is μ_i, for $i \in S$ and zero otherwise, we have $c = v_0(\alpha A - B)$ and thus v_0 gives the desired optimal process.

§5. SOME EXAMPLES

In this section we illustrate the foregoing theory by some numerical examples.

EXAMPLE 1: The model involves 3 basic processes and 4 goods. The process vectors are

$$a_1 = (0, 1, 0, 0) \qquad b_1 = (1, 0, 0, 0)$$
$$a_2 = (1, 0, 0, 1) \qquad b_2 = (0, 0, 2, 0)$$
$$a_3 = (0, 0, 1, 0) \qquad b_3 = (0, 1, 0, 1).$$

The model is regular, in fact, it is irreducible, hence $\alpha_M = \beta_m$, so it suffices to find vectors v and p such that $\alpha(v) = \beta(p)$, for the common value will then be the expansion coefficient. One verifies directly that the vectors

$$v = \left(2^{-\frac{1}{3}}, 2^{-\frac{2}{3}}, 1\right), \quad p = \left(1, 2^{-\frac{1}{3}}, 2^{-\frac{2}{3}}, 0\right)$$

satisfy the condition and

$$\alpha(v) = \beta(p) = \sqrt[3]{2} \ .$$

Note that G_4 is overproduced, since $\alpha_4(v) = \sqrt[3]{4} > \sqrt[3]{2}$, and hence $\pi_4 = 0$.

It is easy to give examples of models for which α_M and β_m are not equal. One need only consider a composite $\mathcal{M}$ of two models $\mathcal{M}'$ and $\mathcal{M}''$ operating simultaneously. Suppose also that $\mathcal{M}'$ and $\mathcal{M}''$ produce distinct sets of goods and have technological expansion coefficients $\alpha_{M'} < \alpha_{M''}$. Then $\beta_m \leqq \beta_{m'}$ since $\beta_m = \min \beta(p)$, and $\beta_{m'} \leq \alpha_{M'}$ by Corollary 1. Finally $\alpha_M \geqq \alpha_{M''}$ and hence $\beta_m < \alpha_M$.

In the next example we show that we can have $\beta_m < \alpha_M$ even for indecomposable models.

EXAMPLE 2. The example involves five processes and six goods.

$$\begin{aligned}
a_1 &= (0, 1, 0, 0, 0, 0) & b_1 &= (1, 0, 0, 1, 0, 0)\\
a_2 &= (1, 0, 1, 0, 0, 0) & b_2 &= (0, 1, 0, 0, 0, 0)\\
a_3 &= (0, 0, 0, 1, 0, 0) & b_3 &= (0, 0, 1, 0, 0, 0)\\
a_4 &= (0, 0, 1, 0, 0, 1) & b_4 &= (0, 0, 0, 0, 2, 0)\\
a_5 &= (0, 0, 0, 0, 1, 0) & b_5 &= (0, 0, 0, 1, 0, 1).
\end{aligned}$$

Note that the submodel consisting of the last three processes is exactly the model of Example 1 and therefore has expansion coefficient $\sqrt[3]{2}$. On the other hand the submodel consisting of the first three processes has expansion coefficient 1 as can be seen by setting

$$v = (1, 1, 1, 0, 0), \quad p = (1, 1, 0, 0, 0, 0).$$

Thus $\alpha_M = \sqrt[3]{2}$, $\beta_m = 1$. The model is indecomposable since the process (a_3, b_3) belongs to both of the submodels.

In this example the above vectors v and p as well as the vectors

$$v' = \left(0, 0, 2^{-\frac{1}{3}}, 2^{-\frac{2}{3}}, 1\right) \quad \text{and} \quad p' = \left(0, 0, 1, 2^{-\frac{1}{3}}, 2^{-\frac{2}{3}}, 0\right)$$

give rise to the von Neumann equilibria of Theorem 3. Thus we see that a von Neumann model without some condition such as regularity may have a multiplicity of equilibria. This situation has been investigated by Kemeny, Morgenstern and Thompson [5].

EXAMPLE 3. This model involves 5 processes and 4 goods. It is not regular since the optimal process does not use all goods. Nevertheless, $\alpha_M = \beta_m$.

$$\begin{aligned} a_1 &= (0, 1, 0, 0) & b_1 &= (2, 0, 0, 0) \\ a_2 &= (1, 0, 0, 0) & b_2 &= (0, 0, 2, 0) \\ a_3 &= (0, 0, 1, 0) & b_3 &= (0, 2, 0, 0) \\ a_4 &= (0, 0, 0, 1) & b_4 &= (0, 0, 1, 0) \\ a_5 &= (0, 1, 0, 0) & b_5 &= (0, 0, 0, 1). \end{aligned}$$

There are two submodels consisting of the first three and the last three processes. We assert that $\alpha_M = \beta_m = 2$, obtained by choosing $v = (1, 1, 1, 0, 0)$ and $p = (1, 1, 1, 1)$. We will have proved the assertion if we can show that $\alpha_M \leqq 2$ and $\beta_m \geqq 2$. To prove the first part, suppose $\alpha_M > 2$ and let $v = (\lambda_1, \ldots, \lambda_5)$ be optimal. Since (a_3, b_3) occurs in both submodels, $\lambda_3 > 0$ and we may assume $\lambda_3 = 1$. Since the expansion rate $\alpha_2(v)$ must exceed 2, we get

$$\lambda_1 + \lambda_5 < 1 . \tag{5}$$

Similarly, from $\alpha_1(v)$ one gets

$$\lambda_2 < \lambda_1, \tag{6}$$

and from $\alpha_3(v)$

$$2\lambda_2 + \lambda_4 > 2, \tag{7}$$

and from $\alpha_4(v)$

$$2\lambda_4 < \lambda_5. \tag{8}$$

From (5) and (6), $\lambda_2 + \lambda_5 < 1$, whence, from (8) $\lambda_2 + 2\lambda_4 < 1$ or $-2\lambda_2 - 4\lambda_4 > -2$. Adding this to (7) gives $-3\lambda_4 > 0$, a contradiction since $\lambda_4 \geqq 0$.

Now assume $\beta_m < 2$ and $p = (\pi_1, \ldots, \pi_4)$ is optimal. Then $\pi_1 > 0$ for if not, since $\beta_2(p) < \infty$, $\pi_3 = 0$, and since $\beta_3(p) < \infty$, $\pi_2 = 0$, and, since $\beta_5(p) < \infty$, $\pi_4 = 0$. Assume then $\pi_1 = 1$. Then since $\beta_1(p) < 2$, $\pi_2 > 1$, and since $\beta_3(p) < 2$, $\pi_3 > 1$, but this means $\beta_2(p) = 2\pi_3/\pi_1 > 2$, a contradiction.

The above example shows that the condition of regularity is not necessary in order that $\alpha_M = \beta_m$. The problem of finding weaker sufficient conditions presents an interesting question for further study.

§6. THE LEONTIEF MODEL

In this section we discuss expansion for the special case of the Leontief model. A Leontief model is a von Neumann model satisfying the following additional conditions

(i) There are the same number of goods as basic processes.

(ii) The only output of the process (a_i, b_i) is the good G_i.

Assumption (ii) means that the output matrix of a Leontief model is a diagonal matrix. If we now normalize the basic processes (a_i, b_i) so that a_i is the input vector required to produce one unit of G_i, then we need not write down the output matrix at all since the model is completely described by giving its input matrix A. If v is an optimal intensity vector and α_M the expansion coefficient of $\mathcal{M}$, then from the definition of optimality,

$$\alpha_M vA \leqq v.$$

We now show that for Leontief models the above inequality becomes an equation. This result and the others of this section follow easily from, and in many cases are equivalent to, known theorems on matrices with positive coefficients. We include them here for the sake of completeness and also because our proofs are, as far as we know, as direct and elementary as any to be found in the literature.

THEOREM 6. For Leontief models if v is an optimal intensity vector then

$$\alpha_M vA = v.$$

(In other words, there is no overproduction in an optimal process.)

PROOF. Suppose there is an optimal vector $v = (\lambda_1, \ldots, \lambda_n)$ such that $\alpha_M vA \leq v$, that is $\alpha_M(\sum_i \lambda_i \alpha_{ij}) < \lambda_j$ for at least one index j. Strict inequality cannot hold for all j for then α_M could be increased and would not be the true expansion coefficient. Suppose now that v has been so chosen that the strict inequality above holds for as many coordinates as possible. By suitably reordering we may suppose

$$\alpha_M \sum_i \lambda_i \alpha_{ij} < \lambda_j, \qquad j < k \le n, \tag{9}$$

$$\alpha_M \sum_i \lambda_i \alpha_{ij} = \lambda_j, \quad \text{for} \quad j \ge k. \tag{10}$$

We now assert

$$\lambda_i \alpha_{ij} = 0 \quad \text{for} \quad i < k, \qquad j \geqq k, \tag{11}$$

for if this were not the case then, say, $\lambda_1 \alpha_{1k} > 0$. We could then replace λ_1 by $\lambda_1(1 - \epsilon)$, where $\epsilon > 0$ but ϵ is sufficiently small so that inequalities (9) remain valid. But this would decrease the left hand side of equation (10) for $j = k$ giving

$$\alpha_M \sum_i \lambda_i \alpha_{ik} < \lambda_k,$$

contradicting the way in which v was chosen.

Now let $v' = (\lambda_1, \ldots, \lambda_{k-1}, 0, \ldots, 0)$. If we substitute v' for v in (9) we see that the inequality is if anything strengthened, and if v is replaced by v' in (10) then from (11) both sides of the equations are zero. But under these conditions one could again increase α_M without disturbing relations (9) and (10) contrary to the definition of α_M. This completes the proof.

Note that the conclusion of the theorem implies that v is an eigenvector of A corresponding to the eigenvalue $1/\alpha_M$. Since A is an arbitrary non-negative matrix we have incidentally proved the well known fact that a non-negative matrix has non-negative eigenvalues and vectors. (This connection has also been observed by Woodbury [7].)

We proceed to investigate the submodels of a Leontief model. Let S be a subset of the indices $1, \ldots, n$. Then the processes a_i, $i \in S$ form a submodel of the Leontief model $\mathcal{M}$ if and only if $\alpha_{ij} = 0$ for all $i \in S$, $j \notin S$. For Leontief models this is easily seen to be equivalent to the definition of Section 4. We now observe:

LEMMA. For Leontief models the intersection of submodels is a submodel.

PROOF. Let S and S' be subsets of subscripts corresponding to submodels of $\mathcal{M}$. If $i \in S \cap S'$ and $j \notin S \cap S'$ then either $j \notin S$ or $j \notin S'$ and in either case $\alpha_{ij} = 0$. By the remark above $S \cap S'$ corresponds to a submodel.

Note that this lemma does not hold for von Neumann models in general as shown by Examples 2 and 3 of the previous section in which the process (a_3, b_3) is the intersection of submodels but is not itself a submodel.

COROLLARY. The irreducible submodels of $\mathcal{M}$ are disjoint and no good is an input to more than one irreducible submodel.

PROOF. The first assertion follows at once from the lemma. If G_j were an input to two irreducible submodels $\mathcal{M}'$ and $\mathcal{M}''$, it would also be produced by both so that the jth process must belong both to $\mathcal{M}'$ and $\mathcal{M}''$ contrary to the first assertion of the corollary.

This corollary states that, by suitably reordering, the matrix A of a Leontief model decomposes in the following manner.

$$A = \begin{pmatrix} A_1 & 0 & \cdots & 0 & 0 \\ 0 & A_2 & \cdots & 0 & 0 \\ \vdots & \vdots & \ddots & \vdots & \vdots \\ 0 & 0 & \cdots & A_k & 0 \\ \hline & & A' & & \end{pmatrix}$$

where the submatrices A_i are the input matrices of the irreducible submodels and the rectangular matrix A' corresponds to those processes belonging to no irreducible submodel. Letting α_i be the expansion rate of the submodel A_i, we get

THEOREM 7. $\alpha_M = \max_i \alpha_i$.

PROOF. Let $v = (\lambda_1, \ldots, \lambda_n)$ be any optimal intensity vector and let $\mathcal{M}'$ be the submodel of $\mathcal{M}$ consisting of processes a_i such that $\lambda_i > 0$, say, $a_i \in \mathcal{M}'$ for $i \leqq r$. If $\mathcal{M}'$ is irreducible the theorem is proved. If not let $\mathcal{M}''$ be the irreducible submodel of $\mathcal{M}'$ having the highest expansion rate $\alpha_{M''}$. We may suppose $\mathcal{M}''$ consists of processes a_i, $i \leq s < r$.

By Theorem 6

(12) $$\alpha_M \sum_{i=1}^{r} \lambda_i \alpha_{ij} = \lambda_j \quad \text{for all} \quad j.$$

Let $v'' = (\lambda_1, \ldots, \lambda_s, 0, \ldots, 0)$ then

$$\alpha_M \sum_{i=1}^{s} \lambda_i \alpha_{ij} \leqq \lambda_j \quad \text{for} \quad j \leqq s, \tag{13}$$

since we have if anything decreased the left side of (12). But v'' is an intensity vector for the submodel $\mathcal{M}''$, hence $\alpha_{M''} \geqq \alpha(v'')$ and, on the other hand, (13) shows that $\alpha(v'') \geqq \alpha_M$. Hence $\alpha_{M''} = \alpha_M$ and since $\mathcal{M}''$ is irreducible the result follows.

COROLLARY. If the process a_k belongs to no irreducible submodel then $\lambda_k = 0$.

PROOF. Let v be the intensity vector of the theorem. It suffices to show that for $i \leq r$, a_i belongs to some irreducible submodel. The vector v'' above is optimal, hence by Theorem 6 inequalities (13) become equations,

$$\alpha_M \sum_{i=1}^{s} \lambda_j \alpha_{ij} = \lambda_j ,$$

and combining with (12), we get, for $j \leqq s$

$$\alpha_M \sum_{i=s+1}^{r} \lambda_i \alpha_{ij} = 0. \tag{14}$$

Since $\lambda_i > 0$ for $i \leq r$, we must have $\alpha_{ij} = 0$ for $s < i \leq r$, $j \leqq s$. But this means that $a_{s+1}, \ldots, a_r$ form a submodel of $\mathcal{M}'$, and repeating the argument if necessary, it follows that $\mathcal{M}'$ is the union of irreducible submodels.

The above theorem and corollary reduces the study of a Leontief model to the study of its irreducible submodels. For this case we obtain the following concise result.

THEOREM 8. For irreducible Leontief models the optimal intensity and price vectors are positive and uniquely determined up to multiplication by a positive constant.

PROOF. An optimal intensity vector $v = (\lambda_1, \ldots, \lambda_n)$ must be positive for if not the processes a_i for which $\lambda_i > 0$ would form a submodel. If $v' = (\lambda_1', \ldots, \lambda_n')$ is a second such vector, let $\mu = \max \{\lambda_i'/\lambda_i\}$, say, $\mu = \lambda_1'/\lambda_1$. Let $v'' = \mu v - v' = (0, \lambda_2'', \ldots, \lambda_n'') \geqq$

But v'' satisfies

$$\alpha_M v''A = \alpha_M(\mu v - v')A = \alpha_M \mu v A - \alpha_M v'A = (\mu v - v') = v''.$$

From the first assertion of the theorem, v'' cannot be optimal since $\lambda_1'' = 0$, hence $v'' = 0$ so that $v' = \mu v$ as was to be shown. A precisely analogous argument proves the uniqueness and positivity of the optimal price vector.

BIBLIOGRAPHY

[1] von NEUMANN, J., "Uber ein ökonomisches Gleichungsystem und ein Verallgemeinung des Brouwerschen Fixpunktsatzes," Ergebnisse eines Mathematischen Kolloquiums, No. 8, Vienna, 1937. Translated in Review of Economic Studies, 1945-46.

[2] LOOMIS, L. H., "On a theorem of von Neumann," Proc. Nat. Acad. Sci. 32 (1946), pp. 213-215.

[3] GEORGESCU-ROEGEN, N., "The aggregate linear production function and its applications to von Neumann's economic model," Cowles Commission Series, #13, John Wiley and Sons, New York (1951) pp. 98-115.

[4] STEINITZ, E., "Bedingt konvergente Reihen und konvexe systeme," Jour. fur reine und angewandte math. bd. 143 (1913), pp. 153-154.

[5] KEMENY, J. G., MORGENSTERN, O., and THOMPSON, G. L., "A generalization of the von Neumann model of an expanding economy," Econometrica, to appear.

[6] THOMPSON, G. L., "On the solution of a game-theoretic problem," this Study.

[7] WOODBURY, MAX A., "Characteristic roots of input output matrices," Economic Activity Analysis, edited by Oskar Morgenstern, Wiley (1954) pp. 365-382.

David Gale

Brown University

A BIBLIOGRAPHY
ON
LINEAR INEQUALITIES AND RELATED SYSTEMS

The bibliography below has been prepared for inclusion in this Study as part of the work of the Office of Naval Research Logistics Project, Department of Mathematics, Princeton University. The items were assembled by Mrs. Lily Atiyah and Mr. James H. Griesmer under the supervision of the editors.

In such a ramified subject as linear inequalities, no bibliography could claim completeness. The selection of references given here is a personal choice, evidencing a bias in favor of research that has been stimulated, directly or indirectly, by von Neumann's theory of games, linear programming, and related economic models. It is most complete in the area of linear programming and pays slight attention to the subjects of convex sets, the theory of games proper, or papers with primarily economic content. Exceptions to this loosely formulated policy occur whenever a book or paper contains material that bears directly on a paper in this Study. In general, the items included are readily available through normal library channels or by application to a source listed in the reference. For the literature up to 1934 concerning basic properties of convex sets, the reader is referred to "Theorie der konvexen Körper" by T. Bonnesen and W. Fenchel, Ergebnisse der Mathematik 3, 1, Berlin 1934, New York 1948. The classical literature on linear inequalities is covered thoroughly by T. S. Motzkin, "Beiträge zur Theorie der linearen Ungleichungen," Inaugural-Dissertation Basel, Jerusalem 1936. These references are complemented by the historical notes and bibliography of W. Fenchel, "Convex Cones, Sets, and Functions," Princeton, 1953. Research in the theory of games forms the core of the bibliographies appended to "Contributions to the Theory of Games," Vol. I and II, Annals of Math. Studies Nos. 24 and 28, Princeton 1950 and 1953, while many of the relevant papers from mathematical economics are to be found in the bibliography of "Activity Analysis of Production and Allocation," Cowles Commission Monograph No. 13, New York, 1951, edited by T. C. Koopmans.

[1] ABLOW, C. M., and BRIGHAM, A., "An analog solution of programming problems," J. Operations Res. Soc. Amer. 3 (1955), 388-394.

[2] AGMON, S., "The relaxation method for linear inequalities," Canad. J. Math. 6 (1954), 382-392.

[3] ANTOSIEWICZ, H. A., ed., Proceedings of the Second Symposium in Linear Programming, Vols. 1 and 2, Directorate of Management Analysis, DCS/Comptroller, Headquarters U. S. Air Force, Washington, D. C., 1955.

[4] ——————, "A theorem on alternatives for pairs of matrices," Pacific J. Math. 5 (1955), 641-642.

[5] ——————, and HOFFMAN, A. J., "A remark on the smoothing problem," Management Science 1 (1954-55), 92-95.

[6] ARROW, KENNETH J., and DEBREU, GERARD, "Existence of an equilibrium for a competitive economy," Econometrica 22 (1954), 265-290.

[7] BANACH, S., Théorie des Opérations Linéaires, Warsaw, 1932.

[8] BARANKIN, E. W., "Some investigations in linear programming," in [233], 68-73.

[9] BATCHELOR, JAMES H., "A commercial use of linear programming," in [3], 103-116.

[10] BEALE, E. M. L., "An alternative method for linear programming," Proc. Cambridge Philos. Soc. 50 (1954), 513-523.

[11] ——————, "Cycling in the dual simplex algorithm," Naval Res. Logist. Quart. 2 (1955), 269-275.

[12] BECKENBACH, E. F., "Convex functions," Bull. Amer. Math. Soc. 54 (1948), 439-460.

[13] BECKMANN, M., "Aktivitäts-analyse der Produktion und des Wirtschaftens," Zeitschrift für die gesamte Staatswissenschaft 109 (1953), 629-644.

[14] ——————, and MARSCHAK, T., "An activity analysis approach to location theory," in [3], 331-379.

[15] BELLMAN, RICHARD, Dynamic Programming (RAND Corporation Research Study) Princeton, 1957.

[16] BLUMENTHAL, LEONARD M., "Metric methods in linear inequalities," Duke Math. J. 15 (1948), 955-966.

[17] ——————, "Two existence theorems for systems of linear inequalities," Pacific J. Math. 2 (1952), 523-530.

[18] BOHNENBLUST, H. F., and KARLIN, S., "On a theorem of Ville," Contributions to the Theory of Games, Vol. I, 155-160. Annals of Mathematics Studies, No. 24, Princeton, 1950.

[19] ——————, KARLIN, S., and SHAPLEY, L. S., "Solutions of discrete, two-person games," Contributions to the Theory of Games, Vol. I, 51-72. Annals of Mathematics Studies, No. 24, Princeton, 1950.

[20] BOLDYREFF, A. W., "Determination of the maximal steady state flow of traffic through a railroad network," J. Operations Res. Soc. Amer. 3 (1955), 443-465.

[21] BOLES, JAMES N., "Linear programming and farm management analysis," J. Farm Econ. 37 (1955), 1-24.

[22] BOWMAN, E. H., "Production scheduling by the transportation method of linear programming," J. Operations Res. Soc. Amer. 4 (1956), 100-103.

BRIGHAM, A., see Ablow, C. M.

[23] BROWN, G. W.. "Iterative solution of games by fictitious play," Chapter XXIV of [182], 374-376.

[24] ———, and KOOPMANS, T. C., "Computational suggestions for maximizing a linear function subject to linear inequalities," Chapter XXV of [182], 377-380.

[25] ———, and von NEUMANN, J., "Solutions of games by differential equations," Contributions to the Theory of Games, Vol. I, 73-79. Annals of Mathematics Studies, No. 24, Princeton, 1950.

[26] de BRUIJN, N. G., and van DANTZIG, D., "Inequalities concerning determinants and systems of linear equations," Proc. Kon. Nederl. Akad. Wetensch. Amsterdam, Ser. A, 55 (1952), 315-321.

[27] BURGER, E., "On extrema with side conditions," Econometrica 23 (1955), 451-452.

BURROWS, G. L., see Waugh, F. V.

[28] CAHN, A. S., "The warehouse problem," Bull. Amer. Math. Soc. 54 (1948), 1073 (abstract).

[29] CARVER, W. B., "Systems of linear inequalities," Ann. of Math. 23 (1921-22), 212-220.

[30] CERNIKOV, S. N., "A generalization of Kronecker-Capelli's theorem on systems of linear equations," Mat. Sbornik, N.S. 25 (57) (1944), 437-448. (Russian, English summary.)

[31] ———, "Systems of linear inequalities," Uspehi Mat. Nauk, N.S. 8, No. 2 (54), (1953), 7-73. (Russian).

[32] CHARNES, A., "Constrained games and linear programming," Proc. Nat. Acad. Sci. U.S.A. 38 (1953), 639-641.

[33] ———, "Optimality and degeneracy in linear programming," Econometrica 20 (1952), 160-170.

[34] ———, and COOPER, W. W., "Linear programming," Scientific American (August, 1954), 21-23.

[35] ———, and COOPER, W. W., "The stepping stone method of explaining linear programming calculations in transportation problems," Management Science 1 (1954-55), 49-69.

[36] ———, and COOPER, W. W., "Generalizations of the warehousing model," Operation Res. Q. 6 (1955), 131-172.

[37] ———, COOPER, W. W., and FARR, D., "Linear programming and profit preference scheduling for a manufacturing firm," J. Operations Res. Soc. Amer. 1 (1953), 114-129.

[38] CHARNES, A., COOPER, W. W., and FERGUSON, R. O., "Optimal estimation of executive compensation by linear programming," Management Science 1 (1954-55), 138-151.

[39] ———, COOPER, W. W., and HENDERSON, A., Introduction to Linear Programming, New York, Wiley, 1953.

[40] ———, COOPER, W. W., and MELLON, B., "Blending aviation gasolines - a study in programming interdependent activities in an integrated oil company," Econometrica 20 (1952), 135-159.

[41] ———, COOPER, W. W., and MELLON, B., "A model for programming and sensitivity analysis in an integrated oil company," Econometrica 22 (1954), 193-217.

[42] ———, COOPER, W. W., and MELLON, B., "A model for optimizing production by reference to cost surrogates," Econometrica 23 (1955), 307-323 (also in [3], 117-150).

[43] ———, and LEMKE, C. E., "Computational problems of linear programming," Proc. of the Assoc. for Computing Machinery, Pittsburgh, Pa. (May, 1952), 97-98.

[44] ———, and LEMKE, C. E., "The minimization of non-linear separable convex functionals," Naval Res. Logist. Quart. 1 (1954), 301-312.

[45] CHIPMAN, JOHN S., "Computational problems in linear programming," Rev. of Econ. and Stat. 35 (1953), 342-349.

[46] ———, "Linear programming," Rev. of Econ. and Stat. 35 (1953), 101-117.

COOPER, W. W., see Charnes, A.

[47] DANSKIN, J. M., "Linear programming in the face of uncertainty: example of a failure," in [3], 39-53.

[48] ———, "Mathematical treatment of a stockpiling problem," Naval Res. Logist. Quart. 2 (1955), 99-109.

van DANTZIG, D., see de Bruijn, N. G.

[49] DANTZIG, G. B., "Programming in a linear structure," Econometrica 17 (1949), 73-74.

[50] ———, "Programming of interdependent activities: II. Mathematical Model," Econometrica 17 (1949), 200-211. (Reprinted in revised form as Chapter II of [182], 19-32.)

[51] ———, "Application of the simplex method to a transportation problem," Chapter XXIII of [182], 359-373.

[52] ———, "Maximization of a linear function of variables subject to linear inequalities," Chapter XXI of [182], 339-347.

[53] ———, "Linear programming," Problems for the Numerical Analysis of the Future (National Bureau of Standards Applied Math. Series 15), 18-21, Washington, 1951.

[54] ———, "A note on a dynamic Leontief model with substitution," Econometrica 21 (1953), 179 (abstract).

[55] ———, "A proof of the equivalence of the programming problem and the game problem," Chapter XX of [182], 330-335.

[56] DANTZIG, G. B., "Linear programming under uncertainty," Management Science 1 (1954-55), 197-206.

[57] ———————, "Upper bounds, secondary constraints, and block triangularity," Econometrica 23 (1955), 174-183.

[58] ———————, "Developments in linear programming," in [3], 667-685.

[59] ———————, FORD, L. R., Jr., and FULKERSON, D. R., "A primal-dual algorithm for linear programs," this Study.

[60] ———————, and FULKERSON, D. R., "On the min-cut max-flow theorem for networks," this Study.

[61] ———————, and FULKERSON, D. R., "Minimizing the number of tankers to meet a fixed schedule," Naval Logist. Res. Quart. 1 (1954), 217-222.

[62] ———————, FULKERSON, D. R., and JOHNSON, S., "Solution of a large scale traveling salesman problem," J. Operations Res. Soc. Amer. 2 (1954), 393-410.

[63] ———————, and HOFFMAN, A. J., "Dilworth's theorem on partially ordered sets," this Study.

[64] ———————, and JOHNSON, S., "A production smoothing problem," in [3], 151-176.

[65] ———————, and ORCHARD-HAYS, W., "The product form for the inverse in the simplex method," Math. Tables Aids Comput. 8 (1954), 64-67.

[66] ———————, and ORDEN, A., "A duality theorem based on the simplex method," in [233], 51-55.

[67] ———————, ORDEN, A., and WOLFE, PHILIP, "Method for minimizing a linear form under linear inequality restraints," Pacific J. Math. 5 (1955), 183-195.

[68] ———————, and WALD, A., "On the fundamental lemma of Neyman and Pearson," Ann. Math. Statist. 22 (1951), 87-93.

———————, see Ferguson, R. O.

———————, see Fulkerson, D. R.

———————, see Wood, Marshall K.

[69] DAVIS, C., "The intersection of a linear subspace with the positive orthant," Michigan Math. J. 1 (1952), 163-168.

[70] ———————, "The theory of positive linear dependence," Amer. J. Math. 76 (1954), 733-746.

[71] ———————, "Remarks on a previous paper," Michigan Math. J. 2 (1953-4), 23-25.

[72] ———————, "Linear programming and computers: Part I," Computers and Automation, Vol. 4, No. 7 (1955), 10-17.

[73] ———————, "Linear programming and computers: Part II," Computers and Automation, Vol. 4, No. 8 (1955), 10-16.

[74] DEBREU, G., "The coefficient of resource utilization," Econometrica 19 (1951), 273-292.

DEBREU, G., see Arrow, Kenneth J.

[75] DIEUDONNÉ, J., "La dualité dans les espaces vectoriels topologiques," Ann. Ecole Normale Sup. 59 (1942), 107-139.

[76] DILWORTH, R. P., "A decomposition theorem for partially ordered sets," Ann. of Math. 51 (1950), 161-166.

[77] DINES, L. L., "Systems of linear inequalities," Ann. of Math. (2) 20 (1918-1919), 191-199.

[78] ———, "Convex extensions and linear inequalities," Bull. Amer. Math. Soc. 42 (1936), 353-365.

[79] ———, "On convexity," Amer. Math. Monthly 45 (1938), 199-209.

[80] ———, and McCOY, N. H., "On linear inequalities," Trans. Roy. Soc. Canada, Sect. III (3) 27 (1933), 37-70.

[81] DORFMAN, R., Application of Linear Programming to the Theory of the Firm, University of California, Berkeley, 1951.

[82] ———, "Mathematical, or "linear", programming," American Economic Review 43 (1953), 797-825.

[83] ———, "Application of the simplex method to a game theory problem," Chapter XXII of [182], 348-358.

[84] ———, SOLOW, R., and SAMUELSON, P. A., Linear Programming and Economic Analysis (RAND Corporation Research Study) New York, 1956.

[85] DUFFIN, R. J., "Infinite programs," this Study.

[86] DULMAGE, L., and HALPERIN, I., "On a theorem of Frobenius-König and J. von Neumann's game of Hide and Seek," Trans. Roy. Soc. Canad. Section III, 49 (1955), 23-29.

[87] DWYER, P. S., "The solution of the Hitchcock transportation problem with the method of reduced matrices," Engineering Research Institute Report, University of Michigan, 1955.

[88] ———, "Multiple assignments of persons to jobs," Proc. 1954 Invit. Conf. Testing Prob., Educational Testing Service, Princeton, 1955.

[89] ———, "Solution of the personnel classification problem with the method of optimal regions," Psychometrika 19 (1954), 11-16.

[90] EASTERFIELD, T. E., "A combinatorial algorithm," J. London Math. Soc. 21 (1946), 219-226.

[91] EISEMANN, K., "Linear programming," Quart. Appl. Math. 13 (1955), 209-232.

[92] EGERVÁRY, E., "Matrixok combinatorius tulájdonsagaírol," Mat. és Fiz. Lapok 38 (1931), 16-28 (translated as "On combinatorial properties of matrices," by H. W. Kuhn, Office of Naval Research Logistics Project Report, Department of Mathematics, Princeton University (1953)).

[93] FAN, KY, "Fixed-point and minimax theorems in locally convex topological linear spaces," Proc. Nat. Acad. Sci. U.S.A. 38 (1952), 121-126.

[94] FAN, KY, "Minimax theorems," Proc. Nat. Acad. Sci. U.S.A. 39 (1953), 42-47.

[95] ————, "On systems of linear inequalities," this Study.

[96] FARKAS, J., "Über die theorie der einfachen Ungleichungen," J. Reine Angew. Math. 124 (1902), 1-24.

FARR, D., see Charnes, A.

[97] FARRELL, M. J., "An application of activity analysis to the theory of the firm," Econometrica 22 (1954), 291-302.

[98] FAVARD, J., "Sur les zéros réels des polynomes," Bull. Soc. Math. France 59 (1931), 229-255.

[99] ————, Les Théorèmes de la Moyenne pour les Polynomes, (Actualités Scient. et. Industr., No. 302), Hermann, Paris, 1936.

[100] FENCHEL, W., "On conjugate convex functions," Canad. J. Math. 1 (1949), 73-77.

[101] ————, Convex Bodies, (Lecture Notes) Stanford University, 1950.

[102] ————, Convex Cones, Sets, and Functions (Lecture Notes by D. W. Blackett) Office of Naval Research Logistics Project Report, Department of Mathematics, Princeton University, 1953.

[103] ————, "A remark on convex sets and polarity," Medd. Lunds Univ. Mat. Sem. (Supplement-band tillägnat Marcel Riesz) 1952, 82-89.

[104] FERGUSON, R. O., and DANTZIG, G. B., "Problem of routing aircraft," Aero. Engineering Rev. 14 (1955), 51-55.

————, see Charnes, A.

[105] FINSLER, P., "Über das Vorkommen definiter und semidefiniter Formen in Scharen quadratischer Formen," Comment. Math. Helv. 9 (1937), 188-192.

[106] FISCHER, WALTER D., and SCHRUBEN, LEONARD W., "Linear programming applied to feed- mixing under different price conditions," Journal of Farm Economics 35 (1953), 471-483.

[107] FLOOD, M. M., "On the Hitchcock distribution problem," Pacific J. Math. 3 (1953), 369-386.

[108] ————, "Application of transportation theory to scheduling a military tanker fleet," J. Operations Res. Soc. Amer. 2 (1954), 150-162.

[109] ————, "The traveling salesman problem," J. of the Operations Res. Soc. Amer. 4 (1956), 61-75.

[110] FORD, L. R. Jr., and FULKERSON, D. R., "Maximal flow through a network," Canad. J. Math., to appear.

————, see Dantzig, G. B.

[111] FORSYTHE, G. E., "Solving linear algebraic equations can be interesting," Bull. Amer. Math. Soc. 59 (1953), 299-329.

[112] FOULKES, J., "Linear programming and structural design," in [3], 117-184.

[113] FOX, L., "Practical solution of linear equations and inversion of matrices," Contributions to the Solution of Systems of Linear Equations and the Determination of Eigenvalues, edited by O. Taussky, Nat. Bureau of Standards, App. Math. Series 39, Washington, D. C., 1954, 1-54.

FREUND, see King, R. A.

[114] FULKERSON, D. R., and DANTZIG, G. B., "Computation of maximal flows in networks," Naval Res. Logist. Quart. 2 (1955), 277-283.

——————, see Dantzig, G. B.

——————, see Ford, L. R. Jr.

[115] GADDUM, J. W., "A theorem on convex cones with applications to linear inequalities," Proc. Amer. Math. Soc. 3 (1952), 957-960.

[116] ——————, HOFFMAN, A. J., and SOKOLOWSKY, D., "On the solution of the caterer problem," Naval Res. Logist. Quart. 1 (1954), 223-229.

[117] GAINEN, L., "Linear programming in bid evaluations," in [3], 29-38.

[118] ——————, HONIG, D., and STANLEY, E. D., "Linear programming in bid evaluation," Naval Res. Logist. Quart. 1 (1954), 48-52.

[119] GALE, DAVID, "The law of supply and demand," Math. Scand. 3 (1955), 155-169.

[120] ——————, "Convex polyhedral cones and linear inequalities," Chapter XVII of [182], 287-297.

[121] ——————, "Mathematics and economic models," American Scientist 44 (1956), 33-44.

[122] ——————, "Neighboring vertices on a convex polyhedron," this Study.

[123] ——————, "The closed linear model of production," this Study.

[124] ——————, KUHN, H. W., and TUCKER, A. W., "Linear programming and the theory of games," Chapter XIX of [182], 317-329.

[125] ——————, and SHERMAN, S., "Solutions of finite two-person games," Contributions to the Theory of Games, Vol. I, 37-49. Annals of Mathematics Studies, No. 24, Princeton, 1950.

[126] GASS, S. I., "A first feasible solution to the linear programming problem," in [3], 495-508.

[127] ——————, and SAATY, T. L., "The parametric objective function," J. Operations Res. Soc. Amer. 2 (1954), 316-319.

[128] ——————, and SAATY, T. L., "The computational algorithm for the parametric objective function," Naval Res. Logist. Quart. 2 (1955), 39-45.

[129] ——————, and SAATY, T. L., "Parametric objective function (part 2) - generalization," J. Operations Res. Soc. Amer. 3 (1955), 395-401.

[130] GEORGESCU-ROEGEN, N., "The aggregate linear production function and its applications to von Neumann's economic model," Chapter IV of [182], 98-115.

[131] GEORGESCU-ROEGEN, N., "Limitationality, limitativeness, and economic equilibrium," in [3], 295-330.

[132] GERSTENHABER, MURRAY, "Theory of convex polyhedral cones," Chapter XVIII of [182], 298-316.

[133] GLEYZAL, A., "An algorithm for solving the transportation problem," to appear in J. Res. Nat. Bur. Standards.

[134] GLICKSBERG, I. L., "A further generalization of the Kakutani fixed-point theorem, with application to Nash equilibrium points," Proc. Amer. Math. Soc. 3 (1952), 170-174.

[135] GOLDMAN, A. J., "Resolution and separation theorems for polyhedral convex sets," this Study.

[136] ————, and TUCKER, A. W., "Polyhedral convex cones," this Study.

[137] ————, and TUCKER, A. W., "Theory of linear programming," this Study.

[138] GOLDSTEIN, L., "The problem of contract awards," in [233], 147-154.

————, see Orden, A.

[139] GORDAN, P., "Über die Auflösungen linearer Gleichungen mit reelen coefficienten," Math. Ann. 6 (1873), 23-28.

[140] GUNTHER, P., "Use of linear programming in capital budgeting," J. Operations Res. Soc. Amer. 2 (1955), 219-224.

[141] HADAMARD, J., "Sur les operations fonctionelles," C. R. Acad. Sci. Paris 136 (1903), 351-354.

[142] HALL, P., "On representatives of subsets," J. London Math. Soc. 10 (1935), 26-30.

[143] HALMOS, P. R., Measure Theory, Van Nostrand, New York, 1950.

[144] ————, and VAUGHAN, HERBERT E., "The marriage problem," Amer. J. Math. 72 (1950), 214-215.

HALPERIN, I., See Dulmage, L.

[145] HARRISON, J. O., "Linear programming and operations research," Operations Research for Management, 217-237, Baltimore, 1954.

[146] HELLER, I., "On the traveling salesman's problem," in [3], 643-665.

[147] ————, "On the problem of shortest path between points," I and II, Bull. Amer. Math. Soc. 59 (1953), 551 (abstracts).

[148] ————, "The traveling salesman's problem, Part I, basic facts," The George Washington University Logistics Research Project, June, 1954.

[149] ————, "Geometric characterization of cyclic permutations," Bull. Amer. Math. Soc. 61 (1955), 227 (abstract).

[150] ————, and TOMPKINS, C. B., "Extension of a theorem of Dantzig," this Study.

[151] HENDERSON, A., and SCHLAIFER, R., "Mathematical programming," Harvard Business Review 32 (1954), 73-100.

HENDERSON, A., see Charnes, A.

[152] HERMITE, C., "Une question relative à la théorie des nombres," J. Math. Pures Appl. 14 (1849), 21-30.

[153] HERSTEIN, I. N., "Some mathematical methods and techniques in economics," Quart. Appl. Math. 11 (1953), 249-262.

[154] HESTENES, M. R., and McSHANE, E. J., "A theorem on quadratic forms and its application in the calculus of variations," Trans. Amer. Math. Soc. 47 (1940), 501-512.

[155] HILDRETH, C., and REITER, S., "On the choice of a crop rotation plan," Chapter XI of [182], 177-188.

[156] HITCHCOCK, F. L., "Distribution of a product from several sources to numerous localities," J. Math. Phys. (M.I.T.) 20 (1941), 224-230.

[157] HOFFMAN, A. J., "On approximate solutions of systems of linear inequalities," J. Res. Nat. Bur. Standards, 49 (1952), 263-265.

[158] ——————, "How to solve a linear programming problem," in [3], 397-424.

[159] ——————, and JACOBS, W. W., "Smooth patterns of production," Management Science 1 (1954-1955), 86-91.

[160] ——————, and KRUSKAL, J. B., "Integral boundary points of convex polyhedra," this Study.

[161] ——————, and KUHN, H. W., "On systems of distinct representatives," this Study.

[162] ——————, and KUHN, H. W., "Systems of distinct representatives and linear programming," Amer. Math. Monthly, to appear.

[163] ——————, MANNOS, M., SOKOLOWSKY, D., and WIEGMANN, N. A., "Computational experience in solving linear programs," J. Soc. Indust. Appl. Math. 1 (1953), 17-33.

[164] ——————, and WIELANDT, H. W., "The variation of the spectrum of a normal matrix," Duke Math. J. 20 (1953), 37-39.

——————, see Antosiewicz, H. A.

——————, see Dantzig, G. B.

——————, see Gaddum, J. W.

HONIG, D., see Gainen, L.

[165] HOOD, W. C., "Linear programming and the firm," Canad. J. of Econ. 18 (1952).

[166] HOUSEHOLDER, A. S., "Terminating and non-terminating iterations for solving linear systems," J. Soc. Indust. Appl. Math. 3 (1955), 67-72.

[167] HOUTHAKKER, H. S., "On the numerical solution of the transportation problem," J. Operations Res. Soc. Amer. 3 (1955), 210-214.

[168] JACKSON, J. R., "On the existence problem of linear programming," Pacific J. Math. 4 (1954), 29-36.

[169] JACOBS, W. W., "The caterer problem," Naval Res. Logist. Quart. 1 (1954), 154-165.

[170] ————, "Military applications of linear programming," in [3], 1-27.

————, see Hoffman, A. J.

[171] JACOBSON, NATHAN, Lectures in Abstract Algebra, Van Nostrand, New York, 1953.

JOHNSON, S., see Dantzig, G. B.

[172] KAKUTANI, S., "A generalization of Brouwer's fixed-point theorem," Duke Math. J. 8 (1941), 451-459.

[173] KANTOROVITCH, L., "On the translocation of masses," Dokl. Akad. Nauk S.S.R. 37 (1942), 199-201.

KARLIN, S., see Bohnenblust, H. F.

[174] KEMENY, JOHN G., "Game-theoretic solution of an economic problem," Progress Report No. 2 (1956), The Dartmouth Mathematics Project.

[175] ————, MORGENSTERN, OSKAR, and THOMPSON, GERALD, L., "A generalization of the von Neumann model of an expanding economy," Econometrica, to appear.

[176] KING, R. A., "Some applications of activity analysis in agricultural economics," Journal of Farm Economics 35 (1953), 823-833.

[177] ————, and FREUND, "A procedure for solving a linear programming problem," Jour. Paper No. 563, No. Carolina Agric. Exp. Station (July 1953).

[178] KLEE, V. L., Jr., "Convex sets in linear spaces," Duke Math. Jour. 18 (1951), 443-466, 875-883.

[179] KOHN, J. J., Linear Inequalities and Polyhedral Convex Cones, Office of Naval Research Project Report, Department of Mathematics, Princeton University, 1956.

[180] KÖNIG, D., Theorie der Endlichen und Unendlichen Graphen, Chelsea Publishing Co., New York, 1950.

[181] KOOPMANS, T. C., "Optimum utilization of the transportation system," Econometrica 17, supplement (1949), 136-146.

[182] ————, ed., Activity Analysis of Production and Allocation, Cowles Commission Monograph No. 13, Wiley, New York, 1951.

[183] ————, "Uses of prices," Proc. of the Conference on Operations Research in Production and Inventory Control, Case Inst. of Tech. (1954), 1-7.

[184] ————, "Analysis of production as an efficient combination of activities," Chapter III of [182], 33-97.

[185] ————, "Activity analysis and its applications," Amer. Econ. Rev. 43 (1953), 406-414.

[186] ————, and REITER, S., "A model of transportation," Chapter XIV of [182], 222-259.

————, see Brown, G. W.

KRUSKAL, J. B., see Hoffman, A. J.

[187] KUHN, H. W., "A combinatorial algorithm for the assignment problem," Issue 11 of Logistics Papers, George Washington University Logistics Research Project, 1954.

[188] ———, Lectures on the Theory of Games, Office of Naval Research Logistics Project Report, Department of Mathematics, Princeton, 1953.

[189] ———, "The Hungarian method for solving the assignment problem," Naval Res. Logist. Quart. 2 (1955), 83-97.

[190] ———, "On certain convex polyhedra," Bull. Amer. Math. Soc. 61 (1955), 557 (abstract).

[191] ———, "A note on "The law of supply and demand"," Math. Scand. 3 (1956).

[192] ———, "On a theorem of Wald," this Study.

[193] ———, Solvability and consistency for systems of linear equations and inequalities," Amer. Math. Monthly 63 (1956), 217-232.

[194] ———, and TUCKER, A. W., "Nonlinear programming," Proceedings of the Second Berkeley Symposium on Mathematical Statistics and Probability (ed. J. Neyman), 481-492, University of California, Berkeley, 1951.

[195] ———, and TUCKER, A. W., eds., Contributions to the Theory of Games, Vols. I and II. Annals of Mathematics Studies, Nos. 24 and 28, Princeton, 1950 and 1953.

[196] ———, and TUCKER, A. W., eds., Linear Inequalities and Related Systems, Annals of Mathematics Studies, No. 38, Princeton, 1956.

———, see Gale, David.

———, see Hoffman, A. J.

[197] LEMKE, C. E., "The dual method of solving the linear programming problem," Naval Res. Logist. Quart. 1 (1954), 48-54.

———, see Charnes, A.

[198] LOOMIS, L. H., "On a theorem of von Neumann," Proc. Nat. Acad. Sci. U.S.A. 32 (1946), 213-215.

[199] MANN, H. B., and RYSER, H. J., "Systems of distinct representatives," Amer. Math. Monthly 60 (1953), 397-401.

MANNOS, M., see Hoffman, A. J.

[200] MARKOWITZ, HARRY, "Concepts and computing procedures for certain X_{ij} programming problems," in [3], 509-565.

MARSCHAK, T., see Beckmann, M.

[201] MARTIN, A. D., "Mathematical programming of portfolio selections," Management Science 1 (1954-55), 152-166.

[202] MAYBERRY, J. P., "A geometrical interpretation of the simplex method," in [233], 56-67.

[203] MAZUR, S., "Über konvexe Mengen in linearen normierten Raumen," Studia Math. 4 (1933), 70-84.

[204] McCLOSKEY, J. C., and TREFETHEN, F. M., eds., Operations Research for Management, Baltimore, 1954.

McCOY, N. H., see Dines, L. L.

[205] McKENZIE, L. W., "On equilibrium in Graham's model of world trade and other competitive systems," Econometrica 22 (1954), 147-161.

[206] ———, "Specialization and efficiency in world production," Rev. Economic Studies 21 (1954), 165-180.

[207] ———, "Competitive equilibrium with dependent consumer preferences," in [3], 277-294.

[208] McKINSEY, J. C. C., Introduction to the Theory of Games, McGraw-Hill, New York, 1952.

McSHANE, E. J., see Hestenes, M. R.

MELLON, B., see Charnes, A.

[209] MILLS, H. D., "Marginal values of linear programs and matrix games," this Study.

[210] MINKOWSKI, H., Geometrie der Zahlen, Leipzig, 1910.

[211] MORGENSTERN, O., ed., Economic Activity Analysis, Wiley, New York, 1954.

[212] ———, and von NEUMANN, J., Theory of Games and Economic Behavior, (3rd edition), Princeton, 1953.

———, see Kemeny, John G.

[213] MORTON, G., "Notes on linear programming," Economica 18 (1951), 397-411.

[214] MOTZKIN, T. S., Beiträge zur Theorie der Linearen Ungleichungen, Inaugural Dissertation, Basel, Jerusalem, 1936.

[215] ———, "Two consequences of the transposition theorem on linear inequalities," Econometrica 19 (1951), 184-185.

[216] ———, "The multi-index transportation problem," Bull. Amer. Math. Soc. 58 (1952), 494 (abstract).

[217] ———, "The assignment problem," Proc. Sixth Symp. in Applied Math. (Amer. Math. Soc.), New York, 1956.

[218] ———, "The probability of solvability of linear inequalities," in [3], 607-611.

[219] ———, "New techniques for linear inequalities and optimization," in [233], 15-27.

[220] ———, "Remarks on the history of linear inequalities," in [233], 179 (abstract).

[221] ———, and SCHOENBERG, I. J., "The relaxation method for linear inequalities," Canad. J. Math. 6 (1954), 393-404.

[222] MOTZKIN, T. S., RAIFFA, H., THOMPSON, G. L., and THRALL, R. M., "The double description method," Contributions to the Theory of Games, Vol. II, 51-73. Annals of Mathematics Studies, No. 28, Princeton, 1953.

[223] von NEUMANN, J., "Zur theorie der Gesellschaftsspiele," Math. Ann. 100 (1928), 295-320.

[224] ——————, "Some matrix-inequalities and metrization of matric-space," Mitt. Forsch. Inst. Math. Mech. Univ. Tomsk, 1 (1937), 286-299.

[225] ——————, "Über ein okonomisches Gleichungsystem und ein Verallgemeinung des Brouwerschen Fixpunktsatzes," Ergebnisse eines Mathematischen Kolloquiums, No. 8, 1937 (translated in Rev. Economic Studies, 1945-46).

[226] ——————, "A certain zero-sum two-person game equivalent to the optional assignment problem," Contributions to the Theory of Games, Vol. II, 5-12. Annals of Mathematics Studies, No. 28, Princeton, 1953.

[227] ——————, "A numerical method to determine optimum strategy," Naval Res. Logist. Quart. 1 (1954), 109-115.

——————, see Brown, G. W.

——————, see Morgenstern, O.

[228] NIKAIDO, H., "On von Neumann's minimax theorem," Pacific J. Math. 4 (1954), 65-72.

[229] NORMAN, R. Z., "On the convex polyhedra of the symmetric traveling salesman problem," Bull. Amer. Math. Soc. 61 (1955), 557 (abstract).

ORCHARD-HAYS, W., see Dantzig, G. B.

[230] ORDEN, A., "Solution of systems of linear inequalities on a digital computer," Proc. of the Assoc. for Computing Machinery, Pittsburgh, Pa., (May 1952), 91-95.

[231] ——————, "Survey of research on mathematical solutions of programming problems," Management Science 1 (1954-55), 170-172.

[232] ——————, "Application of the simplex method to a variety of matrix problems," in [233], 28-50.

[233] ——————, and GOLDSTEIN, L., eds., Symposium on Linear Inequalities and Programming, (Project SCOOP, No. 10) Directorate of Management Analysis, DCS/Comptroller, Headquarters U. S. Air Force, Washington, D. C., 1952.

——————, see Dantzig, G. B.

——————, see Votaw, D. F.

[234] PRAGER, W., "On the role of congestion in transportation problems," Z. für Ange. Math. Mech. 35 (1955), 264-268.

[235] RADNER, ROY, "The linear team: an example of linear programming under uncertainty," in [3], 381-396.

RAIFFA, H., see Motzkin, T. S.

[236] REITER, S., "Trade barriers in activity analysis," Rev. Economic Studies 20 (1953).

REITER, S., see Hildreth, C.

__________, see Koopmans, T. C.

[237] ROBINSON, J., "An iterative method of solving a game," Ann. Math. 54 (1951), 296-301.

[238] ROSANDER, A. C., "The use of linear programming to improve the quality of decisions," Industrial Quality Control 12 (1956), 11-16.

[239] ROSENBLOOM, P. C., "Quelques classes de problèmes extrémaux," Bull. Soc. Math. France 79 (1951), 1-58.

RYSER, H. J., see Mann, H. B.

[240] SAATY, T. L., "The number of vertices of a polyhedron," Amer. Math. Monthly 62 (1955), 326-331.

__________, see Gass, S. I.

[241] SALINE, LINDON E., "Quadratic programming of interdependent activities for optimum performance," Trans. A.S.M.E. 78 (1956), 37-46.

[242] SALVESON, M. E., "On a quantitative method in production planning and scheduling," Econometrica 20 (1952), 554-590.

[243] __________, "The assembly line balancing problem," in [3], 55-101.

[244] SAMUELSON, P. A., "Linear programming and economic theory," in [3], 251-272.

[245] __________, Foundations of Economic Analysis, Cambridge, Massachusetts, 1948.

[246] __________, "Spatial price equilibrium and linear programming," Amer. Econ. Review 42 (1952), 282-303.

__________, see Dorfman, R.

[247] SANDGREN, L., "On convex cones," Math. Scand. 2 (1954), 19-28, and 3 (1955), 170.

[248] SCHELL, EMIL, D., "Distribution of a product by several properties," in [3], 615-642.

SCHLAIFER, R., see Henderson, A.

[249] SCHLESINGER, K., "Über die Produktionsgleichungen der okonomischen Wertlehre," Ergebnisse eines mathematischen Kolloquiums, No. 6 (1933-34), 10-11.

[250] SCHOENBERG, I. J., "Convex domains and linear combinations of continuous functions," Bull. Amer. Math. Soc. 39 (1933), 273-280..

__________, see Motzkin, T. S.

SCHRUBEN, LEONARD W., see Fischer, Walter D.

[251] SCHWAN, H. T., "Practical linear programming applications," Industrial Quality Control 12 (1956), 4-8.

SHAPLEY, L. S., see Bohnenblust, H. F.

[252] SHAPLEY, L. S., and SNOW, R. N., "Basic solutions of discrete games," Contributions to the Theory of Games, Vol. I, 27-35. Annals of Mathematics Studies, No. 24, Princeton, 1950.

——————, see Bohnenblust, H. F.

SHERMAN, S., see Gale, David.

[253] SIMON, H. A., "Effects of technological change in a linear model," Chapter XV of [182], 260-277 (with Comments by A. Coale and Yale Brozen, 277-281).

[254] SLADE, J. J., Jr., "Some observations on formal models for programming," Trans. A.S.M.E. 78 (1956), 47-53.

[255] SLATER, M. L., "A note on Motzkin's transposition theorem," Econometrica 19 (1951), 185-186.

SNOW, R. N., see Shapley, L. S.

SOKOLOWSKY, D., see Gaddum, J. W.

——————, see Hoffman, A. J.

SOLOW, R., see Dorfman, R.

STANLEY, E. D., see Gainen, L.

[256] STEINITZ, E., "Bedingt konvergente Reihen und konvexe systeme," J. Reine Angew. Math. 143 (1913), 153-154.

[257] STIEMKE, E., "Über positive Lösungen homogener linearer Gleichungen," Math. Ann. 76 (1915), 340-342.

[258] STIGLER, GEORGE, J., "The cost of subsistence," Journal of Farm Economics 27 (1945), 303-314.

[259] STOKES, R. W., "A geometric theory of solution of linear inequalities," Trans. Amer. Math. Soc. 33 (1931), 782-805.

[260] SYMONDS, G. H., "Mathematical programming as an aid to decision making," Advanced Management 20 (1955), 11-17.

[261] ——————, Linear Programming: The Solution of Refinery Problems, Esso Standard Oil Co., New York, 1955.

[262] THOMAS, J. M., "Positive solutions of binomial inequalities," Duke Math. J. 7 (1940), 291-297.

[263] THOMPSON, GERALD, L., "On the solution of a game-theoretic problem," Bull. Amer. Math. Soc. (1956), (abstract).

——————, see Kemeny, John G.

——————, see Motzkin, T. S.

[264] ——————, "A game-theoretic solution of an economic problem," this Study.

[265] THORNDIKE, ROBERT L., "The problem of classification of personnel," Psychometrika 15 (1950), 215-235.

[266] THRALL, R. M., "Some results in non-linear programming," in [3], 471-493.

——————, see Motzkin, T. S.

[267] TINTNER, G., "Stochastic linear programming with applications to agricultural economics," in [3], 197-228.

[268] TOMPKINS, C. B., "Projection methods in calculation," in [3], 425-448.

———, see Heller, I.

TREFETHEN, F. M., see McCloskey, J. C.

[269] TUCKER, A. W., "Extensions of theorems of Farkas and Stiemke," Bull. Amer. Math. Soc. 56 (1950), 57 (abstract).

[270] ———, "Linear inequalities and convex polyhedral sets," in [3], 569-602.

[271] ———, "A skew-symmetric matrix theorem," Bull. Amer. Math. Soc. 61 (1955), 135 (abstract).

[272] ———, "Theorems of alternatives for pairs of matrices," in [233], 180-181.

[273] ———, Game Theory and Programming (Notes of lectures at the N.S.F. Summer Institute for Mathematics Teachers at Oklahoma Agricultural and Mechanical College) College Bookstore, Stillwater, Oklahoma, 1955.

[274] ———, "Dual systems of homogeneous linear relations," this Study.

[275] ———, "Linear programming," Industrial Quality Control 12 (1956), 8-11.

———, see Gale, David.

———, see Goldman, A. J.

———, see Kuhn, H. W.

VAUGHAN, HERBERT E., see Halmos, P. R.

[276] VILLE, J., "Sur la théorie generale des jeux où intervient l'habilitē des joueurs," Traité du Calcul des Probabilités et de ses Applications, by E. Borel and collaborators, Vol. 4, Part 2, 105-113, Paris, 1938.

[277] VAZSONYI, ANDREW, "Optimizing a function of additively separated variables subject to a simple restriction," in [3], 453-469.

[278] VOTAW, D. F., Jr., "Methods of solving some personnel-classification problems," Psychometrika 17 (1952), 255-266.

[279] ———, "Programming under conditions of uncertainty," in [3], 187-195.

[280] ———, and ORDEN, A., "Personnel assignment problem," in [233], 155-163.

[281] WALD, A., "Über die eindeutige positive Lösbarkeit der neuen Produktionsgleichungen," Ergebnisse eines mathematischen Kolloquiums, No. 6 (1933-34), 12-20.

[282] ———, "Über die Produktionsgleichungen der okonomischen Wertlehre," Ergebnisse eines mathematischen Kolloquiums, No. 7 (1934-35), 1-6.

[283] WALD, A., "Über einige Gleichungssysteme der mathematischen Okonomie," Zeitschrift für Nationalokonomie 7, No. 5 (1936), 637-670 (translated in Econometrica 19 (1951), 368-403).

——————, see Dantzig, G. B.

[284] WAUGH, F. V., and BURROWS, G. L., "A short cut to linear programming," Econometrica 23 (1955), 18-29.

[285] WEYL, H., "Elementare Theorie der konvexen polyeder," Comm. Math. Helv. 7 (1935), 290-306 (translated in Contributions to the Theory of Games, Vol. I, 3-18, Annals of Mathematics Studies, No. 24, Princeton, 1950).

[286] WHITIN, T. M., "Classical theory, Graham's theory, and linear programming in international trade," Quart. J. of Econ. 67 (1953), 520-544.

WIEGMANN, N. A., see Hoffman, A. J.

WIELANDT, H. W., see Hoffman, A. J.

[287] WILLIAMS, N., "An application of linear programming to the selection of raw materials," Appl. Statist. 4 (1955), 22-31.

[288] WOLFE, PHILIP, "Determinateness of polyhedral games," this Study.

——————, see Dantzig, G. B.

[289] WOOD, MARSHALL K., and DANTZIG, G. B., "Programming of interdependent activities: I. General Discussion," Econometrica 17 (1949), 193-199 (reprinted in revised form as Chapter I of [182], 15-18).

PRINCETON MATHEMATICAL SERIES

Edited by Marston Morse and A. W. Tucker

1. The Classical Groups
   By HERMANN WEYL ....314 pp. $6.00
2. Topological Groups
   By L. PONTRJAGIN (translated by Emma Lehmer) ....310 pp. $6.00
3. An Introduction to Differential Geometry
   By LUTHER PFAHLER EISENHART ....316 pp. $6.00
4. Dimension Theory
   By WITOLD HUREWICZ and HENRY WALLMAN ....174 pp. $3.75
5. Analytical Foundations of Celestial Mechanics
   By AUREL WINTNER ....460 pp. $7.50
6. The Laplace Transform
   By DAVID VERNON WIDDER ....416 pp. $7.50
8. Theory of Lie Groups: I
   By CLAUDE CHEVALLEY ....288 pp. $4.00
9. Mathematical Methods of Statistics
   By HARALD CRAMÉR ....570 pp. $7.50
10. Several Complex Variables
    By S. BOCHNER and W. T. MARTIN ....216 pp. $4.00
11. Introduction to Topology
    By S. LEFSCHETZ ....226 pp. $4.50
12. The Topology of Surfaces and their Transformations
    By JAKOB NIELSEN and WERNER FENCHEL ....In preparation
13. Algebraic Curves
    By ROBERT J. WALKER ....210 pp. $4.00
14. The Topology of Fibre Bundles
    By NORMAN STEENROD ....232 pp. $5.00
15. Foundations of Algebraic Topology
    By SAMUEL EILENBERG and NORMAN STEENROD ....342 pp. $7.50
16. Functionals of Finite Riemann Surfaces
    By MENAHEM SCHIFFER and DONALD C. SPENCER ..464 pp. $8.00
17. Introduction to Mathematical Logic, Vol. I
    By ALONZO CHURCH ....384 pp. $7.50
18. Algebraic Geometry
    By S. LEFSCHETZ ....242 pp. $5.00
19. Homological Algebra
    By H. CARTAN and S. EILENBERG ....406 pp. $7.50
20. The Convolution Transform
    By D. V. WIDDER and I. I. HIRSCHMANN .... 276 pp. $5.50
21. Geometric Integration Theory
    By HASSLER WHITNEY ....In press

PRINCETON UNIVERSITY PRESS
PRINCETON, NEW JERSEY